1997
Stage____

G000123558

BU___
U.K. O____

January 1997

Contents

1997 Stagecoach Bus Handbook

The 1997 Stagecoach Bus Handbook is the fourth edition of this Bus Handbook dedicated to the various bus fleets of Stagecoach Holdings, both within the United Kingdom and overseas.

Although this book has been produced with the encouragement of, and in co-operation with, Stagecoach management, it is not an official Stagecoach fleet list and the vehicles included are subject to variation, particularly as substantial new vehicle deliveries lead to older vehicles being 'cascaded' to other subsidiaries. Some vehicles listed are no longer in regular use on service but are retained for special purposes or preserved by the company. The services operated and the allocation of vehicles to subsidiary companies are subject to variation at any time, although accurate at the time of going to print. The contents are correct to January 1997, and include the vehicles of Swebus of Stockholm which joined the group in September 1996 and enlarged Lancasgire operation following the purchase of Hyndburn, and Burnley Borough Council's announcement on 31st October of its intention to sell its 50% share of Burnley & Pendle Transport to Stagecoach.

The publishers would be glad to hear from readers should any information be available which corrects or enhances that given in this publication, or to receive any suitable photographs for use in future editions, particularly those covering the overseas operations.

Principal Editors: Bill Potter and David Donati

Acknowledgements:
We are grateful to Andy Jarosz, Mark Jameson, Colin Lloyd, Richard Smiles, Malcolm Tranter, the PSV Circle and the Management and officials of Stagecoach Holdings and their operating companies for their kind assistance and co-operation in the compilation of this book.
To keep up to date with the fleets we recommend *Buses*, published monthly by Ian Allan Ltd and for more in-depth information the news sheets of the PSV Circle.

The front cover photo is by Bill Potter, the frontispieces for the UK is in conjunction with Bluebird and the overseas by Kenya Bus. The rear cover photographs are by Stagecoach International and Tony Wilson.

ISBN 1 897990 24 3
Published by *British Bus Publishing* Ltd
The Vyne, 16 St Margarets Drive, Wellington,
Telford, Shropshire, TF1 3PH
© British Bus Publishing Ltd, January 1997

Stagecoach

The Stagecoach Group is one of the larger private sector operators of buses in the United Kingdom, with a growing involement in surface transport throughout the world. This Bus Handbook details the latest fleets of constituent companies, both in Britain and overseas in Africa, Portugal, Scandinavia and New Zealand.

Stagecoach can trace its roots back to a small self-drive caravan and caravanette rental business which was formed in Perth in 1976. Trading as Gloagtrotter (later GT Coaches), the business expanded a couple of years later to include minibus private hire under the original partnership of Ann Gloag, now Executive Director of Stagecoach Holdings, and her husband, Robin. Her brother, Brian Souter, now Executive Chairman (an accountant by profession), joined the fledgling organisation in 1980 just prior to its starting regular long distance services at which time the Stagecoach name was adopted, at the suggestion of Ann's other brother, David. This move into regular services was made possible by coach deregulation, introduced in the 1980 Transport Act.

Stagecoach was born out of deregulation and privatisation. The freedom of deregulation and the opportunities of privatisation have facilitated the rapid growth of Stagecoach.

The first service began in October 1980, an overnight run from Dundee to London. Subsequently further legs were added that brought in Aberdeen and Glasgow to form a network of coach services. Soon a network of express services was developed that operated throughout Scotland and ran south of the border to London via Manchester and Birmingham. The quality of vehicle provided on these services quickly improved, exotic foreign double deck coaches in a bright uncontroventional livery becoming the norm from 1982 onwards in marked contrast to the traditional single deck coaches with a rather dowdy image used by their main competitor - The Scottish Bus Group.

In December 1982 Mrs Gloag's husband left the business and set up his own company trading as Highwayman Coaches at Errol near Perth. In tandem with the coach service expansion, a number of school contracts had been secured. These were operated primarily with second hand Bristol Lodekkas and, by the mid 1980s, Stagecoach was the largest operator of that type, with a fleet of over 20. In December 1980 Stagecoach took its first step into regular bus service operation when the Perth to Errol route of A & C McLennan of Spittalfield was taken over. It was this route which five years later was to see the birth of the

'Provincial Routemaster Revival' which was started by Stagecoach when it introduced Routemasters between Perth and Errol in the spring of 1985. In the early 1980s a number of other Scottish coach operations were absorbed into Stagecoach including Adamson & Low of Edinburgh and Bennetts of Kilwinning in Ayrshire, although both were subsequently disposed of. After a period of consolidation, a further expansion into local bus services was achieved when, in November 1985, the remaining business of McLennan's of Spittalfield was purchased. This gave the Stagecoach company a significant presence in the Tayside region, and most importantly McLennan's extensive workshops and engineering facilities at Spittalfield which were needed to maintain the ever-growing express coach fleet.

The 1985 Transport Act resulted in the deregulation of bus services outside of London. As implementation of the Act drew near, the Stagecoach company prepared its plans for a major expansion in the bus market. A new company was formed called Magicbus, and on 26th October 1986 it commenced operating a number of services in Glasgow. The vehicles utilised were primarily Routemasters formerly with London Buses or Northern General and these vehicles brought back conductor operation to the city along with the Routemasters of Kelvin and Clydeside. At the same time there was some expansion of services in Tayside, Stagecoach taking over commercially a number of rural routes left for the tendering process by Strathtay Scottish, including the routes north of Perth to Aberfeldy and Pitlochry.

With established operations in Tayside and Glasgow, and an extensive network of express services, the Stagecoach team considered for the first time acquiring operators outside its native Scotland, and took an interest in the pending privatisation of National Bus Company's subsidiaries. An unsuccessful bid for City of Oxford did not deter the directors who turned their attention to Hampshire Bus. A new holding company, Skipburn Limited, was formed by directors Brian Souter and Ann Gloag together with their uncle Fraser McColl and the General Manager of Hampshire Bus. Hampshire Bus together with Pilgrim Coaches were successfully purchased on 2nd April 1987. The new owners did not waste time in rationalising their new acquisition, with Pilgrim Coaches, which had been loss-making from the outset, closing down on 26th April 1987. By 3rd October, the Southampton area operations had been sold to Southern Vectis who formed a new company, trading as Solent Blue Line, to operate the routes. The residual Hampshire Bus operation continues as part of the Stagecoach South company with depots at Andover, Basingstoke and Winchester.

In 1987 Derek Scott joined the board as Finance Director, and has subsequently played a key role in shaping the growth of the group,

In December 1980 Stagecoach took its first step into regular bus service operation when the Perth to Errol route of A & C McLennan of Spittalfield was taken over. It was this route which five years later was to see the birth of the 'Provincial Routemaster Revival' which was started by Stagecoach when it introduced Routemasters between Perth and Errol in the spring of 1985. Shown here is DGS625, a Leyland Tiger PS1/2 which carries a body built by McLennan in 1951. It was purchased for the Stagecoach Special Event fleet in 1989 and is liveried for the Loch Earn 'Trundler' service which it operated in 1996 and will do in 1997. *Phillip Stephenson*

becoming Company Secretary in 1996. While still digesting Hampshire Bus, the Stagecoach board turned its attention to the acquisition of a second NBC subsidiary. This time Cumberland was the target and, following a successful offer, Stagecoach took control of Cumberland Motor Services on 23rd July 1987. The Cumberland operations were based at Whitehaven with depots in Carlisle, Penrith, Keswick, Workington and Millom. The new owners quickly recast the Carlisle city network and introduced crew-operated Routemasters to that city. The Cumberland company acquired a number of its competitors during 1988 including Yeowart's of Whitehaven and Kirkpatrick of Brigham, near Cockermouth.

In July 1987 the McColl interests in Skipburn were acquired. However, further expansion of the group was still being sought. Under the NBC privatisation rules only three subsidiaries could be acquired by any purchaser. However, Hampshire Bus and Pilgrim Coaches had been classed as one unit, Cumberland a second and, therefore, Stagecoach was able to acquire United Counties as its third NBC company. The area of operation encompassed Bedford, Corby, Huntingdon, Kettering and Northampton and was the group's first presence in the Midlands. As with Cumberland, it was not long before the potential of Routemasters was realised and the Corby and Bedford networks received a fleet of these vehicles soon after the Stagecoach acquisition.

During 1988 Ewan Brown joined the board of directors in a non-executive capacity. Being a Merchant Banker by profession, and a former director of the Scottish Transport Group, he brought valuable skills and knowledge to the management team.

Up to this point the Stagecoach Group had acquired three NBC companies. All were operating a typical mix of National Bus Company standard vehicles which primarily consisted of Leyland Nationals and Leopards, and Bristol VRTs. Additionally, the fleet in Scotland was mainly secondhand Routemasters and Bristol Lodekkas together with Volvo B58 and Neoplan coaches for the express network. Vehicles in Scotland were in the now standard Stagecoach livery of white with blue, red and mustard (later to become orange) stripes and it was decided that in order to provide flexibility and enable vehicles to be transferred between fleets, all vehicles in the group would be painted in this corporate style. Very quickly the new livery began to appear on all three English fleets.

New vehicle purchases had to be made in order that the bus companies could maintain and develop their business into the 1990s and early purchases of Alexander-bodied Mercedes 709 minibuses and Leyland Olympians were to be a portent of large numbers of vehicles of these types in years to come. The importance of investing in new vehicles, and its consequent increase in patronage and reduction of maintenance costs, has continued to the present.

The most significant event of 1988 was the private placing of a quantity of Stagecoach shares with institutional investors. This raised £5 million and set the financial scene for Stagecoach to develop into a major force within the bus industry. It was also a sign of things to come, that is the Stock Market flotation five years later.

1989 saw the first Stagecoach acquisition overseas when, in March of that year, it purchased a 51% share in United Transport Malawi Limited from United Transport International, a British Electric Traction (BET) Subsidiary.

The vehicles operated in Africa are somewhat strange to British eyes with large numbers of ERF Trailblazer and Leyland Victory single deckers, all built to meet the rough African conditions where much mileage is run on dirt roads. Stagecoach did, however, introduce double decker operation to the Malawi fleet with Daimler CVG6 double deckers previously operated in Hong Kong by the Kowloon Motor Bus Company. All of these, together with a Bristol FLF, are now withdrawn as the company has taken delivery of Dennis Dragons, former Durban single-decks and new single-decks. City services and long distance express routes are operated from depots based in Blantyre (Makata Road and Chichiri), Lilongwe and Mzuzu.

Having ventured into Africa, Stagecoach soon returned to the acquisition trail in England. East Midland Motor Services had been sold to its management by NBC, but in April 1989 the management decided to sell its entire share holding, Stagecoach being the purchaser. The operation was conducted under East Midland, Mansfield & District, and Rainworth Travel names in the East Midland area, and in addition there were two Frontrunner operations, one based in Essex and the other in north west Derbyshire and eastern Greater Manchester. The Frontrunner South East operation was quickly sold on to Ensign Bus of Purfleet while the Derbyshire/Manchester operation was absorbed by Ribble. This left the East Midland management to concentrate in its own territory and soon its coaching operations were consolidated into Rainworth Travel which was renamed Midland Travel. The bus operations are based on Worksop, Chesterfield and Mansfield and, as with other acquisitions, former London Routemasters were again tried, this time in Mansfield where Routemaster operation lasted until 1991. In May 1993 the Midland Travel coaching operation was sold to Skills of Nottingham.

Only a matter of days after the East Midland acquisition, a further company was acquired from its management. Ribble Motor Services Limited, based in the north west of England, had been bought by its management team and had subsequently purchased, from United Transport, the Bee Line Buzz Company - a large minibus operation based in Manchester, together with the Zippy minibus operation based in Preston.

Having added two major bus companies in North West England to one it already owned, Stagecoach embarked upon a reorganisation and rationalisation of its interests in the area. The Barrow-in-Furness municipal undertaking had been in financial difficulties for some time, following heavy competition with Ribble, and its services and depot were acquired in May 1989. For operational control reasons, and to align with the county boundaries, Ribble's South Cumbrian and Lake District operations were transferred to Cumberland Motor Services which also took control in Barrow. This concentrated Cumberland into the county of Cumbria and Ribble into Lancashire and Greater Manchester. In September of 1989 Ribble sold its Bee Line Buzz subsidiary and some of its own Ribble Manchester operations to the Drawlane Group though it retained the Preston-based Zippy minibuses, a name now used for all Ribble minibus operations. Having lost depots at Barrow, Ulverston and Kendal to Cumberland and the Manchester operation passing to Drawlane, Ribble was left to concentrate on the central area which consists of the Lancashire towns of Blackburn, Bolton, Chorley, Clitheroe, Fleetwood, Lancaster, Morecambe and Preston.

Despite the activity in England there were still changes taking place in Scotland during 1989. On 19th June new bus services in and around the cities of Perth and Dundee were introduced, primarily in competition with Strathtay Scottish, whose managing director, Neil Renilson was recruited by the group at the same time. This new network was branded Perth Panther and, after a prolonged period of competition, in which both operators used Routemasters on Perth City services, Strathtay closed their Crieff depot and operations in 1991 and their Perth depot and operations in the summer of 1993.

Perhaps the most surprising development of 1989 was the decision by Stagecoach to sell the express coach operations that had been the genesis of the company. On 4th August 1989 the company announced the sale of its express network to National Express who re-branded the operation as Caledonian Express. With this sale Stagecoach clearly indicated that it was to concentrate on local bus operations in future. The Scottish operations saw further expansion when Inverness Traction was purchased from receivership in November. Inverness Traction had been competing with Highland Scottish on town services in Inverness since 1987. Stagecoach placed this Inverness operation under the Magicbus and Perth Panther management, and renamed the Magicbus company Stagecoach Scotland Ltd as the holding company for its Glasgow, Tayside and Inverness operations. All of these operations were carving out their market through head to head competition with established state-owned operators, whereas in England established operators had been purchased, and competitive pressures were the other way round.

The south coast of England was not neglected either. In August 1989 the management of Southdown decided to sell out to Stagecoach. This brought a sixth former NBC subsidiary into the fold and Stagecoach then acquired, in October, the operations of Portsmouth City Bus from Southampton City Bus who held 75% and a workers co-operative which owned the remaining 25%. In December 1989 Hastings and District was added when the management sold the company which it had bought from NBC.

In 1990 there was expansion overseas with the purchase of Gray Coach Lines of Toronto, Canada. This brought to the Stagecoach Group an extensive network of express coach services throughout eastern Canada together with Niagara Falls sightseeing tours and the Toronto City/Airport express coach service. The venture proved to be unsuccessful in financial terms and the Group's interest in Gray Coach Lines was sold to Greyhound Lines of Canada in December 1992, but not before a number of Stagecoach Scotland Bristol FLFs had been transferred for sightseeing tour work.

One result of the large expansion on the south coast of England was an inquiry by the Monopolies and Mergers Commission and the DTI subsequently instructed Stagecoach to divest themselves of Portsmouth City Bus, and this operation was subsequently sold to Transit Holdings in January 1991. The South of England subsidiaries that remained were then restructured and consolidated in April 1992 when a new company, Stagecoach South Limited, was given overall control of Hastings Buses, Southdown and Hampshire Bus. As part of the reorganisation Southdown was split into two operating companies, Sussex Coastline Buses and South Coast Buses, the latter also taking in Hastings Buses. The Southdown name was discontinued, and South Coast Buses operates at Eastbourne and Hastings with Coastline Buses trading from Chichester, Havant and Worthing.

Following on from the privatisation of NBC the Government decided to extend privatisation to the Scottish Bus Group. It was decreed that only two companies could be acquired by any one purchaser and Stagecoach completed its quota with the purchase of Bluebird Northern and Fife Scottish during the first half of 1991. Bluebird is based in Aberdeen and also has depots at Ballater, Elgin, Fyvie, Macduff, Peterhead and Stonehaven, together with several outstations. Bluebird was acquired in March and its archaic legal company name of Northern Scottish Omnibuses Ltd was quickly changed to Bluebird Buses Ltd. Bluebird was placed under common management with Stagecoach Scotland Ltd and its fleet renumbered into a single series.

By July of 1991 the Fife company was also under the Stagecoach umbrella. In line with the company name operations are concentrated in the Kingdom of Fife with depots at Aberhill (Methil), Cowdenbeath, Dunfermline, Glenrothes, Kirkcaldy and St Andrews. In the autumn of 1991 Stagecoach Scotland further expanded when it took over the remaining Inverness and Easter Ross area operations from Highland, adding some 30 extra buses to the Inverness Traction Fleet, plus the former Highland depot at Tain.

With two former SBG companies now under its wing, plus the Perth and Inverness operations, Stagecoach had established a strong presence on the eastern side of Scotland. In line with Stagecoach policy the corporate colours started to appear on the newly-acquired fleets and fleet renewal commenced, primarily involving Alexander-bodied Mercedes minibuses and Leyland Olympians. There were also transfers north of the border of vehicles from the English companies which resulted in some unfamiliar types of vehicle being introduced into Scotland, especially ECW-bodied Bristol VRTs. The VRT had been despised by SBG with all its initial examples being exchanged for NBC-owned Bristol FLFs.

November 1991 saw further expansion in Africa following BETs decision to divest itself of local bus operations throughout the world and Stagecoach saw potential in acquiring its Kenya operations to add to those of Malawi. As a result of the deal Stagecoach now has a 75% share of Kenya Bus Services (Nairobi), and a 51% share in Kenya Bus Services (Mombasa). The remaining share holdings are held by the local city councils and both operations are maintained under franchising arrangements. As in Malawi the ERF Trailblazer and Leyland Victory tend to dominate the fleets though there are a number of unusual vehicles including some manufactured by Isuzu in Japan.

There is one company in the Stagecoach Group which plays a not insignificant part in the UK transport system as a whole, but operates no buses. National Transport Tokens was formed in the 1970s to manufacture and distribute concessionary travel tokens to various bodies, mostly local authorities and a minority shareholding came to Stagecoach with the purchase of Ribble in April 1989. The aluminium tokens produced by National Transport Tokens are accepted by a variety of operators in lieu of cash fares, including bus companies, taxi firms and rail services and currently NTTs annual turnover is £12m. Stagecoach bought a controlling interest in the company in March 1992 and its headquarters were moved from Manchester to Preston.

In October 1992 Brian Cox, Managing Director of Stagecoach South, and Barry Hinkley, Managing Director of North West joined the main board as executive appointments while Muir Russell and Barry Sealey (who had also previously been a director of the Scottish Transport Group) joined as non-executive directors in December. Muir Russell (who had expected to complete a three-year term) resigned in January 1995 following his promotion within The Scottish Office.

It came as a significant surprise in April 1992 when Stagecoach decided to sell another of its initial operations. Having disposed of the express network the deal was now to sell the Glasgow-based Magicbus operation to Kelvin Central Buses. The vehicles transferred included some newly-delivered Dennis Darts and a substantial number of Bristol VRTs and Routemasters, and the Glasgow depot was also acquired by Kelvin. The Magicbus name and Stagecoach livery continued in use with Kelvin Central until 1993 as part of the deal.

1992 also saw further expansion of the southern fleet when Stagecoach acquired Alder Valley's operations based at depots in Aldershot, Alton and Hindhead. Alder Valley had been through a particularly disturbed time having had a number of owners since privatisation from NBC and suffering from subsequent fragmentation. The operation acquired by Stagecoach was placed under the Stagecoach South umbrella and is operated under the brand name Hants & Surrey.

Having seen the deregulation and privatisation process in the United Kingdom the New Zealand Government decided to embark on a similar course of action. In October 1992 the Wellington City Transport undertaking was privatised and Stagecoach was the successful bidder. There are three companies involved: Wellington City Transport, with a depot at Karori and an outstation at Kilbirnie; Cityline Auckland based at Papakura and Cityline Hutt Valley with depots at Lower Hutt and Stokes Valley. With its new undertaking, Stagecoach now has experience of operating MAN and Hino vehicles but more interestingly, is now operating electric traction. The Wellington City Transport fleet contains over seventy Volvo trolleybuses while Wellington City Transport's share in Harbour City Cable Car Limited has resulted in Stagecoach having an operating interest in this funicular railway.

Overseas developments in 1992 were not confined to Africa and New Zealand. For some time Stagecoach had held a stake in Speedybus Enterprises Limited of Hong Kong, whose primary functions were to sell advertising space on double deckers it supplied to Chinese municipal bus companies, and to import vehicles to China through Hong Kong. Speedybus also supplied Hong Kong double deckers to Stagecoach Malawi. In 1992 Stagecoach Hong Kong Ltd was formed to tender for bus services in Hong Kong, and to gain an operating base in the colony. (Speedybus was primarily a bus dealer and bus advertising contractor rather than an operator, and Stagecoachs 50% interest was disposed of in 1993). In 1994 the company commenced operating services on two commuter routes with five Volvo B10Ms. These vehicles were almost the same as the Stagecoach standard Alexander PS-bodied Volvo B10Ms except that they were fitted with air conditioning to cope with the humid Hong Kong climate. In 1995 six tri-axle Volvo Olympians joined the operation and a second residents route was introduced. The Hong Kong operations were sold in the summer of 1996 after attempts to enlarge the business through the tendering/franchising process had been unsuccessful.

In the spring of 1993 Lancaster City Council expressed an intention to sell its municipal bus undertaking, much of the network operated comprised joint services with Ribble. As Ribble already had a substantial presence in Lancaster and the surrounding area, Stagecoach was not expected to be a bidder for the operation. However, in order to protect its interests in the area, Ribble registered many of Lancaster City's routes and subsequently the City Council decided to liquidate their undertaking, selling the depot and some twelve buses to Ribble during 1993. As a result of this acquisition Ribble was able to close its own, smaller, depot in Morecambe and move into the former council depot in Heysham.

Expansion in the south of England continued in 1993 when the management of East Kent sold their company. This is yet another former NBC subsidiary that was purchased by a management team. Again the new acquisition had been placed under the control of Stagecoach South and it now trades under the Stagecoach East Kent name. The East Kent purchase brought with it depots at Ashford, Canterbury, Thanet (Westwood), Dover, Folkestone and Herne Bay and contained a typical mix of former NBC vehicles with Leyland Nationals, Bristol VRs and Olympians together with a substantial number of minibuses. In addition, it contained several MCW and Scania products. In 1994 East Kent purchased four Dennis low-floor vehicles with Berkhof bodies for the Canterbury Park and Ride service, these being the first such vehicles in the Stagecoach Group with more of the type delivered during 1996 for a Greater Manchester PTE contract.

While the Government had not legislated for the privatisation of municipal bus companies, a number of councils took the opportunity to sell before the end of 1993 to allow all of the income from the sale to be used on other projects. (The proportion for reallocation has since been reduced to 75% when sold before 31st March 1997).

Grimsby Cleethorpes Transport was jointly owned by the Boroughs of Grimsby and Cleethorpes and the two councils decided to sell the undertaking through a competitive tendering process and Stagecoach were the successful bidder. The deal was completed in November 1993 and has now brought the Stagecoach livery to South Humberside. The vehicles acquired are of a typical municipal nature and included substantial numbers of Dennis Dominators and Lances. The last of the five Lances delivered in 1993 was painted into Stagecoach livery before delivery. Grimsby Cleethorpes is operated as a division of the East Midland company.

The 1000th new bus to join Stagecoach was handed over to Ann Gloag and Brian Souter on the opening day of Coach & Bus 93; this was a Volvo B6 destined for United Counties. Stagecoach has been the largest UK purchaser of new buses in recent years, and has invested heavily in renewing its fleet and offering passengers modern, comfortable vehicles. The order for new vehicles for delivery in 1995 was the largest annual order for buses in the UK since privatisation began in the 1980s. Purchasing policy for the year continued to be based on Volvo double deck and single deck chassis together with Mercedes-Benz minibuses, though Dennis have supplied the Dart and Javelin in significant numbers. Alexander with assembly plants in Scotland and Northern Ireland are the preferred bus body builder with Plaxton as the coach body supplier, although some vehicles have been bodied by Northern Counties, particularly for the Groups urban operations.

December 1993 saw a further major acquisition by Stagecoach Holdings. Western Travel Ltd was formed on the privatisation of the Cheltenham and Gloucester company from NBC. Cheltenham and Gloucester operates in both the cities mentioned in its title together with services in Swindon and the Cotswolds based on Stroud. Western Travel itself went on the acquisition trail as part of the NBC privatisation process and acquired the Midland Red South company which brought with it operations in Leamington Spa, Nuneaton, Rugby, Stratford-upon-Avon and Warwick. Western Travel had also secured the eastern part of the National Welsh operation trading as Red & White, adding operations around the Red & White historical base of Monmouthshire and the eastern valleys of South Wales. A further 650 vehicles were added to the Stagecoach Group with this purchase, the first being painted into corporate colours in December 1993.

1993 also saw the company become listed on the London Stock Exchange. The successful 1993 share flotation attracted much publicity and the proceeds gave the group access to considerable additional funds with which to expand. Some 18,000 (over 90%) of Stagecoachs UK employees are now shareholders, following the Buy One Get One Free (BOGOF) offer in 1991 and the award of free shares twice each year from 1994 based on up to 3% of pre-tax profits.

1994 saw the bus industry's consolidation accelerate and Stagecoach's development move into the larger metropolitan markets in which it had previously had limited operations. The year opened with the launch of Stagecoach Manchester at the end of January. Although a division of Ribble, it traded separately under its own brand name on the long established 192 route from central Manchester to Hazel Grove south of Stockport. Originally set up as a unit with sixteen B6s, rapid passenger growth called for more and larger vehicles, and the year finished with 23 B10Ms allocated to the route. In the autumn of 1995 this operation, with the vehicles, was sold to EYMS Group Ltd who also operated south Manchester services through their Finglands subsidiary.

The first full scale acquisition of 1994 was of Western Scottish, a former SBG company, which was owned by its management and employees. Western is based at Ayr with other depots at Cumnock, Dumfries Kilmarnock and Stranraer, and a number of sub-depots both on the mainland and on the Isles of Arran and Bute. The operating area runs from the southern outskirts of Glasgow right down to Annan where the services meet those of Stagecoach North West's Cumberland division while the fleet comprised 340 vehicles, including a large number of different chassis and bodies. Shortly after aquisition the legal company name was changed to Western Buses Limited.

In July 1994 Busways Travel Services Ltd became a subsidiary company of Stagecoach. Busways Travel Services Ltd was a private limited company established by the Transport Act 1985 to acquire the bus undertaking of Tyne and Wear Passenger Transport Executive.

Busways commenced trading in October 1986 under the ownership of the PTA, though its origins can be found in the municipal transport undertakings in Newcastle upon Tyne, South Shields and Sunderland, and also the private companies acquired in 1973 (Armstrong and Galley) and 1975 (Economic). In May 1989 the management/employee buyout was successfully completed. Fifty-one per cent of the shares were purchased by the management of ten while 49% were purchased for employees through an ESOP. The Tyne and Wear Omnibus Company Ltd was acquired in November 1989 and in August 1993 Busways acquired a majority shareholding in Welcome Passenger Transport Ltd.

With a fleet of 590 buses and coaches Busways provides mainly urban local bus services in the Newcastle upon Tyne, South Shields and Sunderland areas whose combined population is approximately half a million. The acquisition represented an important development for the group because Busways mainly provides services in the densely populated metropolitan area of Tyne and Wear. Stagecoach had not previously had a significant presence in a metropolitan area as Stagecoach was effectivly excluded from all the earlier privatisations of 'municipals in South Yorkshire, Aberdeen, Tyneside, Teeside, West Midlands and West Yorkshire because of councils unwillingness to open up to competitive tendering. The controversial Manchester privatisation also seemed biased against 'outsiders such as British Bus and Stagecoach.

Because of the strength of the Busways brand names in the local market the group agreed that Busways should retain its distinctive liveries once Busways joined the group and the presentation of trading names was revised to include reference to group membership. However, during 1995 corporate livery was introduced following a local employee decision after market research showed the group livery to have a more modern image.

Also in the summer of 1994, Stagecoach announced its intention to buy a 20% share in Mainline, the former South Yorkshire PTE bus operation based on Sheffield, Doncaster and Rotherham. In October, however, the Office of Fair Trading decided to investigate this purchase the result being a requirement for Stagecoach to divest its interest. While a sale to FirstBus was agreed, an appeal against the principle of forced divestment was lost in the London courts.

The breakthrough into London bus operation was achieved in September 1994 with the purchase of London Buses' subsidiaries East

The tender for services for 1996/97 on Arran has been awarded to Western Buses who operate several 'tourist' services on the island. To augment the service buses, Western's 1074, YYS174 has been placed in service in the traditional MacBraynes livery. This Bedford C5Z1 carries a Duple Vista body and joined the Western fleet in that livery in 1970. *Tony Wilson*

London and Selkent being announced as part of the privatisation of the capital's red bus fleets. In the case of East London this returned Stagecoach operations to that area of the city following the disposal of East Midland's Frontrunner South East in 1989 to Ensign Bus of Purfleet. Both companies run local suburban services in their respective areas of London as well as trunk routes into the central area. East London's fleet comprises 600 buses operating out of depots at Leyton, Barking, East Ham and Stratford, while Selkent's has 450 buses operating from depots at Bromley, Catford, Plumstead and Orpington, since closed as a result of the Roundabout route tender losses.

A few weeks later saw further expansion in the urban areas of the north east of England, with the acquisition of Cleveland Transit early in the month, and along with it 51% of the share capital of formerly troubled Kingston upon Hull City Transport. The remaining 49% of Kingston upon Hull City transport owned by the ESOP was also acquired. Days later, Darlington City Transport, which had been experiencing financial problems for some time, ceased trading after Busways established a competing network of services in the town, and with it the birth of Stagecoach Darlington. In the middle of the following month Hartlepool Transport joined Stagecoach in an agreed sale.

Hartlepool, also based in the county of Cleveland, employed some 145 staff and operated 68 vehicles. In 1995 the management of the Darlington operation was transferred from Busways to Cleveland.

November 1994 was planned to see the return of Stagecoach into Glasgow with the introduction of Stagecoach Glasgow, a 69 vehicle quality operation, in similar fashion to the Manchester unit. However, two days before Stagecoach Glasgow was due to commence operations, Strathclyde Buses announced they would sell 20% of their shares to Stagecoach in a similar style deal to the Mainline share exchange, and the Stagecoach Glasgow operation, staff and 18 Volvo B10Ms passed to SBL. Like the Mainline operation, this holding attracted the attention of the Monopolies and Mergers Commission who, after investigation, instructed divestment. A legal appeal was lost in July 1996, although the DTI agreed in an out of court settlement not to seek any undertakings against Stagecoach in Strathclyde(apart from separate undertakings in respect of A1) or South Yorkshire.

Further expansion in 1995 commenced in January with the acquisition of A1 Service. This was a complex sale in that Ayrshire Bus Owners was the last Scottish co-operative bus company and was owned by nine separate members. Stagecoach took 75 vehicles with the purchase, not all constituent members sold all their vehicles, and Stagecoach declined to purchase some of the most elderly vehicles. As a result of this and an urgent need to replace many of those acquired, Leyland Titans and Bristol VRs were transferred from other companies to ensure operational needs were met. During the year no less than 21 new Volvo Olympians and many modern mid-life vehicles were placed with this operation to replace the very elderly A1 fleet which had been the subject of a Traffic Commissioners maintenance hearing and warning shortly prior to the sale to Stagecoach.

Despite the small scale of this operation Secretary of State for Trade and Industry directed the Monopolies and Mergers Commission to inquire into the purchase. Much criticism of the MMC has been voiced over this inquiry as each investigation costs the taxpayer a considerable amount of money and consumes valuable management time and energy. It was widely commented on at the time that often larger acquisitions by other groups were being cleared without referral. In November the report was published allowing the retention of the operation providing certain conditions on fares and service levels were adhered to.

June 1995 saw the announcement of a joint venture with Montagu Private Equity to buy part of Rodoviária de Lisboa, the main operator in and around the Portuguese capital. The main towns served are Cascais, Estoril and Sintra, with the 900mm gauge Sintra tram operation included. Some 75 buses and 160 staff from two depots and associated services transferred on 1st January 1996. This purchase brought many AECs and early Volvo products including bendi-buses into the group, though many of the older examples have started to be replaced with the arrival of the first Scania single-deck buses.

In New Zealand Stagecoach acquired the operations of Cesta Travel in Wellington, which brought one additional vehicle to the fleet and Stokes Valley Coaches of Upper Hutt. The Runcimans Motors business was acquired with bus services taken into the Cityline Hutt Valley operation initially while the remaining contract and hire business was acquired subsequently, retaining a local identity.

In July 1995 Stagecoach confirmed the acquisition of ailing Chesterfield Transport following an Extraordinary General Meeting at which 99% of Chesterfield's employees voted in favour of the take over. The Chesterfield operation was placed under East Midlands management who moved its local depot to Stonegravels depot off Sheffield Road. This acquisition too became the subject of a Monopolies and Mergers Commission enquiry with vehicle repainting delayed pending the outcome of the MMC enquiry. Ten much travelled B10Ms were transferred in from Ribble. This purchase was cleared during 1996 allowing the fleet to be renumbered and brought together.

October brought Coach and Bus 95 at which four Stagecoach buses were exhibited by various suppliers. Mercedes-Benz displayed the 800th 709D for the group, destined for Cumberland. On the Northern Counties stand was the last of 52 Volvo Olympians destined for Selkent from the 1995 order. Also in red livery was an Alexander-bodied Dennis Dart for East London but the main Stagecoach attraction was the Volvo B10L demonstrator for the group. It operated in the Fife fleet for a year along side new B10Ms and featured the Säffle-designed body built by Alexander as its Ultra model, and was returned to Volvo after its one year trial.

The investment in new vehicles continued during the year with some 627 new vehicles delivered in the year ending 30th April. This represented a total expenditure in excess of £40 million. At Coach and Bus 95 substantial corporate orders were announced totalling over 1000 buses for delivery during 1996. In a statement Brian Souter said "The level of investment in new vehicles demonstrates our continued commitment to maintain our operating costs at the lowest possible levels, while at the same time offering our customers the highest standard of safety and comfort."

1996 was another year of outstanding growth with pre-tax profits up 34% despite adverse weather and fuel duty increases. In Scotland, Bluebird was granted the Royal Warrant for services to the Royal Family with vehicles at Ballater now displaying the Royal Coat of Arms.

Western Buses saw the greatest change with many services revised and new routes introduced, including several Stagecoach Express inter-urban services providing links from the centres of operation to Glasgow and Edinburgh. Fife intoduced the first articulated coaches on its X27 service from Glasgow, these to be joined by some Plaxton-bodied examples from the ten to be used nationwide. The north west of England saw the acquisition of GM Buses South (now Stagecoach Manchester) in February after several months of speculation. Earlier, the initial Manchester unit was sold to Finglands to ensure there was no conflicting competition issues. Also in the north west, Ribble secured the Hyndburn operations during September, the services to be provided from several Ribble depots as the purchase did not include the Hyndburn operation buildings in Accrington.

Busways and Transit now form the north east England operations. Highlights of 1996 here were the introduction of a Green Route in Stockton and the restructuring of Busways engineering and administration functions. The addition of 59 new buses was the largest delivery in the area for some twenty years. The midlands fleets were joined by Cambus early in 1996 and the administration of Cambus and Chesterfield Transport have now been integrated into East Midlands at Chesterfield. The MMC report presented to Parliament shortly after the last edition was published noted that Chesterfield Transport could have collapsed if Stagecoach had not made the merger offer. Following the merger with Cambus undertakings were agreed with the MMC that the divestment of the Huntingdon depot and Milton Keynes operations of Cambus would be made.

In the west of England two operation units now function, Stagecoach West and Stagecoach Devon. All three divisions of Stagecoach West (Cheltenham & Gloucester, Midland Red South and Red & White) received new single deck buses and minibuses during the year with the Volvo B10Ms being devoted to the important corridors of Nuneaton-Coventry, Cheltenham-Gloucester and Newport-Tredegar. The Devon operation was formed by the amalgamation into one company with two operational divisions for Exeter and Torbay, the latter acquiring open-top Bristol VRs to re-instate regular big-bus services in the Torquay area. 185 vehicles were delivered to Stagecoach South during the year, some 25% of the fleet strength. Stagecoach South also received Titans from Selkent as part of a group policy to cascade urban vehicles to lighter duties at mid-life and help minimise whole-life costs.

1996 in Africa saw a further batch of 30 ERF Trailblazer chassis for Speedlink express services between Lilongwe and Blantyre and other cities. Some 36 second-hand single-decks from Durban City Transport are also being introduced to Blantyre to replace life-expired vehicles

The group was awarded a seven-year franchise for South West Trains in December 1995 and took over operations in February 1996. One of the early developments has been the introduction of bus/rail feeder services between Romsey-Winchester and Bordon-Liphook using buses provided by East London though operated by Stagecoach South. Then newly-liveried train and rail link bus share the same platform at Waterloo on launch day. *Stagecoach Holdings*

including the last of the former KMB double-decks from Hong Kong. During March 1996 the small Hong Kong operation was sold, the B10Ms moving to New Zealand while the Olympians remain on the colony, passing to Citybus.

The group was awarded a seven-year franchise for South West Trains in December 1995 and took over operations in February 1996. SWT operates urban and main line passenger rail services from London Waterloo to over 200 stations principally in south west London, Surrey, Hampshire and Dorset using 1022 vehicles, mainly electric multiple units and Class 159 diesel rail cars. One of the early developments has been the introduction of bus/rail feeder services between Romsey-Winchester and Bordon-Liphook using buses provided by East London though operated by Stagecoach South. The Isle of Wight rail line franchise was also awarded to Stagecoach during 1996.

August 1996 saw the aquisition of Porterbrook leasing Company MEBO Limited, one of three railway rolling stock leasing operators (ROSCO). This operation owns over 35% of the rail stock which is then leased to the various operators for them to operate. Porterbrook Group has its headquarters in Derby. It owns 3774 vehicles of rolling stock and supplies units to 16 of the 25 train operating companies. Approxamately 70 per cent of Porterbrook's rolling stock is leased for eight to ten years

The group was awarded a seven-year franchise for South West Trains in December 1995 and took over operations in February 1996. SWT operates urban and main line passenger rail services from London Waterloo to over 200 stations principally in south west London, Surrey, Hampshire and Dorset using 1022 vehicles, mainly electric multiple units and Class 159 diesel rail cars. Shown here is the first unit to carry the adapted Network South East livery which uses the Stagecoach colours in a modified version on the bus livery. *Stagecoach Holdings*

of which the Government have guaranteed up to 80 per cent of the rentals payable to Porterbrook during these intitial periods. To allow the Stagecoach to manage both South West Trains, and in November the Department of Trade and Industry indicated that it would accept certain undertakings in respect of this acquisition in lieu of reference to the MMC.

Swebus was finally acquired on 2nd October, though the announcement that Stagecoach was the preferred bidder was made several weeks earlier. Swebus has a fleet of approximately 3,450 buses. 90% of these are commuter buses of which 87% are operate d in Sweden. The remainder of the fleet consists of express buses and hire coaches. The principal operations are in Sweden and the largest component of this operation are tendered services for various authorities. In Denmark and Norway, Swebus' operations are also focused on this type of service. As a result small batches of vehicles are often supplied to match the tender with some 200 buses, of various lengths and specifications, planned for delivery in 1997.

In Noveber 1996 Bluebird won the prestigious Bus Company of the year award, at a ceremony in London where the Managing Director, Neil Renilson, received the award from John Watts, Minister of Transport.

Some 625 vehicles have been ordered for 1997 delivery for Stagecoach's British fleets was announced in November. The double-deck requirement will be met by 140 Volvo Olympians of which forty will be bodied by Northern Counties to London specification. One houndred minibuses will be delivered during the year, and these will be the new Mercedes-Benz Vario model and will have Plaxton's Beaver 2 bodywork. Fifty low-floor Dennis Darts, with Alexander ALX200 bodies augment the ninty Volvo B6BLEs from the 1996 delivery order that are just entering service. Requirements for full single-deck and coach needs will be met with the Volvo B10M. Fifteen will carry Expressliner 2 bodies and 60 Interurbans from Plaxton while the buses will be built by Alexander (160) and Northern Counties (100). In additon, options have been taken on five batches, each of 50 further vehicles, and should these options be taken up, then one vehicle in eight will be replaced. The Darts are SLFs and signal a first switch to low floor units for general replacement. In addition, five Northern Counties-bodied Volvo B10BLEs will be trialed with Manchester and used on the 192 service early in 1997. If successful, then upto a quarter of the B10M order may be changed to low-floor buses.

As 1997 commences the corporate livery of white with orange, red and blue stripes is now a familiar sight throughout the United Kingdom and is also highly visible in a number of countries overseas. The company strives to develop its policy of expansion within the whole sphere of transport and the stated ambition of the group is to develop into a truly global surface transport provider, with a turnover of £2 billion by the year 2000.

Of one thing we can be certain. When writing the 1998 edition there will be a lot of further developments to report. Growth and development have been one of the hallmarks of Stagecoach for the past sixteen years, and surely will be so for 1997 as well!

BLUEBIRD

Bluebird Buses Ltd, Guild Street, Aberdeen, Grampian, AB9 2DR

Depots : Hillview Road, East Tullos, Aberdeen; Montgarrie Road, Alford; Golf Road, Ballater; Castleton Place, Braemar; March Road, Buckie; Stirling Road, Crieff; Pinefield, Elgin; North Road, Forres; Hanover Street, Fraserburgh; Schoolhill, Fyvie; Burnett Road, Inverness; Union Road, Macduff; Longside Road, Mintlaw; Ruthvenfield Road, Perth; St Peter Street, Peterhead; Spittalfield; Spurryhillock Ind Est, Stonehaven; Bellabeg, Strathdon and Scotsburn Road, Tain. **Outstations** : Ellon; Castle Street, Fochabers and Inverurie.

002-007		Leyland Olympian ONLXB/1R	Alexander RL		H45/32F	1981		
002	SSA2X	**004**	SSA4X	**005**	SSA5X	**006**	SSA6X	**007**	SSA7X
003	SSA3X							

008	K508ESS	Leyland Olympian ON2R50G13Z4	Alexander RL	DPH43/27F	1992	
009	K509ESS	Leyland Olympian ON2R50G13Z4	Alexander RL	DPH43/27F	1992	
010	K510ESS	Leyland Olympian ON2R50G13Z4	Alexander RL	DPH43/27F	1992	
011	K511ESS	Leyland Olympian ON2R50G13Z4	Alexander RL	DPH43/27F	1992	
012	TSO12X	Leyland Olympian ONLXB/1R	Eastern Coach Works	H45/32F	1982	Ex Stagecoach, 1994
013	TSO13X	Leyland Olympian ONLXB/1R	Eastern Coach Works	H45/32F	1982	Ex Stagecoach, 1994
014	TSO14X	Leyland Olympian ONLXB/1R	Eastern Coach Works	H45/32F	1982	Ex Stagecoach, 1994
015	K515ESS	Leyland Olympian ON2R50G13Z4	Alexander RL	DPH43/27F	1992	
016	TSO16X	Leyland Olympian ONLXB/1R	Eastern Coach Works	H45/32F	1982	Ex Stagecoach, 1994
017	TSO17X	Leyland Olympian ONLXB/1R	Eastern Coach Works	H45/32F	1982	Ex Stagecoach, 1994
018	K518ESS	Leyland Olympian ON2R50G13Z4	Alexander RL	DPH43/27F	1992	
019	OMS910W	Leyland Olympian B45-6LXB	Eastern Coach Works	H45/32F	1981	Ex Stagecoach, 1994

020-025		Leyland Olympian ONLXB/1R	Eastern Coach Works		H45/32F	1982	Ex Stagecoach, 1994
020	TSO20X	**022**	9492SC	**023**	TSO23X	**024**	TSO24X	**025**	TSO15X
021	TSO21X							

026	L26JSA	Volvo Olympian YN2RV18Z4	Northern Counties Palatine I	DPH43/25F	1993	
027	L27JSA	Volvo Olympian YN2RV18Z4	Northern Counties Palatine I	DPH43/25F	1993	
028	L28JSA	Volvo Olympian YN2RV18Z4	Northern Counties Palatine I	DPH43/25F	1993	
029	TSO29X	Leyland Olympian ONLXB/1R	Eastern Coach Works	H45/32F	1982	Ex Stagecoach, 1994
030	TSO30X	Leyland Olympian ONLXB/1R	Eastern Coach Works	H45/32F	1982	Ex Stagecoach, 1994
031	TSO31X	Leyland Olympian ONLXB/1R	Eastern Coach Works	H45/32F	1982	Ex Stagecoach, 1994
032	TSO32X	Leyland Olympian ONLXB/1R	Eastern Coach Works	H45/32F	1982	Ex Stagecoach, 1994

Bluebird vehicles based at Inverness and Tain depots carry IT fleetnames for the Inverness Traction operation. Seen heading for the town centre is Leyland Olympian 027, L27JSA, one of three bodied by Northern Counties and fitted with dual purpose seating.
Malc McDonald

Most of Bluebird's Alexander T-type vehicles have received a mid-life refurbishment and now have seats with corporate moquette. This can be seen through the windows of 163, JSA101V, as it heads from Buckie to Aberdeen on tendered service 308. *Phillip Stephenson*

033-060

		Leyland Olympian ONLXB/1R*		Alexander RL		H45/32F*	1983-85	*044 is DPH41/29F		
								*049 has a 5LXCT engine		

033	YSO33Y	039	YSO39Y	045	A45FRS	051	B351LSO	056	B356LSO
034	YSO34Y	040	YSO40Y	046	A46FRS	052	B352LSO	057	B357LSO
035	YSO35Y	041	YSO41Y	047	A47FRS	053	B353LSO	058	B358LSO
036	YSO36Y	042	YSO42Y	048	B348LSO	054	B354LSO	059	B359LSO
037	YSO37Y	043	YSO43Y	049	B349LSO	055	B355LSO	060	B360LSO
038	YSO38Y	044	A44FRS	050	B350LSO				

061-066

		Leyland Olympian ONLXB/1RV		Alexander RL		DPH43/27F	1986		
061	C461SSO	063	C463SSO	064	MHS4P	065	MHS5P	066	C466SSO
062	C462SSO								

067-071

		Leyland Olympian ONLXB/1RV		Alexander RL		H47/30F	1986		
067	C467SSO	068	C468SSO	069	C469SSO	070	C470SSO	071	GSO1V

072	UWV605S	Bristol VRT/SL3/6LXB	Eastern Coach Works	CO43/31F	1977	Ex East Midland, 1992
074	UWV611S	Bristol VRT/SL3/6LXB	Eastern Coach Works	CO43/31F	1978	Ex Stagecoach South, 1996
075	UWV613S	Bristol VRT/SL3/6LXB	Eastern Coach Works	CO43/31F	1978	Ex Stagecoach South, 1996
076u	MAU146P	Bristol VRT/SL3/6LX	Eastern Coach Works	H39/31F	1976	Ex Stagecoach, 1992
077	VTV171S	Bristol VRT/SL3/6LXB	Eastern Coach Works	H43/31F	1978	Ex Stagecoach South, 1996
078	EAP996V	Bristol VRT/SL3/6LXB	Eastern Coach Works	H43/31F	1980	Ex Stagecoach South, 1996
079u	EAP983V	Bristol VRT/SL3/6LXB	Eastern Coach Works	H43/31F	1980	Ex Stagecoach South, 1996
082	OCY910R	Bristol VRT/SL3/501	Eastern Coach Works	H43/31F	1977	Ex East Midland, 1992

085-089

		Leyland Olympian ONLXB/1RV		Alexander RL		DPH43/27F	1987		
085	D385XRS	086	D386XRS	087	D387XRS	088	D388XRS	089	D389XRS

Photographed in Elgin is Bluebird 131, RRS46R, a Leyland Leopard with Duple Dominant I bodywork which, despite being 20 years old, is still very presentable. Bluebird use Leyland Leopards with high-back seating on several of the longer deeply rural routes that are operated on local authority tenders let to the lowest bidders, hence the use of fully depreciated vehicles. *Malc McDonald*

090-099

Leyland Olympian ON2R56G13Z4 Alexander RL   DPH47/27F 1991-92

090	J120XHH	**092**	J122XHH	**097**	J197YSS	**098**	J198YSS	**099** J199YSS
091	J121XHH	**096**	J196YSS					

100	L100JLB	Volvo Olympian YN2RV18Z4	Northern Counties Palatine I	DPH43/25F	1993	
101	L101JSA	Volvo Olympian YN2RV18Z4	Northern Counties Palatine I	DPH43/25F	1993	
102	L102JSA	Volvo Olympian YN2RV18Z4	Northern Counties Palatine I	DPH43/25F	1993	
103	FDV810V	Bristol VRT/SL3/6LXB	Eastern Coach Works	H43/31F	1980	Ex Stagecoach, 1994
104	JAK209W	Bristol VRT/SL3/6LXB	Eastern Coach Works	H43/31F	1980	Ex Western Scottish, 1995
105	FDV816V	Bristol VRT/SL3/6LXB	Eastern Coach Works	H43/31F	1980	Ex Stagecoach, 1994
106	UWV608S	Bristol VRT/SL3/6LXB	Eastern Coach Works	CO43/31F	1977	Ex Stagecoach, 1991
107	FDV819V	Bristol VRT/SL3/6LXB	Eastern Coach Works	H43/31F	1980	Ex Stagecoach, 1994
108	UWV609S	Bristol VRT/SL3/6LXB	Eastern Coach Works	CO43/31F	1977	Ex Stagecoach, 1991
109	FDV840V	Bristol VRT/SL3/6LXB	Eastern Coach Works	H43/31F	1980	Ex Stagecoach, 1994
110	JAK210W	Bristol VRT/SL3/6LXB	Eastern Coach Works	H43/31F	1980	Ex Stagecoach, 1994
111	KWA213W	Bristol VRT/SL3/6LXB	Eastern Coach Works	H43/31F	1981	Ex Western Scottish, 1995
112	JAK212W	Bristol VRT/SL3/6LXB	Eastern Coach Works	H43/31F	1980	Ex Stagecoach, 1994
113	HWG207W	Bristol VRT/SL3/6LXB	Eastern Coach Works	H43/31F	1980	Ex Western Scottish, 1995
114	KWA219W	Bristol VRT/SL3/6LXC	Eastern Coach Works	H43/31F	1981	Ex Western Scottish, 1995
115	FAO429V	Bristol VRT/SL3/6LXB	Eastern Coach Works	H43/31F	1980	Ex Western Scottish, 1995
116	EWE205V	Bristol VRT/SL3/6LXB	Eastern Coach Works	H43/31F	1980	Ex Western Scottish, 1995
117	KKY222W	Bristol VRT/SL3/6LXB	Eastern Coach Works	H43/31F	1981	Ex Western Scottish, 1995
120	SAO410R	Bristol VRT/SL3/501	Eastern Coach Works	H43/31F	1977	Ex Cumberland, 1991
122	SAO412R	Bristol VRT/SL3/501	Eastern Coach Works	H43/31F	1977	Ex Cumberland, 1991
123	EWE202V	Bristol VRT/SL3/6LXB	Eastern Coach Works	H43/31F	1980	Ex Western Scottish, 1995
124	KWA215W	Bristol VRT/SL3/6LXC	Eastern Coach Works	H43/31F	1981	Ex Western Scottish, 1995
125	KWA216W	Bristol VRT/SL3/6LXC	Eastern Coach Works	H43/31F	1981	Ex Western Scottish, 1995
126	KRM430W	Bristol VRT/SL3/6LXB	Eastern Coach Works	H43/31F	1980	Ex Western Scottish, 1995
128	RJT155R	Bristol VRT/SL3/6LXB	Eastern Coach Works	H43/31F	1977	Ex Stagecoach, 1992
131	RRS46R	Leyland Leopard PSU3E/4R	Duple Dominant I	C49F	1977	
132	RRS47R	Leyland Leopard PSU3E/4R	Duple Dominant I	C49F	1977	
133	RRS48R	Leyland Leopard PSU3E/4R	Duple Dominant I	C49F	1977	
134	PRA109R	Leyland Leopard PSU3C/4R	Alexander AT	C49F	1976	Ex East Midland, 1995

135	RRS50R	Leyland Leopard PSU3E/4R	Duple Dominant I	C49F	1977	
136	PRA110R	Leyland Leopard PSU3C/4R	Alexander AT	C49F	1976	Ex East Midland, 1995
137	PRA112R	Leyland Leopard PSU3C/4R	Alexander AT	C49F	1976	Ex East Midland, 1995
138	RRS53R	Leyland Leopard PSU3E/4R	Duple Dominant I	C49F	1977	

139-144

		Leyland Leopard PSU3E/4R	Alexander AT	DP49F	1979	

139	CRS60T	141	CRS62T	142	CRS63T	143	CRS68T	144	CRS69T
140	CRS61T								

145	CRS70T	Leyland Leopard PSU3E/4R	Duple Dominant I	C49F	1979	
146	CRS71T	Leyland Leopard PSU3E/4R	Duple Dominant I	C49F	1979	
147	CRS73T	Leyland Leopard PSU3E/4R	Duple Dominant I	C49F	1979	
148	CRS74T	Leyland Leopard PSU3E/4R	Duple Dominant I	C49F	1979	
149u	OSJ635R	Leyland Leopard PSU3C/3R	Alexander AY	B53F	1977	Ex East Midland, 1995
150u	OSJ643R	Leyland Leopard PSU3C/3R	Alexander AY	B53F	1977	Ex East Midland, 1995
151u	OSJ644R	Leyland Leopard PSU3C/3R	Alexander AY	B53F	1977	Ex East Midland, 1995

152-158

		Leyland Leopard PSU3E/4R	Alexander AYS	DP49F*	1980	Ex Stagecoach, 1994
						*155/7 are B53F

152	GSO89V	154	GSO91V	156	GSO93V	157	GSO94V	158	GSO95V
153	GSO90V	155	GSO92V						

160	KRS531V	Leyland Leopard PSU3E/4R	Duple Dominant II Express	C49F	1980	
161	KRS532V	Leyland Leopard PSU3E/4R	Duple Dominant II Express	C49F	1980	
162w	OSJ634R	Leyland Leopard PSU3C/3R	Alexander AY	B53F	1977	Ex East Midland, 1995
163	JSA101V	Leyland Leopard PSU3F/4R	Alexander AT	DP49F	1980	
164	JSA102V	Leyland Leopard PSU3F/4R	Alexander AT	DP49F	1980	
165	JSA103V	Leyland Leopard PSU3F/4R	Alexander AT	DP49F	1980	
166	JSA104V	Leyland Leopard PSU3F/4R	Alexander AT	DP49F	1980	
167	4585SC	Leyland Leopard PSU3G/4R	Duple Dominant II Express	C49F	1981	Ex Stagecoach, 1994
169	NUF276	Leyland Leopard PSU3G/4R	Duple Dominant II Express	C49F	1981	Ex Stagecoach, 1994
170	VLT272	Leyland Leopard PSU3G/4R	Duple Dominant II Express	C49F	1981	Ex Stagecoach, 1994
171	866NHT	Leyland Leopard PSU3G/4R	Duple Dominant II Express	C49F	1981	Ex Stagecoach, 1994
172	145CLT	Leyland Leopard PSU3E/4R	Duple Dominant II Express	C53F	1980	Ex Western Scottish, 1995
188	DWF188V	Bristol VRT/SL3/6LXB	Eastern Coach Works	H43/31F	1979	Ex Stagecoach, 1994
190	DWF190V	Bristol VRT/SL3/6LXB	Eastern Coach Works	H43/31F	1979	Ex Stagecoach, 1994
191	DWF191V	Bristol VRT/SL3/6LXB	Eastern Coach Works	H43/31F	1979	Ex Stagecoach, 1994
193	DWF193V	Bristol VRT/SL3/6LXB	Eastern Coach Works	H43/31F	1979	Ex Stagecoach, 1994
213	HNE252V	Leyland Leopard PSU5C/4R	Duple Dominant II Express	C53F	1980	Ex Stagecoach, 1994
214	HNE254V	Leyland Leopard PSU5C/4R	Duple Dominant II Express	C53F	1980	Ex Stagecoach, 1994
215	JND260V	Leyland Leopard PSU5C/4R	Duple Dominant II Express	C53F	1980	Ex Stagecoach, 1994
216	XRM772Y	Leyland Leopard PSU5C/4R	Duple Dominant III	C57F	1983	Ex Hardie's Coaches, Aberchirder, 1994
217w	D523KSE	Bedford YNV Venturer	Duple 320	C57F	1986	Ex Hardie's Coaches, Aberchirder, 1994
221	WFS135W	Leyland Leopard PSU3F/4R	Alexander AYS	B53F	1980	Ex Stagecoach, 1994
223	WFS137W	Leyland Leopard PSU3F/4R	Alexander AYS	B53F	1980	Ex Stagecoach, 1994
230	D435RYS	Mercedes-Benz 609D	Scott	C24F	1987	Ex Airpark, Linwood, 1990
231	D436RYS	Mercedes-Benz 609D	Scott	C24F	1987	Ex Airpark, Linwood, 1990
233	E364YGB	Mercedes-Benz 609D	Scott	C24F	1988	Ex Airpark, Linwood, 1990
234	E842KAS	Mercedes-Benz 609D	Reeve Burgess	C23F	1988	Ex Glenlivet & District, 1990
235	E947BHS	Mercedes-Benz 609D	Scott	C24F	1988	Ex Whitelaw, Stonehouse, 1990
236	F77HAU	Mercedes-Benz 609D	Scott	C24F	1988	Ex Skills, Sheffield, 1990
237	F164XCS	Mercedes-Benz 609D	Scott	C24F	1989	Ex Clyde Coast, Ardrossan, 1990
238	F862FWB	Mercedes-Benz 609D	Whittaker	C24F	1989	Ex Metcalfe, Ferryhill, 1990
239	D322MNC	Mercedes-Benz 609D	Made-to-Measure	DP25F	1986	Ex Fife Scottish, 1994
241	C901HWF	Mercedes-Benz L608D	Reeve Burgess	DP19F	1985	Ex Fife Scottish, 1994

256-292

		Mercedes-Benz 709D	Alexander Sprint	B25F*	1990	Ex Stagecoach, 1991-94
						*279-292 are B23F

256	G256TSL	262	G262TSL	275	G275TSL	283	G283TSL	288	G288TSL
257	G257TSL	270	G270TSL	276	G276TSL	284	G284TSL	289	G289TSL
258	G258TSL	271	G271TSL	277	G277TSL	285	G285TSL	290	G290TSL
259	G259TSL	272	G272TSL	278	G278TSL	286	G286TSL	291	G291TSL
260	G260TSL	273	G273TSL	279	G279TSL	287	G287TSL	292	G292TSL
261	G261TSL	274	G274TSL	282	G282TSL				

293	E713LYU	Mercedes-Benz 811D	Optare StarRider	B28F	1988	Ex Western Scottish, 1995
294	E714LYU	Mercedes-Benz 811D	Optare StarRider	B28F	1988	Ex Western Scottish, 1995
295	F169FWY	Mercedes-Benz 811D	Optare StarRider	B26F	1989	Ex Western Scottish, 1995
296	F177FWY	Mercedes-Benz 811D	Optare StarRider	B26F	1989	Ex Western Scottish, 1995

297	F180FWY	Mercedes-Benz 811D	Optare StarRider	B26F	1989	Ex Western Scottish, 1995
298	G86KUB	Mercedes-Benz 811D	Optare StarRider	B26F	1989	Ex Western Scottish, 1995
299	L550JFS	Mercedes-Benz 814D	Dormobile Routemaker	B33F	1993	Ex John G Gordon, Dornoch, 1996
301	L301JSA	Mercedes-Benz 709D	Alexander Sprint	DP25F	1993	
302	L302JSA	Mercedes-Benz 709D	Alexander Sprint	DP25F	1993	
303	L303JSA	Mercedes-Benz 709D	Alexander Sprint	DP25F	1993	

304-314

Mercedes-Benz 709D — Alexander Sprint — DP25F — 1990 — Ex Stagecoach, 1991-94

304	G193PAO	307	G196PAO	309	G198PAO	311	G200PAO	313	G202PAO
305	G194PAO	308	G197PAO	310	G199PAO	312	G201PAO	314	G203PAO
306	G195PAO								

315-321

Mercedes-Benz 709D — Alexander Sprint — DP25F — 1993-94

| 315 | L315JSA | 317 | M317RSO | 319 | M319RSO | 320 | M320RSO | 321 | M321RSO |
| 316 | L316JSA | 318 | M318RSO | | | | | | |

336-352

Mercedes-Benz 709D — Alexander Sprint — B25F — 1996

336	N636VSS	340	N640VSS	344	P344ASO	347	P347ASO	350	P350ASO
337	N637VSS	341	P341ASO	345	P345ASO	348	P348ASO	351	P351ASO
338	N638VSS	342	P342ASO	346	P346ASO	349	P349ASO	352	P352ASO
339	N639VSS	343	P343ASO						

421	A116ESA	Leyland Tiger TRBTL11/2R	Alexander P	B52F	1983	
422	A117ESA	Leyland Tiger TRBTL11/2R	Alexander P	B52F	1983	
423	A118ESA	Leyland Tiger TRBTL11/2R	Alexander P	B52F	1983	

424-430

Leyland Tiger TRBLXB/2RH — Alexander P — B52F — 1984

| 424 | A121GSA | 426 | A123GSA | 428 | A125GSA | 429 | A126GSA | 430 | A127GSA |
| 425 | A122GSA | 427 | A124GSA | | | | | | |

431	PES190Y	Leyland Tiger TRCTL11/3R	Duple Laser	C55F	1983	Ex Fife Scottish, 1994
433	A940XGG	Leyland Tiger TRCTL11/3R	Duple Laser	C51F	1984	Ex Fife Scottish, 1994
434	A941XGG	Leyland Tiger TRCTL11/3R	Duple Laser	C51F	1984	Ex Fife Scottish, 1994
435	A942XGG	Leyland Tiger TRCTL11/3R	Duple Laser	C51F	1984	Ex Fife Scottish, 1994

442-446

Leyland Tiger TRCTL11/2RP — Alexander TC — C51F* — 1985 — *443 is C49F; 446 is C47F

| 442 | TSV718 | 443 | TSV719 | 444 | TSV720 | 445 | TSV721 | 446 | TSV722 |

447	126ASV	Leyland Tiger TRBTL11/2R	Alexander TE	C51F	1983	Ex Kelvin Scottish, 1986
448	127ASV	Leyland Tiger TRBTL11/2R	Alexander TE	C51F	1983	Ex Kelvin Scottish, 1986
449	128ASV	Leyland Tiger TRBTL11/2R	Alexander TE	C51F	1983	Ex Kelvin Scottish, 1986

The 1996 delivery of Alexander Sprint minibuses for Bluebird have entered service at Inverness where they have displaced earlier examples. Pictured shortly after delivery 349, P349ASO, is one of the batch built at Alexander's assembly unit in Belfast.
Murdoch Currie

450-454 Leyland Tiger TRCTL11/3RH Alexander TC C57F 1987

| 450 | D744BRS | 451 | LSK547 | 452 | LSK548 | 453 | 147YFM | 454 | BSK756 |

455	HSK760	Leyland Tiger TRCLXC/2RH	Duple 320	C53F	1986	Ex Central Scottish, 1989
456	C111JCS	Leyland Tiger TRCLXC/2RH	Duple 320	C53F	1986	Ex Central Scottish, 1989
458	WAO643Y	Leyland Tiger TRCTL11/2R	Alexander TE	C47F	1983	Ex Ribble, 1994
459	RIB4309	Leyland Tiger TRCTL11/2R	Alexander TE	C49F	1983	Ex East Midland, 1991

460-465 Leyland Tiger TRCTL11/3R Duple Laser C53F 1984 Ex National Welsh, 1992

| 460 | AAX600A | 462 | AKG232A | 463 | AAX589A | 464 | AAX601A | 465 | AKG162A |
| 461 | AAX631A | | | | | | | | |

466	NIB4138	Leyland Tiger TRCTL11/3RH	Duple Laser	C51F	1984	Ex Stagecoach, 1994
467	NIB5455	Leyland Tiger TRCTL11/3RH	Duple Laser	C51F	1984	Ex Stagecoach, 1994
468	A663WSU	Leyland Tiger TRBTL11/2RP	Alexander TE	DP53F	1983	Ex Kelvin Central, 1993

491-499 Volvo B6-9.9M Alexander ALX200 B40F 1996

| 491 | P491BRS | 493 | P493BRS | 495 | P495BRS | 497 | P497BRS | 499 | P499BRS |
| 492 | P492BRS | 494 | P494BRS | 496 | P496BRS | 498 | P498BRS | | |

501-512 Dennis Dart 9.8SDL3017 Alexander Dash B41F 1992

501	J501FPS	504	J504FPS	507	J507FPS	509	J509FPS	511	J511FPS
502	J502FPS	505	J505FPS	508	J508FPS	510	J510FPS	512	J512FPS
503	J503FPS	506	J506FPS						

513-522 Dennis Dart 9.8SDL3017 Alexander Dash B40F 1993

| 513 | K101XHG | 515 | K103XHG | 517 | K105XHG | 519 | K107XHG | 521 | K109XHG |
| 514 | K102XHG | 516 | K104XHG | 518 | K106XHG | 520 | K108XHG | 522 | K110XHG |

527-544 Volvo B10M-62 Plaxton Premiére Interurban DP51F 1994

527	M527RSO	531	M531RSO	535	M535RSO	539	M539RSO	542	M542RSO
528	M528RSO	532	M532RSO	536	M536RSO	540	M540RSO	543	M543RSO
529	M529RSO	533	M533RSO	537	M537RSO	541	M541RSO	544	M544RSO
530	M530RSO	534	M534RSO	538	M538RSO				

545	1412NE	Volvo B10M-61	Van Hool Alizée	C53F	1986	Ex Hardie's Coaches, Aberchirder, 1994
546	TSV778	Volvo B10M-61	Van Hool Alizée	C53F	1986	Ex Hardie's Coaches, Aberchirder, 1994
547	TSV779	Volvo B10M-61	Van Hool Alizée	C53F	1987	Ex Rainworth Travel, 1992
548	TSV780	Volvo B10M-61	Van Hool Alizée	C53F	1987	Ex Shearings, 1991
549	TSV781	Volvo B10M-61	Van Hool Alizée	C53F	1987	Ex Shearings, 1991
550	CSU920	Volvo B10M-61	Van Hool Alizée	C53F	1987	Ex Rainworth Travel, 1992
551	CSU921	Volvo B10M-61	Van Hool Alizée	C53F	1987	Ex Shearings, 1991
552	CSU922	Volvo B10M-61	Van Hool Alizée	C53F	1987	Ex Shearings, 1991
553	CSU923	Volvo B10M-61	Van Hool Alizée	C53F	1987	Ex Shearings, 1991
554	F277WAF	Volvo B10M-61	Duple 320	C56F	1989	Ex Scotravel, Elgin, 1995
555	DDZ8844	Volvo B10M-61	Duple 320	C57F	1989	Ex Scotravel, Elgin, 1995
556	MIB7416	Volvo B10M-61	Plaxton Paramount 3500 III	C53F	1988	Ex Western Buses, 1996
557	F424GGB	Volvo B10M-61	Plaxton Paramount 3?00 III	C57F	1988	Ex Gray, Fochabers, 1996
558	UOT648	Volvo B10M-61	Van Hool Alizée	C53F	1988	Ex Eastons, Inverurie, 1996
559	OSK784	Volvo B10M-61	Duple 320	C53F	1988	Ex Eastons, Inverurie, 1996

561-570 Volvo B10M-60 Plaxton Premiére Interurban DP51F 1993 561/70 ex Stagecoach, 1994

| 561 | K561GSA | 563 | K563GSA | 565 | K565GSA | 567 | K567GSA | 569 | K569GSA |
| 562 | K562GSA | 564 | K564GSA | 566 | K566GSA | 568 | K568GSA | 570 | K570GSA |

Opposite, top: **The 1997 new year heralds the displacement of Routemasters on Perth town service and the introduction of the first of ninety Volvo B6BLE buses for Stagecoach. These carry the new Alexander ALX200 body.** *Iain Smart*
Opposite, bottom: **The Mercedes-Benz 709D has almost eliminated the other types of minibuses with the introduction of 400 of the type across the group during 1996. One of the earlier group deliveries is seen here as Bluebird 278, G278TSL.** *Malc McDonald*

Ten Dennis Darts were placed into service with Bluebird in July 1993 and followed on from a dozen delivered the previous year. Most are allocated to Inverness, but four including 521, K109XHG shown here, are based in Aberdeen for outer suburban services. *Phillip Stephenson*

571-578

| | | | | | | | | | Volvo B10M-55 | | Alexander PS | B49F | 1993 | Ex Stagecoach, 1994 |

571	K571LTS	573	K573LTS	575	K575LTS	577	K577LTS	578	K578LTS
572	K572LTS	574	K574LTS	576	K576LTS				

579	L579JSA	Volvo B10M-60	Plaxton Premiére Interurban	DP51F	1993
580	L580JSA	Volvo B10M-60	Plaxton Premiére Interurban	DP51F	1993
581	L581JSA	Volvo B10M-60	Plaxton Premiére Interurban	DP51F	1993
582	N582XSA	Volvo B10M-62	Plaxton Premiére Interurban	DP51F	1996
583	N583XSA	Volvo B10M-62	Plaxton Premiére Interurban	DP51F	1996
584	N584XSA	Volvo B10M-62	Plaxton Premiére Interurban	DP51F	1996
585	L585JSA	Volvo B10M-60	Plaxton Premiére Interurban	DP51F	1993
586	L586JSA	Volvo B10M-60	Plaxton Premiére Interurban	DP51F	1993
587	L587JSA	Volvo B10M-60	Plaxton Premiére Interurban	DP51F	1993
588	L588JSA	Volvo B10M-60	Plaxton Premiére Interurban	DP51F	1993

589-598

| | | | | | | | | | Volvo B10M-55 | | Alexander PS | DP48F | 1994 |

589	M589OSO	591	M591OSO	593	M593OSO	595	M595OSO	597	M597OSO
590	M590OSO	592	M592OSO	594	M594OSO	596	M596OSO	598	M598OSO

618	N618USS	Volvo B10M-62	Plaxton Expressliner 2	C44FT	1995	
619	N619USS	Volvo B10M-62	Plaxton Expressliner 2	C44FT	1995	
620	N620USS	Volvo B10M-62	Plaxton Expressliner 2	C44FT	1995	
623	J455FSR	Volvo B10M-61	Plaxton Paramount 3500 III	C46FT	1991	Ex Express Travel, 1994
624	J456FSR	Volvo B10M-61	Plaxton Paramount 3500 III	C46FT	1992	Ex Speedlink, 1994
625	P625NSE	Volvo B10M-62	Plaxton Expressliner 2	C44FT	1997	
626	P626NSE	Volvo B10M-62	Plaxton Expressliner 2	C44FT	1997	

628-634

| | | | | | | | | | Volvo B10M-62 | | Plaxton Premiére Interurban | DP51F | 1996 |

628	N148XSA	630	N150XSA	632	N152XSA	633	N153XSA	634	N154XSA
629	N149XSA	631	N151XSA						

The 1997 Stagecoach Bus Handbook

Special event vehicles - traditional liveries

602	EDS50A	AEC Routemaster R2RH	Park Royal	H36/28R	1960	Ex Stagecoach, 1994
603	NSG636A	AEC Routemaster R2RH	Park Royal	H36/28R	1962	Ex Stagecoach, 1994
604	YTS820A	AEC Routemaster 2R2RH	Park Royal	H36/28R	1963	Ex Stagecoach, 1994
605	USK625	AEC Routemaster R2RH	Park Royal	H36/28R	1961	Ex Stagecoach, 1994
606	ALD968B	AEC Routemaster 2R2RH	Park Royal	H36/28R	1964	Ex Stagecoach, 1994
607	LDS201A	AEC Routemaster 2R2RH	Park Royal	H36/24R	1963	Ex Stagecoach, 1994
608	490CLT	AEC Routemaster 2R2RH	Park Royal	H32/25R	1962	Ex Selkent, 1994
609	XSL596A	AEC Routemaster 2R2RH	Park Royal	H36/28R	1962	Ex Stagecoach, 1994
614	LDS210A	AEC Routemaster R2RH	Park Royal	H36/28R	1962	Ex Stagecoach, 1994
650u	FES831W	Volvo B58-61	Duple Dominant IV	DP59F	1981	Ex Stagecoach, 1994
651u	NMY643E	AEC Routemaster R2RH2	Park Royal	H32/24F	1967	Ex Kelvin Scottish, 1993
652	GRS343E	Albion Viking VK43AL	Alexander Y	DP40F	1967	Ex Stagecoach, 1994
653	HDV639E	Bristol MW6G	Eastern Coach Works	C39F	1967	Ex preservation, 1996
654u	HGM335E	Bristol FLF6G	Eastern Coach Works	H44/34F	1967	Ex Stagecoach, 1994
655u	HFM561D	Bristol MW6G	Eastern Coach Works	C39F	1966	Ex preservation, 1996
657	DGS625	Leyland Tiger PS1/2	McLennan	C39F	1951	Ex Stagecoach, 1994

Liveries: 618-24 National Express

Previous Registrations:

126ASV	BMS511Y	KRS531V	HSA97V, CSU921
127ASV	BMS513Y	KRS532V	HSA98V, CSU922
128ASV	BMS515Y	L100JLB	L110JSA
1412NE	C325DND	LDS201A	607DYE
145CLT	ORS107W, TSV719, PSO28W	LDS210A	245CLT
147YFM	D439XRS	LSK547	D437XRS
4585SC	ORS106W, TSV718, PSO27W	LSK548	D438XRS
490CLT	From new	MHS4P	C464SSO
866NHT	ORS110W, TSV722, PSO32W	MHS5P	C465SSO
9492SC	TSO19X	MIB7416	F27LTO
A663WSU	A120GLS, WLT976	NIB4138	A45YAK
A940XGG	A507PST, GSU344	NIB5455	A46YAK
A941XGG	A505PST, GSU342	NSG636A	164CLT
A942XGG	A506PST, GSU343	NUF276	ORS108W, TSV720, PSO27W, OVL473
AAX589A	A216VWO	OSK784	E748JAY, A3KRT
AAX600A	A219VWO	PES190Y	VTY130Y, GSU341
AAX601A	A218VWO	RIB4309	A40XHE
AAX631A	A222VWO	TSV718	B328LSA
AKG162A	A223VWO	TSV719	B329LSA
AKG232A	A229VWO	TSV720	B330LSA
BSK756	E640BRS	TSV721	B331LSA
CSU920	D550MVR	TSV722	B332LSA
CSU921	D551MVR	TSV778	C330DND
CSU922	D552MVR	TSV779	D547MVR
CSU923	D553MVR	TSV780	D548MVR
D744BRS	D436XRS, BSK744	TSV781	D549MVR
DGS625	From new	UOT648	E644UNE, LSK874
DDZ8844	F27LTO	USK625	WLT980
EDS50A	WLT560	VLT272	ORS109W, TSV721, PSO31W, LSK528
GSO1V	C471SSO	XSL596A	289CLT
HSK760	C110JCS	YTS820A	599CLT

BURNLEY & PENDLE

Burnley & Pendle Transport Co Ltd; Vicount Central Ltd,
Queensgate, Colne Road, Burnley, Lancashire, BB10 1HH

Stagecoach Holdings has a 50% share of Burnley & Pendle Transport Company Limited. The remaining 50% has been placed for sale by Burnley Council and discussions over this share are currently taking place.

1	OIJ201	Aüwaerter Neoplan N116/3	Aüwaerter Cityliner	C48FT	1991	Ex Parry, Cheslyn Hay, 1994
2	GSU552	Volvo B10M-61	Jonckheere Jubilee P50	C49F	1986	
3	GSU553	Volvo B10M-61	Jonckheere Jubilee P50	C49F	1986	
7	XSU907	Volvo C10M-70	Ramseier & Jenzer	C49FT	1985	Ex Park's, 1990
8	XSU908	Volvo C10M-70	Ramseier & Jenzer	C49FT	1985	Ex Park's, 1990
9	XSU909	Volvo B10M-61	Jonckheere Jubilee P50	C51FT	1986	Ex Parry, Cheslyn Hay, 1990
10	XSU910	Volvo B10M-61	Jonckheere Jubilee P50	C49FT	1987	Ex Parry, Cheslyn Hay, 1990
11	HXI311	Volvo B10M-61	Jonckheere Jubilee P50	C49FT	1988	Ex Parry, Cheslyn Hay, 1991
12	NXI812	Volvo B10MT-53	Van Hool Alizée	C48FT	1989	Ex Rothwell, Heywood, 1991
13	GXI613	Volvo B10MT-50	Plaxton Paramount 4000RS	CH53/12DT	1989	Ex Flight's, 1992
14	NXI414	Volvo B10MT-53	Jonckheere Jubilee P95	CH54/13DT	1985	Ex Flight's, 1988
15	XFK305	Toyota HDB30R	Caetano Optimo	C21F	1992	
16	GXI516	Volvo B10MT-53	Van Hool Astral	C52/13FT	1989	Ex Excelsior, 1995

17-23
Volvo Citybus B10M-55   Alexander PS   B51F   1991

17	H617ACK	19	H619ACK	21	H621ACK	22	H622ACK	23	H623ACK
18	H618ACK	20	H620ACK						

24	J24MCW	Volvo Citybus B10M-50	East Lancashire EL2000	B45F	1992
25	J25MCW	Volvo Citybus B10M-50	East Lancashire EL2000	B45F	1992
26	K26WBV	Volvo Citybus B10M-50	East Lancashire EL2000	B45F	1993
27	K27WBV	Volvo Citybus B10M-50	East Lancashire EL2000	B45F	1993

30-43
Leyland Leopard PSU4E/4R   East Lancashire   B47F   1978-80

30	MFV30T	35	MFV35T	38	DBV38W	40	DBV40W	42	DBV42W
33	MFV33T	36	MFV36T	39	DBV39W	41	DBV41W	43	DBV43W
34	MFV34T								

44-50
Leyland National 2 NL116L11/1R   B52F   1980

44	XRN44V	46	XRN46V	48	XRN48V	49	XRN49V	50	XRN50V
45	XRN45V	47	XRN47V						

51	GSU551	Leyland Tiger TRCTL11/3R	Plaxton Paramount 3500	C53F	1983	
54	GSU554	Leyland Tiger TRCTL11/3R	Duple Laser 1	C53F	1983	Ex GM Buses, 1989
55	XSU905	Leyland Tiger TRCTL11/3R	Duple Laser 1	C55F	1983	Ex GM Buses, 1989
56	XSU906	Mercedes-Benz 709D	Reeve Burgess Beaver	C19F	1987	
57	VFV7V	Leyland Leopard PSU3E/4R	Duple Dominant II	C53F	1979	

61-66
Volvo Citybus B10M-55   Alexander P   DP53F*   1988   *61 is B53F

61	E61JFV	63	E63JFV	64	E64JFV	65	E65JFV	66	E66JFV
62	E62JFV								

67	G67PFR	Volvo Citybus B10M-55	East Lancashire EL2000	B51F	1990	
68	G68PFR	Volvo Citybus B10M-55	East Lancashire EL2000	B51F	1990	
69	BUH239V	Leyland National 2 NL106L11/1R		B44F	1980	Ex National Welsh, 1988
70	BUH240V	Leyland National 2 NL106L11/1R		B44F	1980	Ex National Welsh, 1989
71	BUH241V	Leyland National 2 NL106L11/1R		B44F	1980	Ex National Welsh, 1988
72	FUH32V	Leyland National 2 NL116L11/1R		B49F	1980	Ex Taff Ely, 1988
73	FUH33V	Leyland National 2 NL116L11/1R		B49F	1980	Ex Taff Ely, 1988
74	FUH34V	Leyland National 2 NL116L11/1R		B49F	1980	Ex Taff Ely, 1988

Burnley & Pendle have a fleet of vehicles mostly compatible with the main group. The Colne Road depot has been used by Ribble as an outstation of Clitheroe for some time. Shown here is 101, E101JFV, lettered for the Blackpool Flyer service. *Glyn Matthews*

78	H78CFV	Mercedes-Benz 811D	Alexander AM	B31F	1991		
79	H79CFV	Mercedes-Benz 811D	Alexander AM	B31F	1991		
80w	C80OCW	Mercedes-Benz L608D	Reeve Burgess	B20F	1986		
81	D81UFV	Mercedes-Benz L608D	Sparshatts	B20F	1986		
82w	D82UFV	Mercedes-Benz L608D	Sparshatts	B20F	1986		
83w	D83UFV	Mercedes-Benz L608D	Sparshatts	B20F	1986		
84	E84HRN	Mercedes-Benz 709D	Robin Hood	B29F	1987		

85-90			Mercedes-Benz 811D	Robin Hood	B29F	1987-88	
85	E85HRN	87	E87HRN	88	E88HRN	89	E89HRN	90	E90JHG
86	E86HRN						

91	E91LBV	Mercedes-Benz 709D	Alexander AM	B25F	1988		
92	E92LHG	Mercedes-Benz 709D	Alexander AM	B25F	1988		
93	E93LHG	Mercedes-Benz 709D	Alexander AM	B25F	1988		
94	E94LHG	Mercedes-Benz 709D	Alexander AM	B25F	1988		
95	F995DRN	Mercedes-Benz 709D	Reeve Burgess Beaver	DP25F	1988		
96	G96MRN	Mercedes-Benz 811D	Reeve Burgess Beaver	B31F	1990		
97	G97MRN	Mercedes-Benz 811D	Reeve Burgess Beaver	B31F	1990		
98	G98PCK	Mercedes-Benz 811D	Reeve Burgess Beaver	B31F	1990		
99	G99PCK	Mercedes-Benz 709D	Reeve Burgess Beaver	B23F	1990		
101	E101JFV	Volvo Citybus B10M-50	Alexander RV	DPH47/35F	1988		
102	E102JFV	Volvo Citybus B10M-50	Alexander RV	DPH47/35F	1988		

103-112			Volvo Citybus B10M-50	Alexander RV	H47/37F	1989	
103	F103XCW	105	F105XCW	107	F107XCW	109	F109XCW	111	F111XCW
104	F104XCW	106	F106XCW	108	F108XCW	110	F110XCW	112	F112XCW

Burnley & Pendle currently operate thirteen Leyland Nationals, all of them National 2s of which 45, XRN45V, is seen here. Stagecoach have proposed a major modernisation of the Burnley & Pendle fleet. The remaining 50% holding has been placed for sale by Burnley Council and discussions over this share are currently taking place.

113	H113ABV	Volvo Citybus B10M-50	Alexander RV	H47/37F	1991
114	H114ABV	Volvo Citybus B10M-50	Alexander RV	DPH47/35F	1991
115	H115ABV	Volvo Citybus B10M-50	Alexander RV	DPH47/35F	1991

166-174
Bristol VRT/SL3/6LXB   Eastern Coach Works   H43/31F   1978

| 166 | FFR166S | 168 | FFR168S | 172 | FFR172S | 173 | FFR173S | 174 | FFR174S |
| 167 | FFR167S | | | | | | | | |

175	K75XCW	Optare MetroRider MR03	Optare	B29F	1993
176	J176MCW	Optare MetroRider MR09	Optare	B23F	1992
177	J177MCW	Optare MetroRider MR09	Optare	B23F	1992
178	L178KHG	Optare MetroRider MR17	Optare	B29F	1994
179	L179KHG	Optare MetroRider MR17	Optare	B29F	1994

193-205
Bristol VRT/LL3/6LXB   Alexander AL   H49/35F   1977   Ex Tayside, 1982

| 193 | OSR193R | 195 | OSR195R | 196 | OSR196R | 197 | OSR197R | 205 | OSR205R |

Previous Registrations:

F995DRN	F95VBV, XFK305	GXI613	F705COA	XSU905	ANA53Y, XFK305
GSU551	A201MFR	HXI311	E508KNV	XSU906	E206FRN
GSU552	D202VBV	NXI414	B708EOF, HHG25	XSU907	C641KDS
GSU553	D203VBV	NXI812	G827UMU	XSU908	C661KDS
GSU554	ANA52Y	OIJ201	H166RHE	XSU909	D111BNV
GXI516	XEL14, F94AEL	XFK305	K815TJU	XSU910	E507KNV

Livery: Crimson and cream; white grey and maroon (Viscount Central) 1-3, 7-16, 51/4/5, 115

BUSWAYS

Busways Travel Services Ltd, Manors, Newcastle-upon-Tyne, NE1 2EL

Lane, Slatyford (Newcastle Busways); Wheatsheaf
...urite); Dean Road, South Shields (Economic, South

xpress	C53F	1981	Ex Nottingham, 1988
xpress	C53F	1981	Ex Nottingham, 1988
	C44FT	1993	
	C44FT	1993	
	C44FT	1993	
	C44FT	1993	
	C44FT	1992	Ex Park's, 1993
	C44FT	1992	Ex Park's, 1993
	C44FT	1992	Ex Park's, 1993
	C44FT	1995	
	C25F	1988	Ex Cumberland, 1995
	C44FT	1996	
	C44FT	1996	

B49F 1988-89

116	F116HVK	121	F121HVK
117	F117HVK	122	F122HVK
118	F118HVK	123	F123HVK
119	F119HVK	124	F124HVK
120	F120HVK	125	F125HVK

DP47F 1990
DP47F 1990

H49/37F 1980

215	EJR115W	219	EJR119W
217	EJR117W	222	EJR122W
218	EJR118W	223	EJR123W

H49/37F 1978

287	UVK287T	299	UVK299T
289w	UVK289T	300	UVK300T
290	UVK290T	302	VCU302T
295	UVK295T	303	VCU303T

H49/37F 1980

339	AVK159V	351u	AVK171V
340	AVK160V	359	AVK179V
341u	AVK161V	360w	AVK180V
350	AVK170V	363w	AVK183V

H47/29F 1990

427	H427BNL	429	H429BNL
428	H428BNL	430	H430BNL

H48/35F 1976
H48/31F 1976
H48/31F 1977
H48/33F 1977

42?	H42?BNL	42?		
422	H422BNL	424	H424BNL	426	H426BNL

500	MVK500R	Leyland Atlantean AN68A/2R	Alexander AL
532	MVK532R	Leyland Atlantean AN68A/2R	Alexander AL
544	MVK544R	Leyland Atlantean AN68A/2R	Alexander AL
551	MVK551R	Leyland Atlantean AN68A/2R	Alexander AL

Pictured in South Shields in August 1996 is Busways' 734, N734LTN, a Volvo Olympian with Alexander RL bodywork and one of forty placed in service by Stagecoach shortly after it acquired the operation. The vehicle is lettered for the Economic operation based in that town. *Mark Bailey*

601-665

Leyland Olympian ONLXB/1R   Alexander RH   H45/31F   1985-86

601	C601LFT	615	C615LFT	628	C628LFT	641	C641LFT	654	C654LFT
602	C602LFT	616	C616LFT	629	C629LFT	642	C642LFT	655	C655LFT
603	C603LFT	617	C617LFT	630	C630LFT	643	C643LFT	656	C656LFT
604	C604LFT	618	C618LFT	631	C631LFT	644	C644LFT	657	C657LFT
605	C605LFT	619	C619LFT	632	C632LFT	645	C645LFT	658	C658LFT
606	C606LFT	620	C620LFT	633	C633LFT	646	C646LFT	659	C659LFT
608	C608LFT	621	C621LFT	634	C634LFT	647	C647LFT	660	C660LFT
609	C609LFT	622	C622LFT	635	C635LFT	648	C648LFT	661	C661LFT
610	C610LFT	623	C623LFT	636	C636LFT	649	C649LFT	662	C662LFT
611	C611LFT	624	C624LFT	637	C637LFT	650	C650LFT	663	C663LFT
612	C612LFT	625	C625LFT	638	C638LFT	651	C651LFT	664	C664LFT
613	C613LFT	626	C626LFT	639	C639LFT	652	C652LFT	665	C665LFT
614	C614LFT	627	C627LFT	640	C640LFT	653	C653LFT		

667-676

Leyland Olympian ON2R50C13Z4 Northern Counties Palatine H47/30F   1990-91

667	H667BNL	669	H669BNL	671	H671BNL	673	H673BNL	675	H675BNL
668	H668BNL	670	H670BNL	672	H672BNL	674	H674BNL	676	H676BNL

677-697

Leyland Olympian ONLXB/1RH   Northern Counties   H43/30F   1988   Ex London Buses, 1991

677	E901KYR	682	E909KYR	686	E914KYR	690	E919KYR	694	E923KYR
678	E905KYR	683	E910KYR	687	E915KYR	691	E920KYR	695	E924KYR
679	E906KYR	684	E911KYR	688	E917KYR	692	E921KYR	696	E925KYR
680	E907KYR	685	E912KYR	689	E918KYR	693	E922KYR	697	E927KYR
681	E908KYR								

The 1997 Stagecoach Bus Handbook

Repainting of the Busways fleet into corporate livery is progressing. Seen in Newcastle is Leyland Olympian 691, E920KYR. One of the batch of twenty-one Northern Counties examples acquired from London Buses in 1991 after being displaced from the Bexleybus services. *Phillip Stephenson*

701-740

Volvo Olympian YN2RV18Z4   Alexander RL   H47/28F   1995

701	N701LTN	709	N709LTN	717	N717LTN	725	N725LTN	733	N733LTN
702	N702LTN	710	N710LTN	718	N718LTN	726	N726LTN	734	N734LTN
703	N703LTN	711	N711LTN	719	N719LTN	727	N727LTN	735	N735LTN
704	N704LTN	712	N712LTN	720	N720LTN	728	N728LTN	736	N736LTN
705	N705LTN	713	N713LTN	721	N721LTN	729	N729LTN	737	N737LTN
706	N706LTN	714	N714LTN	722	N722LTN	730	N730LTN	738	N738LTN
707	N707LTN	715	N715LTN	723	N723LTN	731	N731LTN	739	N739LTN
708	N708LTN	716	N716LTN	724	N724LTN	732	N732LTN	740	N740LTN

815-838

Leyland Fleetline FE30AGR   Alexander AL   H44/30F   1977

815w	OCU815R	819	OCU819R	821u	OCU821R	833	RCU833S	837	RCU837S
816	OCU816R	820	OCU820R	822	OCU822R	834	RCU834S	838	RCU838S
818	OCU818R								

901-920

Scania N113CRB   Alexander PS   B51F*   1989   *901-5 are B48F; 906 is B49F

901	F901JRG	905	F905JRG	909	F909JRG	913	F913JRG	917	F917JRG
902	F902JRG	906	F906JRG	910	F910JRG	914	F914JRG	918	F918JRG
903	F903JRG	907	F907JRG	911	F911JRG	915	F915JRG	919	F919JRG
904	F904JRG	908	F908JRG	912	F912JRG	916	F916JRG	920	F920JRG

921-926

Scania N113CRB   Alexander PS   B51F*   1989-90   *926 is B49F

921	G921TCU	923	G923TCU	924	G924TCU	925	G925TCU	926	G926TCU
922	G922TCU								

In 1994 Busways took delivery of four pairs of different buses for evaluation comprising various chassis and body combinations. Shown here is Northern Counties-bodied Scania 952, M952DRG which has high-back seating. All four of the Scania L113s are now allocated to the Byker depot of Newcastle Busways. *Les Peters*

927	G113SKX	Scania N113CRB	Alexander PS	B49F	1989	Ex Scania demonstrator, 1991

928-937			Scania N113CRB		Alexander PS	B51F	1991	
928	H428EFT	930	H430EFT	932	H432EFT	934	H434EFT	936	H436EFT
929	H429EFT	931	H431EFT	933	H433EFT	935	H435EFT	937	H437EFT

938	G108CEH	Scania N113CRB	Alexander PS	B49F	1990	Ex Stevensons, 1993

951	M951DRG	Scania L113CRL	Northern Counties Paladin	B49F	1994
952	M952DRG	Scania L113CRL	Northern Counties Paladin	DP49F	1994
953	M953DRG	Scania L113CRL	Alexander Strider	B51F	1994
954	M954DRG	Scania L113CRL	Alexander Strider	B51F	1994

Opposite: **New buses for Busways have included many single-deck buses with both Dennis Dart and Volvo B10s being placed in service. Representing the fleet here are** *(top)* **Dennis Dart 1740, L740VNL, with Alexander Dash bodywork. The lower picture shows 954, M954DRG, an Alexander Strider-bodied Scania L113. A move for the group to low-floor buses is signalled with five Northern Counties-bodied Volvo B10BLEs to be on trial with Manchester and used on the 192 service early in 1997.** *Gerald Mead/Phillip Stephenson*

1201	M201DRG	Dennis Lance 11SDA3113	Plaxton Verde	B49F	1994
1202	M202DRG	Dennis Lance 11SDA3113	Plaxton Verde	B49F	1994
1203	M203DRG	Dennis Lance 11SDA3113	Plaxton Verde	B49F	1994
1204	M204DRG	Dennis Lance 11SDA3113	Optare Sigma	B47F	1994
1218w	KBB118D	Leyland Atlantean PDR1/1R	MCW	O44/34F	1966
1227	SVK627G	Leyland Atlantean PDR1A/1R	Alexander J	O44/30F	1969

1401-1459

		Mercedes-Benz 709D	Reeve Burgess Beaver	B19F*	1987-88 *1431/49/51/3 are B23F
					1426/9/35/40/2/3/5/50/4-9 are B20F

1401	D401TFT	1425	E425AFT	1432	E432AFT	1443u	E443AFT	1453	E453AFT
1402	D402TFT	1426	E426AFT	1433	E433AFT	1445	E445AFT	1454	E454AFT
1415	D415TFT	1427	E427AFT	1434	E434AFT	1447	E447AFT	1455u	E455AFT
1419	D419TFT	1428	E428AFT	1435u	E435AFT	1449	E449AFT	1456	E456AFT
1421	E421AFT	1429	E429AFT	1437	E437AFT	1450	E450AFT	1457	E457AFT
1422	E422AFT	1430	E430AFT	1440u	E440AFT	1451	E451AFT	1458	E458AFT
1423	E423AFT	1431	E431AFT	1442u	E442AFT	1452	E452AFT	1459	E459AFT
1424	E423AFT								

1461-1500

		Mercedes-Benz 709D	Alexander Sprint	B23F	1996

1461	N461RVK	1469	N469RVK	1477	N477RVK	1485	N485RVK	1493	N493RVK
1462	N462RVK	1470	N470RVK	1478	N478RVK	1486	N486RVK	1494	N494RVK
1463	N463RVK	1471	N471RVK	1479	N479RVK	1487	N487RVK	1495	N495RVK
1464	N464RVK	1472	N472RVK	1480	N480RVK	1488	N488RVK	1496	N496RVK
1465	N465RVK	1473	N473RVK	1481	N481RVK	1489	N489RVK	1497	N497RVK
1466	N466RVK	1474	N474RVK	1482	N482RVK	1490	N490RVK	1498	N498RVK
1467	N467RVK	1475	N475RVK	1483	N4834VK	1491	N491RVK	1499	N499RVK
1468	N468RVK	1476	N476RVK	1484	N484RVK	1492	N492RVK	1500	N501RVK

1635	E635BVK	Renault-Dodge S56	Alexander AM	B25F	1987
1637	E637BVK	Renault-Dodge S56	Alexander AM	B25F	1987

1679-1693

		Optare MetroRider	Optare	B29F	1991-92 Ex Welcome, 1993

1679	J371BNW	1682	J374BNW	1685	J377BNW	1688	J380BNW	1691	K164FYG
1680	J372BNW	1683	J375BNW	1686	J378BNW	1689	K162FYG	1692	K165FYG
1681	J373BNW	1684	J376BNW	1687	J379BNW	1690	K163FYG	1693	K166FYG

1694-1700

		Iveco Daily 59.12	Dormobile Routemaker	B27F	1992 Ex Welcome, 1993

1694	K330RCN	1696	K332RCN	1698	K335RCN	1699	K336RCN	1700	K337RCN
1695	K331RCN	1697	K334RCN						

1701	J701KCU	Dennis Dart 9.8SDL3017	Plaxton Pointer	B40F	1992
1702	J702KCU	Dennis Dart 9.8SDL3017	Plaxton Pointer	B40F	1992

1703-1743

		Dennis Dart 9.8SDL3017*	Alexander Dash	B40F	1992-93 *1723-28 are 9.8SDL3025;
					*1729-43 are 9.8SDL3035

1703	K703PCN	1711	K711PCN	1721	K721PCN	1729	L729VNL	1737	L737VNL
1704	K704PCN	1712	K712PCN	1722	K722PCN	1730	L730VNL	1738	L738VNL
1705	K705PCN	1713	K713PCN	1723	K723PNL	1731	L731VNL	1739	L739VNL
1706	K706PCN	1714	K714PCN	1724	K724PNL	1732	L732VNL	1740	L740VNL
1707	K707PCN	1715	K715PCN	1725	K725PNL	1733	L733VNL	1741	L741VNL
1708	K708PCN	1717	K717PCN	1726	K726PNL	1734	L734VNL	1742	L742VNL
1709	K709PCN	1718	K718PCN	1727	K727PNL	1735	L735VNL	1743	L743VNL
1710	K710PCN	1720	K720PCN	1728	K728PNL	1736	L736VNL		

1744-1759

		Dennis Dart 9.8SDL3035	Plaxton Pointer	B40F	1993

1744	L744VNL	1748	L748VNL	1751	L751VNL	1754	L754VNL	1757	L757VNL
1745	L745VNL	1749	L749VNL	1752	L752VNL	1755	L755VNL	1758	L758VNL
1746	L746VNL	1750	L750VNL	1753	L753VNL	1756	L756VNL	1759	L759VNL

1760-1765

		Dennis Dart 9.8SDL3040	Alexander Dash	B40F	1994

1760	L760ARG	1762	L762ARG	1763	L763ARG	1764	L764ARG	1765	L765ARG
1761	L761ARG								

Busways acquired the Welcome operation in 1993 and this brought into the fleet several Optare MetroRiders. Illustrated here with Blue Bus Services fleet names is 1690, K163FYG.
Phillip Stephenson

1766-1771   Dennis Dart 9.8SDL3040   Plaxton Pointer   B40F   1994

1766	M766DRG	1768	M768DRG	1769	M769DRG	1770	M770DRG	1771	M771DRG
1767	M767DRG								

1772-1785   Dennis Dart SFD412   Alexander Dash   B40F   1996

1772	N772RVK	1775	N775RVK	1778	N779RVK	1781	P781WCN	1784	P784WCN
1773	N773RVK	1776	N776RVK	1779	N780RVK	1782	P782WCN	1785	P785WCN
1774	N774RVK	1777	N7787RVK	1780	P780WCN	1783	P783WCN		

1786-1793   Dennis Dart SLF   Alexander ALX200   B40F   1996-97

1786	P786WVK	1788	P788WVK	1790	P790WVK	1792	P792WVK	1793	P793WVK
1787	P787WVK	1789	P789WVK	1791	P791WVK				

1800w	RAH681F	Bristol RESL6G	Eastern Coach Works	B53F	1968	Ex Buckinghamshire RC, 1994
1805w	EPW516K	Bristol RELL6G	Eastern Coach Works	B53F	1972	Ex Buckinghamshire RC, 1994
1808w	HPW522L	Bristol RELL6L	Eastern Coach Works	B53F	1972	Ex Buckinghamshire RC, 1994

1810-1816   Bristol RELL6L   Eastern Coach Works   B49F*   1972-73 Ex Colchester, 1988
*1810/2 are B53F

1810	YWC16L	1812	OWC720M	1814	OWC723M	1815	SWC25K	1816	SWC26K
1811	YWC18L	1813	OWC722M						

1817-1821   Bristol RESL6G   Eastern Coach Works   B43F   1975   Ex Thamesdown, 1987-88

1817	JMW166P	1818w	JMW167P	1819w	JMW168P	1820	JMW169P	1821	JMW170P

1822u	TDL567K	Bristol RELL6G	Eastern Coach Works	B53F	1971	Ex Catch-a-Bus, 1993

| 1901 | M901DRG | Volvo B10B | Alexander Strider | B51F | 1994 |
| 1902 | M902DRG | Volvo B10B | Alexander Strider | B51F | 1994 |

2201-2217   Volvo B10M-55   Alexander PS   B49F   1995

2201	N201LTN	2205	N205LTN	2209	N209LTN	2212	N212LTN	2215	N215LTN
2202	N202LTN	2206	N206LTN	2210	N210LTN	2213	N213LTN	2216	N216LTN
2203	N203LTN	2207	N207LTN	2211	N211LTN	2214	N214LTN	2217	N217LTN
2204	N204LTN	2208	N208LTN						

2218-2226   Volvo B10M-55   Alexander PS   B49F   1996

| 2218 | P118XCN | 2220 | P120XCN | 2222 | P122XCN | 2224 | P124XCN | 2226 | P126XCN |
| 2219 | P119XCN | 2221 | P121XCN | 2223 | P123XCN | 2225 | P125XCN | | |

Special event vehicles - traditional liveries

1801	ECU201E	Bristol RESL6L	Eastern Coach Works	B45D	1967	Ex Bickers, Coddenham, 1988
1802	TRY118H	Bristol RELL6L	Eastern Coach Works	B48F	1969	Ex Ipswich, 1988
B140	LCU112	Daimler CCG6	Roe	H35/28R	1964	
B141	WBR248	Atkinson PM746HL	Marshall	B45D	1964	Ex Preservation, 1986
B141	FBR53D	Leyland Panther PSUR1/1	Strachan	B47D	1966	Ex Preservation, 1986

Allocations:

Blue Bus Services: 65/6, 218/9/68/77, 302/3, 500/32/44/51,
1401/2/15/9/22/4/5/37/47/52/83-6, 1689-91, 1701/2/44-6/50-3, 1810-7/20/1/32/3.

Economic Services: 117/8/25/7, 270, 675/6, 1749

Favourite: 205/17/23, 319/29/34/8/40/50, 1497-1500, 1714/5/7/21/48/70/1, 1863

Newcastle - Byker: 81-8/90-2, 421-30, 601-6/8-19/5/77-83/90-7, 701-30, 906/18-20/28/9/33-7/51-4,
1421/3/6-30/2-4/61-9.

Newcastle - Slatyford: 204/7/8/11/4/51/4/9, 315/6/8/21/6/30, 620-4/6-49/62/4/5/84-9, 901-5/7-17/21-7/30/1/2/8,
1204, 1470-82, 2201-7/18-26.

South Shields: 115-6/9-24/6, 209/10/2/5/22/48/83/7/90/5/9/300, 731-40, 1201/2/27,
1431/49-51/3/4/6-59/87-96, 1703-12/40-3/54-59/66/9/83-5/91-3.

Sunderland: 101-14, 650-63/7-74, 816/8-20/33/3/7/8, 1203, 1435/40/2/3/5,
1635/7/79-88/92-1700, 1713/8/20/2-39/60-5/72-82/6-90, 1901/2, 2208-17

On loan: 249/322/7/8 (Transit - Darlington); 2227-35 (Ribble - Bolton)

Previous registrations:

| ESU263 | A829PPP | | KSU463 | J422HDS |
| KSU462 | J420HDS | | KSU464 | J424HDS |

One of the latest arrivals with Busways is Alexander-bodied Dart 1782, P782WCN, seen leaving the city centre on route 22 to Thorney Close. Several of the latest batch of B10s have been initially sent to work with Ribble following damage to some 37 vehicles at the Bolton depot over Christmas, 1996. *Mark Bailey*

CAMBUS

Cambus Ltd, 100 Cowley Road, Cambridge CB4 4DN
Viscount Bus & Coach Co Ltd, 351 Lincoln Road, Peterborough, PE1 2PG

Depots: Cowley Road, Cambridge; Kilmaine Close, Cambridge; Wisbech Road, March; Lincoln Road, Peterborough and Station Road, Oundle. **Outstations:** Crowland; Ely; Fowlmere; Haverhill; Littleport; Longstowe; Market Deeping; Newmarket; Royston; St Ives; Sawston; Stamford; Sutton and Wisbech.

| 81 | GAZ4381 | Optare MetroRider MR17 | Optare | B29F | 1999 | CNG Powered |
| 82 | GAZ4382 | Optare MetroRider MR17 | Optare | B29F | 1999 | CNG Powered |

155-169

Volvo B6-9M — Marshall C32 — B32F — 1993

155	L655MFL	158	L658MFL	161	L661MFL	164	L664MFL	168	L668MFL
156	L656MFL	159	L659MFL	162	L662MFL	165	L665MFL	169	L669MFL
157	L657MFL	160	L660MFL	163	L663MFL	167	L667MFL		

200-211

Mercedes-Benz 709D — Alexander Sprint — B25F — 1996 — Ex Western, 1996

200	N614VSS	203	N619VSS	206	N616VSS	208	N620VSS	210	N643VSS
201	N615VSS	204	N641VSS	207	N618VSS	209	N642VSS	211	N644VSS
202	N617VSS	205	N613VSS						

310	F167SMT	Leyland Lynx LX112L10ZR1S	Leyland Lynx	B49F	1989	Ex Miller, Foxton, 1992
311	F168SMT	Leyland Lynx LX112L10ZR1S	Leyland Lynx	B49F	1989	Ex Miller, Foxton, 1992
312	F171SMT	Leyland Lynx LX112L10ZR1S	Leyland Lynx	B49F	1989	Ex Miller, Foxton, 1992

315-319

Volvo B10M-55 — Alexander PS — B49F — 1996

| 315 | P315EFL | 316 | P316EFL | 317 | P317EFL | 318 | P318EFL | 319 | P319EFL |

350	N350YFL	Dennis Dart SFD412	Alexander Dash	B40F	1996	
351	N351YFL	Dennis Dart SFD412	Alexander Dash	B40F	1996	
352	N352YFL	Dennis Dart SFD412	Alexander Dash	B40F	1996	
364	P364APM	Dennis Dart SLF SFD322	Plaxton Pointer	B39F	1996	On evaluation
407	H407GAV	Volvo B10M-60	Plaxton Paramount 3500 III	C53F	1991	
408	J408TEW	Volvo B10M-60	Plaxton Paramount 3500 III	C53F	1992	
409	J409TEW	Volvo B10M-60	Plaxton Paramount 3500 III	C49FT	1992	
421	K911RGE	Volvo B10M-60	Jonckheere Deauville P599	C49FT	1993	Ex Park's, 1994
422	K912RGE	Volvo B10M-60	Jonckheere Deauville P599	C49FT	1993	Ex Park's, 1994

Two Optare MetroRiders have been placed in service with Cambus to operate the City Centre Shuttle. The vehicles are powered by compressed natural gas, and British Gas is working with the company in these trials. The vehicles were given GAZ index marks that resulted in their fleet numbers. Shown in the city is 82, GAZ4382.
Tony Wilson

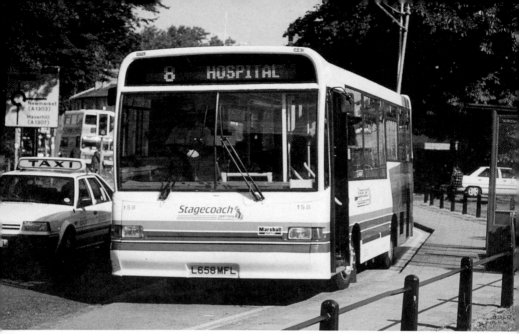

Cambus took delivery of fourteen Volvo B6s in 1993. These were fitted with Marshall bodywork to their C32 design. The type are now receiving corporate livery as shown here. *M H A Flynn*

425	G525LWU	Volvo B10M-60	Plaxton Paramount 3500 III	C49FT	1990	Ex Wallace Arnold, 1994	
426	G526LWU	Volvo B10M-60	Plaxton Paramount 3500 III	C49FT	1990	Ex Wallace Arnold, 1994	
427	G527LWU	Volvo B10M-60	Plaxton Paramount 3500 III	C49FT	1990	Ex Wallace Arnold, 1994	
430	G520LWU	Volvo B10M-60	Plaxton Paramount 3500 III	C49FT	1990	Ex Wallace Arnold, 1994	

431-435

Volvo B10M-60   Plaxton Paramount 3500 III   C48FT*   1991   Ex Wallace Arnold, 1994
*431 is C49FT

431	H649UWR	432	H642UWR	433	H643UWR	434	H652UWR	435	H653UWR

436-444

Volvo B10M-60   Plaxton Premiére 350   C48FT   1992   Ex Wallace Arnold, 1994

436	J706CWT	439	J739CWT	441	J741CWT	443	J743CWT	444	J744CWT
437	J702CWT	440	J740CWT	442	J742CWT				

445-452

Volvo B10M-62   Plaxton Expressliner 2   C49FT   1995

445	N445XVA	447	N447XVA	449	N449XVA	451	N451XVA	452	N452XVA
446	N446XVA	448	N448XVA	450	N450XVA				

	JAH552D	Bristol FLF6G	Eastern Coach Works	O38/32F	1966		
481	A681KDV	Leyland Olympian ONLXB/1R	Eastern Coach Works	H45/32F	1983	Ex North Devon, 1996	
482	A561KWY	Leyland Olympian ONLXB/1R	Eastern Coach Works	H45/32F	1983	Ex Selby & District, 1996	
483	A683KDV	Leyland Olympian ONLXB/1R	Eastern Coach Works	H45/32F	1983	Ex North Devon, 1996	
500	E500LFL	Leyland Olympian ONLXCT/1RH	Optare	DPH43/27F	1988		
501	E501LFL	Leyland Olympian ONLXCT/1RH	Optare	DPH43/27F	1988		
502	E502LFL	Leyland Olympian ONLXCT/1RH	Optare	DPH43/27F	1988		
503	UWW3X	Leyland Olympian ONLXB/1R	Roe	H47/29F	1982	Ex West Yorkshire PTE, 1987	
504	UWW4X	Leyland Olympian ONLXB/1R	Roe	H47/29F	1982	Ex West Yorkshire PTE, 1987	
505	UWW8X	Leyland Olympian ONLXB/1R	Roe	H47/29F	1982	Ex West Yorkshire PTE, 1987	

Opposite, top: **Cambridge has recently introduced three new Dennis Darts to the Park & Ride services previously operated as Millers and using Leyland Lynx. Shown here is 351, N351YFL in the Park & Ride livery and displaying signing for that service.** *Tony Wilson*
Opposite, bottom: **Many vehicles in the Cambus fleet are now receiving corporate livery repaints. Seven Iveco Turbodaily 59s are operated by Cambus and these carry Marshall bodywork of the style taken over after Carlyle ceased bodying. Smartly turned out for Cambridge service 3A is 952, K172CAV.** *Tony Wilson*

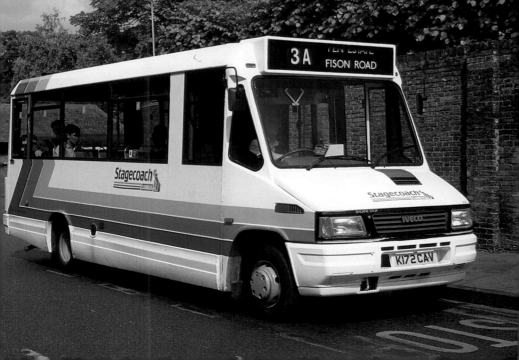

Latest arrivals with Cambus are a large batch of Northern Counties-bodied Volvo Olympians. This batch of fifty two vehicles marks the biggest investment in new buses made by Cambus Holdings. Many of their double-deckers were elderly Bristol VRTs and it is these which Cambus are replacing with the new intake. Shown on one of its first trips out is 529, P529EFL. *M H A Flynn*

506-517

Leyland Olympian ONLXB/1RZ Northern Counties H45/30F 1989

506	F506NJE	509	F509NJE	512	F512NJE	514	F514NJE	516	F516NJE
507	F507NJE	510	F510NJE	513	F513NJE	515	F515NJE	517	F517NJE
508	F508NJE	511	F511NJE						

518	N518XER	Volvo Olympian YN2RV18Z4	Northern Counties Palatine	DPH45/31F	1995
519	N519XER	Volvo Olympian YN2RV18Z4	Northern Counties Palatine	DPH45/31F	1995
520	N520XER	Volvo Olympian YN2RV18Z4	Northern Counties Palatine	DPH45/31F	1995
523	H473CEG	Leyland Olympian ON2R50G13Z4 Leyland		H47/31F	1990
524	H474CEG	Leyland Olympian ON2R50G13Z4 Leyland		H47/31F	1990
525	H475CEG	Leyland Olympian ON2R50G13Z4 Leyland		H47/31F	1990

526-579

Volvo Olympian YN2RV18V3 Northern Counties Palatine H49/33F 1996

526	P526EFL	537	P537EFL	548	P548EFL	559	P559EFL	570	P570EFL
527	P527EFL	538	P538EFL	549	P549EFL	561	P561EFL	571	P571EFL
528	P528EFL	539	P539EFL	550	P550EFL	562	P562EFL	572	P572EFL
529	P529EFL	540	P540EFL	551	P551EFL	563	P563EFL	573	P573EFL
530	P530EFL	541	P541EFL	552	P552EFL	564	P564EFL	574	P574EFL
531	P531EFL	542	P542EFL	553	P5534FL	565	P565EFL	575	P575EFL
532	P532EFL	543	P543EFL	554	P554EFL	566	P566EFL	576	P576EFL
533	P533EFL	544	P544EFL	556	P556EFL	567	P567EFL	577	P577EFL
534	P534EFL	545	P545EFL	557	P557EFL	568	P568EFL	578	P578EFL
535	P535EFL	546	P546EFL	558	P558EFL	569	P569EFL	579	P579EFL
536	P536EFL	547	P547EFL						

735	PWY37W	Bristol VRT/SL3/6LXB	Eastern Coach Works	H43/31F	1981	Ex York City & District, 1990
737	SUB795W	Bristol VRT/SL3/6LXB	Eastern Coach Works	H43/31F	1981	Ex York City & District, 1990
739	URP943W	Bristol VRT/SL3/501	Eastern Coach Works	H43/31F	1981	Ex Buckinghamshire Road Car, 1994

The remaining Bristol VRTs are late-model, series 3 machines some of which may survive the current cull. Seen with the Viscount name used at Peterborough is 772, SUB792W, and one of those which presently survives. *Philip Lamb*

742-746   Bristol VRT/SL3/6LXB   Eastern Coach Works   H43/31F   1980-81

742	VEX295X	743	VEX300X	744	VEX296X	745	VEX303X	746	VEX304X

747	STW24W	Bristol VRT/SL3/6LXB	Eastern Coach Works	H39/31F	1981	Ex Green, Kirkintilloch, 1991
751	VEX298X	Bristol VRT/SL3/6LXB	Eastern Coach Works	H43/31F	1981	
753	VEX289X	Bristol VRT/SL3/6LXB	Eastern Coach Works	H43/31F	1981	
755	VEX293X	Bristol VRT/SL3/6LXB	Eastern Coach Works	H43/31F	1981	
770	SUB790W	Bristol VRT/SL3/6LXB	Eastern Coach Works	H43/31F	1981	Ex Keighley & District, 1990
772	SUB792W	Bristol VRT/SL3/6LXB	Eastern Coach Works	H43/31F	1981	Ex York City & District, 1990
773	SUB793W	Bristol VRT/SL3/6LXB	Eastern Coach Works	H43/31F	1981	Ex York City & District, 1990
774	LWU470V	Bristol VRT/SL3/6LXB	Eastern Coach Works	H43/31F	1980	Ex York City & District, 1990
775	PWY45W	Bristol VRT/SL3/6LXB	Eastern Coach Works	H43/31F	1981	Ex Keighley & District, 1990
777	PWY47W	Bristol VRT/SL3/6LXB	Eastern Coach Works	H43/31F	1981	Ex Keighley & District, 1990
779	PWY49W	Bristol VRT/SL3/6LXB	Eastern Coach Works	H43/31F	1981	Ex Keighley & District, 1990
780	PWY50W	Bristol VRT/SL3/6LXB	Eastern Coach Works	H43/31F	1981	Ex Keighley & District, 1990
781	VEX301X	Bristol VRT/SL3/6LXB	Eastern Coach Works	H43/31F	1981	
782	VEX299X	Bristol VRT/SL3/6LXB	Eastern Coach Works	H43/31F	1981	
784	RAH264W	Bristol VRT/SL3/6LXB	Eastern Coach Works	H43/31F	1980	
788	VAH278X	Bristol VRT/SL3/6LXB	Eastern Coach Works	H43/31F	1981	
789	VAH279X	Bristol VRT/SL3/6LXB	Eastern Coach Works	H43/31F	1981	
790	VAH280X	Bristol VRT/SL3/6LXB	Eastern Coach Works	H43/31F	1981	
791	VEX291X	Bristol VRT/SL3/6LXB	Eastern Coach Works	H43/31F	1981	

952-957   Iveco Daily 59-12   Marshall   B25F   1992

951	K171CAV	953	K173CAV	955	K175CAV	956	K176CAV	957	K177CAV
952	K172CAV	954	K174CAV						

Pictured heading for Impington, to the north of Cambridge, is Cambus 966, K966HUB. Cambus had purchased several of these Optare-built products to replace older, smaller City Pavers prior to becoming part of Stagecoach.
M H A Flynn

960-974

		Optare MetroRider		Optare	B29F	1992-93				
960	J960DWX	**963**	K963HUB	**966**	K966HUB	**969**	K969HUB	**972**	K972HUB
961	J961DWX	**964**	K964HUB	**967**	K967HUB	**970**	K970HUB	**973**	K973HUB
962	J962DWX	**965**	K965HUB	**968**	K968HUB	**971**	K971HUB	**974**	K974HUB

975-979

		Optare MetroRider MR17		Optare		B29F	1995		
975	M975WWR	**976**	M976WWR	**977**	M977WWR	**978**	M978WWR	**979**	M979VWY

981	K391KUA	Optare MetroRider	Optare	B29F	1993
982	K392KUA	Optare MetroRider	Optare	B29F	1993
983	K393KUA	Optare MetroRider	Optare	B29F	1993
984	K975KUB	Optare MetroRider	Optare	B29F	1993
985	J805DWW	Optare MetroRider	Optare	B29F	1992
986	J806DWW	Optare MetroRider	Optare	B29F	1992
987	J807DWW	Optare MetroRider	Optare	B29F	1992
988	M808WWR	Optare MetroRider	Optare	B29F	1995
989	M809WWR	Optare MetroRider	Optare	B29F	1995
990	M810WWR	Optare MetroRider	Optare	B29F	1995
2036	C336SFL	Ford Transit 190	Carlyle	DP16F	1986

Special liveries: White (National Express) 425-7/30-5/9-52; white (Eurolines) 437; green (CNG) 81/2; red & cream (Cambridge Park & Ride) 304/5/10-2/50-2.

Note: All vehicles were formerly Eastern Counties in 1984 subsequently operating for Cambus, Premier or Viscount unless shown otherwise or new later.

CHELTENHAM & GLOUCESTER

Cheltenham & Gloucester Omnibus Company Ltd
Cheltenham District Traction Company Ltd,
Swindon & District Bus Company Ltd,
3/4 Bath Street, Cheltenham, GL50 1YE
Circle Line, Abbey Road Depot, Hempsted, Gloucester GL2 6HU

Depots: Lansdowne Ind Est, Gloucester Road, Cheltenham; London Road, Gloucester; London Road, Stroud and Eastcott Road, Swindon. Outstation: Love Lane, Cirencester.

101-105		Leyland Olympian ONLXB/2RZ	Alexander RL	H51/36F	1990		
101	G101AAD	**102** G102AAD	**103** G103AAD	**104** G104AAD		**105**	G105AAD

106-111		Leyland Titan TNLXB/1RF	Park Royal	H47/26F	1979-80 Ex Thames Transit, 1990		
106	GNF6V	**108** GNF8V	**109** GNF9V	**110** GNF10V		**111**	GNF11V

112-124		Leyland Olympian ONLXB/1R	Roe	H47/29F	1982-83 113 ex Yorkshire Rider, 1987		
112	JHU899X	**115** LWS33Y	**118** LWS36Y	**121** LWS39Y		**123**	LWS41Y
113	UWW7X	**116** LWS34Y	**119** LWS37Y	**122** LWS40Y		**124**	NTC132Y
114	JHU912X	**117** LWS35Y	**120** LWS38Y				

201	JOU160P	Bristol VRT/SL3/501(6LXB)	Eastern Coach Works	H43/28F	1975	
202	MUA872P	Bristol VRT/SL3/6LX	Eastern Coach Works	H43/31F	1975	
204	MOU739R	Bristol VRT/SL3/6LXB	Eastern Coach Works	H43/28F	1976	
205	NHU670R	Bristol VRT/SL3/6LXB	Eastern Coach Works	H43/28F	1976	
208	NWS288R	Bristol VRT/SL3/6LXB	Eastern Coach Works	H43/28F	1977	
209	NWS289R	Bristol VRT/SL3/6LXB	Eastern Coach Works	H43/28F	1977	
213	REU311S	Bristol VRT/SL3/6LXB	Eastern Coach Works	H43/28F	1977	
215	XDV602S	Bristol VRT/SL3/6LXB	Eastern Coach Works	H43/31F	1978	Ex Devon General, 1987
216	XDV606S	Bristol VRT/SL3/6LXB	Eastern Coach Works	H43/31F	1978	Ex Devon General, 1987
217	VOD593S	Bristol VRT/SL3/6LXB	Eastern Coach Works	H43/31F	1978	Ex Devon General, 1987
218	VOD596S	Bristol VRT/SL3/6LXB	Eastern Coach Works	H43/31F	1978	Ex Devon General, 1987
219	VOD597S	Bristol VRT/SL3/6LXB	Eastern Coach Works	H43/31F	1978	Ex Devon General, 1987
222	TWS906T	Bristol VRT/SL3/6LXB	Eastern Coach Works	H43/28F	1979	
223	TWS913T	Bristol VRT/SL3/6LXB	Eastern Coach Works	H43/28F	1979	
224	TWS914T	Bristol VRT/SL3/6LXB	Eastern Coach Works	H43/28F	1979	

Gloucester Citybus names are used for the services in that city which require many of the Roe-bodied Leyland Olympians for the work. In the early 1980s the National Bus Company placed high-bridge orders for the Olympian with Roe, while Eastern Coach Works produced the low-height variant. Cheltenham & Gloucester 121, LWS39Y, is one of two batches ordered for Bristol Omnibus before that company was split prior to its sale. *David Cole*

225-231

						Bristol VRT/SL3/680 (6LXB)	Eastern Coach Works	H43/31F	1981
225	DHW350W	227	EWS740W	229	EWS746W	230	EWS748W	231	EWS751W
226	DHW352W	228	EWS743W						

232	HAH237V	Bristol VRT/SL3/6LXB	Eastern Coach Works	H43/31F	1979	Ex Cambus (Viscount), 1997
233	KVF249V	Bristol VRT/SL3/6LXB	Eastern Coach Works	H43/31F	1980	Ex Cambus (Viscount), 1997
251	MVK521R	Leyland Atlantean AN68A/2R	Alexander AL	H48/33F	1976	Ex Busways, 1996
252	MVK558R	Leyland Atlantean AN68A/2R	Alexander AL	H48/33F	1977	Ex Busways, 1996

302-312

						Leyland National 11351A/1R(DAF)		B52F	1977-79
302	YFB973V	305	PHW989S	307	SAE752S	310	VEU231T	312	TAE644S
303	TAE641S	306	PHW988S	308	TAE642S	311	SAE756S		
314	YFB972V	Leyland National 11351A/1R(DAF)				B52F	1979		

361-375

						Leyland National 2 NL116L11/1R		B52F*	1980	*368 is B52FL (variable)
361	AAE644V	364	AAE648V	367	AAE651V	370	AAE660V	373	BHY997V
362	HIL6075	365	AAE649V	368	YJV806	371	AAE665V	374	BHY998V
363	511OHU	366	AAE650V	369	AAE659V	372	BHY996V	375	BOU6V

376	ARN892Y	Leyland National 2 NL116HLXB/1R	DP52F	1983	Ex Ribble, 1994
377	RHG880X	Leyland National 2 NL116AL11/1R	B52F	1982	Ex Ribble, 1994
378	NHH382W	Leyland National 2 NL116AL11/1R	B52F	1981	Ex Ribble, 1994
379	SHH389X	Leyland National 2 NL116AL11/1R	B52F	1982	Ex Ribble, 1994
380	RRM385X	Leyland National 2 NL116AL11/1R	B52F	1981	Ex Ribble, 1995
381	SNS825W	Leyland National 2 NL116AL11/1R	B52F	1981	Ex Ribble, 1995
382	KHH376W	Leyland National 2 NL116AL11/1R	B52F	1980	Ex Ribble, 1995
383	WAO397Y	Leyland National 2 NL116HLXB/1R	B52F	1982	Ex Busways, 1996
391	LFR860X	Leyland National 2 NL106AL11/1R	B44F	1981	Ex Ribble, 1995
392	LFR861X	Leyland National 2 NL106AL11/1R	B44F	1981	Ex Midland Red, 1995
393	LFR873X	Leyland National 2 NL106AL11/1R	B44F	1981	Ex Midland Red, 1995

401-409

						Volvo B10M-55	Alexander PS	DP48F	1995
401	N401LDF	403	N403LDF	405	N405LDF	407	N407LDF	409	N409LDF
402	N402LDF	404	N404LDF	406	N406LDF	408	N408LDF		

500	VAE499T	Leyland National 10351B/1R		B44F	1978	
501	VAE501T	Leyland National 10351B/1R		B44F	1979	
503	VAE507T	Leyland National 10351B/1R		B44F	1979	
533	G533LWU	Volvo B10M-60	Plaxton Paramount 3500 III	C48FT	1990	Ex Wallace Arnold, 1993
534	G534LWU	Volvo B10M-60	Plaxton Paramount 3500 III	C48FT	1990	Ex Wallace Arnold, 1993
546	G546LWU	Volvo B10M-60	Plaxton Paramount 3500 III	C48FT	1990	Ex Wallace Arnold, 1993
547	G547LWU	Volvo B10M-60	Plaxton Paramount 3500 III	C48FT	1990	Ex Wallace Arnold, 1993
548	G548LWU	Volvo B10M-60	Plaxton Paramount 3500 III	C48FT	1990	Ex Wallace Arnold, 1993

631-645

						Ford Transit 190	Alexander AM	B16F	1985
631	C631SFH	636	C636SFH	640	C640SFH	642	C642SFH	644	C644SFH
632	C632SFH	637	C637SFH	641	C641SFH	643	C643SFH	645	C645SFH
633	C633SFH								

651	C651XDF	Mercedes-Benz L608D	Alexander AM	B20F	1986	
659	C659XDF	Mercedes-Benz L608D	Alexander AM	B20F	1986	
677	F677PDF	Mercedes-Benz 709D	PMT	B25F	1988	
678	F311DET	Mercedes-Benz 709D	Reeve Burgess Beaver	B25F	1988	Ex Reeve Burgess demonstrator, 1989

679-684

						Mercedes-Benz 709D	PMT	B25F	1989
679	G679AAD	681	G681AAD	682	G682AAD	683	G683AAD	684	G684AAD
680	G680AAD								

Opposite, top: **Each of the last three years has seen standard Mercedes-Benz 709D minibuses being delivered to Cheltenham & Gloucester and these have displaced many of the older minibuses. Representing the type with the Swindon & District operation is 711, M711FMR.**
Opposite, bottom: **Stagecoach have been replacing Leyland Nationals with Volvo B10Ms, with the National 1 variant now much in decline. Among surviving National 2s is 379, SHH389X of Stroud Valleys, seen here in Cheltenham. This vehicle was new to Cumberland and came south from Ribble in 1994.** *Malc McDonald/Malc McDonald*

686-703 — Mercedes-Benz 709D — Alexander Sprint — B25F — 1994

686	L686CDD	690	L690CDD	694	L694CDD	697	M697EDD	701	M701EDD
687	L687CDD	691	L691CDD	695	L695CDD	698	M698EDD	702	M702EDD
688	L688CDD	692	L692CDD	696	L696CDD	699	M699EDD	703	M703EDD
689	L689CDD	693	L693CDD						

704-717 — Mercedes-Benz 709D — Alexander Sprint — B25F* — 1995 — *704 is DP25F

704	M704JDG	707	M707JDG	710	M710JDG	713	M713FMR	716	N716KAM
705	M705JDG	708	M708JDG	711	M711FMR	714	M714FMR	717	N717KAM
706	M706JDG	709	M709JDG	712	M712FMR	715	M715FMR		

718-735 — Mercedes-Benz 709D — Alexander Sprint — B25F* — 1996 — *731-5 are DP25F

718	N718RDD	722	N722RDD	726	N726RDD	730	N730RDD	733	N733RDD
719	N719RDD	723	N723RDD	727	N727RDD	731	N731RDD	734	N734RDD
720	N720RDD	724	N724RDD	728	N728RDD	732	N732RDD	735	N735RDD
721	N721RDD	725	N725RDD	729	N729RDD				

803	L803XDG	Mercedes-Benz 811D	Marshall C16	B33F	1993
804	L804XDG	Mercedes-Benz 811D	Marshall C16	B33F	1993
805	L805XDG	Mercedes-Benz 811D	Marshall C16	B33F	1993
806	L806XDG	Mercedes-Benz 811D	Marshall C16	B33F	1993
807	L330CHB	Mercedes-Benz 811D	Marshall C16	B33F	1993 Ex Red & White, 1994
808	K308YKG	Mercedes-Benz 811D	Wright NimBus	B33F	1992 Ex Red & White, 1995

831-845 — Volvo B6-9.9M — Alexander Dash — B40F — 1994

831	L831CDG	834	L834CDG	837	L837CDG	840	L840CDG	843	M843EMW
832	L832CDG	835	L835CDG	838	L838CDG	841	L841CDG	844	M844EMW
833	L833CDG	836	L836CDG	839	L839CDG	842	L842CDG	845	M845EMW

846	L248CCK	Volvo B6-9.9M	Alexander Dash	DP40F	1993 Ex Ribble, 1995
847	M847HDF	Volvo B6-9.9M	Alexander Dash	B40F	1994
848	L709FWO	Volvo B6-9.9M	Alexander Dash	B40F	1994 Ex Red & White, 1995
849	L710FWO	Volvo B6-9.9M	Alexander Dash	B40F	1994 Ex Red & White, 1995
850	L711FWO	Volvo B6-9.9M	Alexander Dash	B40F	1994 Ex Red & White, 1995
851	L712FWO	Volvo B6-9.9M	Alexander Dash	B40F	1994 Ex Red & White, 1995
852	P852SMR	Volvo B6LE	Alexander ALX200	B36F	1997
853	P853SMR	Volvo B6LE	Alexander ALX200	B36F	1997
854	P854SMR	Volvo B6LE	Alexander ALX200	B36F	1997
901	P901SMR	Dennis Dart SF 412	Alexander Dash SFD412	B40F	1997
902	P902SMR	Dennis Dart SF 412	Alexander Dash SFD412	B40F	1997
903	P903SMR	Dennis Dart SF 412	Alexander Dash SFD412	B40F	1997

904-914 — Dennis Dart SLF SFD412 — Alexander ALX200 — B36F — 1996-97

904	P904SMR	907	P907SMR	909	P909SMR	911	P911SMR	913	P913SMR
905	P905SMR	908	P908SMR	910	P910SMR	912	P912SMR	914	P914SMR
906	P906SMR								

Cheltenham & Gloucester were recipients of a batch of Volvo B6s in 1994, and have gained further examples from other fleets since. Shown in Swindon is 844, M844EMW. Three of the new low-floor variant have recently been added to the fleet, and they will be joined shortly by several of the Dennis Darts now in build. *Malc McDonald*

For the longer services, Cheltenham & Gloucester use nine Alexander-bodied B10M most of which carry route branding. Shown leaving Gloucester bus station on service 94 is Cheltenham District 404, N404LDF, lettered for this principal service between the centres. *Les Peters*

Circle-Line:

1055	F55RFS	MCW MetroRider MF150/98	MCW	B25F	1988	Ex Fife Scottish, 1996
1057	F57RFS	MCW MetroRider MF150/98	MCW	B25F	1988	Ex Fife Scottish, 1996
1058	F58RFS	MCW MetroRider MF150/98	MCW	B25F	1988	Ex Fife Scottish, 1996
1060	F60RFS	MCW MetroRider MF150/98	MCW	B25F	1988	Ex Fife Scottish, 1996
1102	E102OUH	Freight Rover Sherpa	Carlyle	B20F	1987	Ex Red & White, 1994
1113	EJR113W	Leyland Atlantean AN68A/2R	Alexander AL	H49/37F	1980	Ex Busways, 1996
1114	NFB114R	Bristol VRT/SL3/6LXB	Eastern Coach Works	H43/27D	1976	Ex City Line, 1993
1137	AKV137V	Leyland Atlantean AN68A/2R	Alexander AL	H49/37F	1980	Ex Busways, 1996
1247	SCN247S	Leyland Atlantean AN68A/2R	Alexander AL	H49/37F	1978	Ex Busways, 1996
1250	SCN250S	Leyland Atlantean AN68A/2R	Alexander AL	H49/37F	1978	Ex Busways, 1996
1255	SCN255S	Leyland Atlantean AN68A/2R	Alexander AL	H49/37F	1978	Ex Busways, 1996
1256	SCN256S	Leyland Atlantean AN68A/2R	Alexander AL	H49/37F	1978	Ex Busways, 1996
1264	SCN264S	Leyland Atlantean AN68A/2R	Alexander AL	H49/37F	1978	Ex Busways, 1996
1310	REU310S	Bristol VRT/SL3/6LXB	Eastern Coach Works	H43/28F	1977	
1364	RIW3364	Leyland Tiger TRCTL11/3R	Plaxton Paramount 3200	C53F	1983	Ex Stagecoach Manchester, 1996
1410	KIB8140	Leyland National 10351A/2R		B22DL	1978	Ex Stagecoach Midland Red, 1996
1467	467WYA	Leyland National 11351A/1R(DAF)		B52F	1978	
1469	A469TUV	Leyland Cub CU335	Wadham Stringer Vanguard	B21FL	1984	Ex LB of Wandsworth, 1992
1493	KGS493Y	Leyland Tiger TRCTL11/3R	Plaxton Paramount 3200	C53F	1983	Ex Stagecoach Manchester, 1996
1499	C499BFB	Ford Transit 190	Dormobile	B16F	1986	Ex Badgerline, 1993
1511	LUL511X	Leyland Cub CU335	Wadham Stringer Vanguard	B21FL	1982	Ex London Residuary Body, 1994
1515	PEU515R	Bristol VRT/SL3/6LXB	Eastern Coach Works	H43/31F	1977	
1545	DNE545Y	Dodge G10	Wadham Stringer	DP30CL	1983	Ex Community Routes, Hattersley, 1993
1581	D581VBV	Freight Rover Sherpa	Dormobile	B16F	1988	Ex Lane, Churchdown, 1994
1603	NFB603R	Leyland National 11351A/1R		B52F	1977	
1604	D604HTC	Iveco 79-14	Robin Hood	B30FL	1987	Ex Gloucestershire CC, 1992
1605	D605HTC	Iveco 79-14	Robin Hood	B30FL	1987	Ex Gloucestershire CC, 1992
1606	D606HTC	Iveco 79-14	Robin Hood	B30FL	1987	Ex Gloucestershire CC, 1996
1617	C617SFH	Ford Transit 190	Alexander AM	B16F	1985	
1621	C621SFH	Ford Transit 190	Alexander AM	B16F	1985	
1626	C626SFH	Ford Transit 190	Alexander AM	B16F	1985	
1639	C639SFH	Ford Transit 190	Alexander AM	B16F	1985	
1663	E663JAD	MCW MetroRider MF150/43	MCW	B25F	1987	

The Circle-Line operation continues to use a green and cream livery though managed as part of Cheltenham & Gloucester. Recently transferred from Busways are Leyland Atlanteans that have displaced older buses. Shown here is 1255, SCN255S. *Colin Lloyd*

1665	E665JAD	MCW MetroRider MF150	MCW	B25F	1987	
1667	E667JAD	MCW MetroRider MF150/43	MCW	B25F	1987	
1676	E676KDG	MCW MetroRider MF150/61	MCW	DP25F	1988	
1693	C693VAD	Leyland Cub CU435	Wadham Stringer Vanguard	B32FL	1986	Ex Gloucestershire CC, 1992
1694	C694VAD	Leyland Cub CU435	Wadham Stringer Vanguard	B32FL	1986	Ex Gloucestershire CC, 1992
1696	C696VAD	Leyland Cub CU435	Wadham Stringer Vanguard	B32FL	1986	Ex Gloucestershire CC, 1992
1697	C697VAD	Leyland Cub CU435	Wadham Stringer Vanguard	B32FL	1986	Ex Gloucestershire CC, 1992
1710	SND710X	Leyland Tiger TRCTL11/3R	Plaxton Supreme V Express	C53F	1982	Ex Cumberland, 1994
1713	WLT713	Leyland Tiger TRCTL11/3RH	Duple Laser 2	C46F	1984	Ex Cumberland, 1994
1726	LHT726P	Bristol VRT/SL3/6LXB	Eastern Coach Works	H43/27D	1976	Ex City Line, 1993
1738	C738CUC	Leyland Cub CU335	Wadham Stringer	B21FL	1986	Ex LB of Wandsworth, 1992
1754	SAE754S	Leyland National 11351A/1R(DAF)		B52F	1978	Ex Bristol, 1983
1801	K801OMW	Mercedes-Benz 811D	Wright NimBus	B33F	1993	
1802	K802OMW	Mercedes-Benz 811D	Wright NimBus	B33F	1993	
1804	6804VC	Leyland Tiger TRCTL11/3RH	Plaxton Paramount 3200 II	C51F	1986	Ex Stagecoach Midland Red, 1996

Operating Units:

Circle-Line:	All 1xxx numbers
Cirencester:	117, 204/15, 401-3, 679/83
Gloucester Citybus:	104/14/21-2, 213/23/4, 303/5/7/8/10/1/4, 391/3, 503,
	680-2/4/7/8/99, 701-3/23-7/33/4, 831-42/8-51.
Stroud Valleys:	115/8-20, 226-31, 362/3/8/76-9/81/2, 500, 632/44/5/51/9/77, 704/18-22/35, 803-8
Swindon & District:	101/2/5/6/8-13/6/23/4, 208/18/9/22, 369-73/80/3, 501, 711-7, 843-5, 901-8.
Cheltenham District:	103, 201/2/5/9/16/25/32/3, 302/5/12/61/4-7/74/5/92, 404-9, 533/4/46-8,
	631/3/6/7/40-3/78/86/9-98, 705-10/28-31, 846/7.
On order:	852-4, 909-14 (for Swindon & District)

Note: All vehicles were formerly Bristol, 1983 unless shown otherwise or new later.

Previous Registrations:

467WYA	TAE645S	HIL6075	AAE646V	WLT713	B108HAO
511OHU	AAE647V	KIB8140	THX249S	YJV806	AAE658V
6804VC	WVT618, C473CAP	RIW3364	KGS491Y, 583TD		

CUMBERLAND

Cumberland Motor Services, PO Box 17, Tangier Street, Whitehaven,
Cumbria, CA28 7XF

Depots : Walney Road, Barrow; Willowholme Ind Est., Carlisle; Station Road, Kendal; Owen Road, Lancaster; Heysham Road, Morecambe and Lillyhall, Workington. **Outstations** Ambleside, Appleby, Askam, Grange, Haverthwaite, Millom, Orton, Penrith, Sedbergh and Ulverston.

1-15
Mercedes-Benz 709D Alexander Sprint B23F 1995

1	N201UHH	4	N204UHH	7	N207UHH	10	N210UHH	13	N213UHH
2	N202UHH	5	N205UHH	8	N208UHH	11	N211UHH	14	N214UHH
3	N203UHH	6	N206UHH	9	N209UHH	12	N212UHH	15	N215UHH

16-33
Mercedes-Benz 709D Alexander Sprint B23F 1996

16	N116YHH	20	N120YHH	24	N124YHH	28	N128YRM	31	N131YRM
17	N117YHH	21	N121YHH	25	N125YHH	29	N129YRM	32	N132YRM
18	N118YHH	22	N122YHH	26	N126YRM	30	N130YRM	33	N133YRM
19	N119YHH	23	N123YHH	27	N127YRM				

35-46
Mercedes-Benz L608D Reeve Burgess B20F 1986-87

35u	D35UAO	37u	D37UAO	39u	D39UAO	43u	D43UAO	45u	D45UAO
36u	D36UAO	38	D38UAO	42u	D42UAO	44	D44UAO	46u	D46UAO

47-53
Mercedes-Benz 709D Alexander Sprint B25F 1988   51-53 ex Hampshire Bus, 1989

47	E47CHH	49	E49CHH	51	E511PVV	52	E512PVV	53	E510PVV
48	E48CHH	50	E50CHH						

54-70
Mercedes-Benz 709D Alexander Sprint B23F* 1990-91 55-70 ex Magicbus, 1990-91
*57-9/61-4 are B25F

54	G178PAO	58	G268TSL	61	G263TSL	64	G266TSL	67	G295TSL
55	G299TSL	59	G269TSL	62	G264TSL	65	G297TSL	68	G294TSL
56	G300TSL	60	G296TSL	63	G265TSL	66	G298TSL	70	G293TSL
57	G267TSL								

71-78
Mercedes-Benz 709D Alexander Sprint B25F 1993

71	K871GHH	73	K873GHH	75	K875GHH	77	K877GHH	78	K878GHH
72	K872GHH	74	K874GHH	76	K876GHH				

Cumberland use an attractive livery for the Lakeland services aimed at tourists to the area. During 1996, the Mercedes-Benz L608Ds have been replaced with the 709 variant. Dedicated to The Honister Rambler service is 78, K878GHH, captured passing through Seatoller in Borrowdale.
Tony Wilson

Cumberland took the first main delivery of Alexander PS-bodied Volvo B10Ms in 1992 placing some 90 vehicles in to service with a mixture of bus and dual-purpose models. Since then two more have the type have been added, while recently one of the original delivery has been transferred to Ribble. The 1995 pair have slightly more powerful engines and are normally found on the Newcastle service. Shown at Carlisle ready for that duty is 789, N789VRM. *Phillip Stephenson*

79-86

		Mercedes-Benz 709D			Alexander Sprint		B25F	1993	Ex Ribble, 1994	
79	K626UFR	81	K622UFR	83	K121XHG	85	L123DRN	86	K113XHG
80	K623UFR	82	K114XHG	84	L126DRN				

87	N327XRP	Mercedes-Benz 709D	Alexander Sprint	DP23F	1996	
88	N328XRP	Mercedes-Benz 709D	Alexander Sprint	DP23F	1996	
89	N329XRP	Mercedes-Benz 709D	Alexander Sprint	DP23F	1996	
101	109DRM	Leyland Tiger TRCTL11/2R	Duple Laser	C50F	1984	
102	A102DAO	Leyland Tiger TRCTL11/2R	Duple Laser	C50F	1984	
103	B103HAO	Leyland Tiger TRCTL11/3RH	Duple Laser 2	C50F	1984	
105	B105HAO	Leyland Tiger TRCTL11/3RH	Duple Laser 2	C53F	1984	
106	B106HAO	Leyland Tiger TRCTL11/3RH	Duple Laser 2	C49F	1984	
107	TCK841	Leyland Tiger TRCTL11/3RH	Duple Laser 2	C46FT	1984	
109	WLT706	Leyland Tiger TRCTL11/3RH	Plaxton Paramount 3500 II	C48FT	1986	
110	WLT824	Leyland Tiger TRCTL11/3RH	Plaxton Paramount 3500 II	C46FT	1986	
111	VRR447	Leyland Tiger TRCTL11/3RH	Plaxton Paramount 3500 II	C48FT	1985	Ex Hampshire Bus, 1988
114	PSU787	Leyland Tiger TRCTL11/3RZ	Duple Caribbean 2	C49FT	1986	Ex East Midland, 1995
120	J120AHH	Volvo B10M-60	Plaxton Expressliner	C46FT	1991	
121	J121AHH	Volvo B10M-60	Plaxton Expressliner	C46FT	1991	

125-132

		Volvo B10M-62			Plaxton Expressliner 2		C46FT	1994-95		
125	L125NAO	127	L127NAO	129	N129VAO	131	N131VAO	132	N132VAO
126	L126NAO	128	N128VAO	130	N130VAO				

Opposite: Two of the special services that work through English Lakeland are seen here. The upper picture shows one of the open-top Bristol VRs used in the area. Based at Keswick for the Borrowdale service 2076, UWV622S, was recently transferred to Cumberland from Ribble. The lower picture shows one of eight Olympians with high-back seating used on the long and picturesque journeys through Lakeland. Service 555 connects Keswick to Lancaster and is marketed as Lakeslink service. Pictured at the Waterhead timing point is 1026, J126XHH. *Tony Wilson*

153	LJC800	Volvo B10M-61	Van Hool Alizée	C48F	1982	Ex Magicbus, 1988
156	PCK335	Leyland Tiger TRCTL11/3RH	Duple Laser 2	C53F	1985	Ex Ribble, 1989
158	DSV943	Volvo B10M-61	Plaxton Paramount 3500 III	C48FT	1987	Ex Wallace Arnold, 1990
159	LJY145	Volvo B10M-61	Plaxton Paramount 3500 III	C48FT	1987	Ex Ribble, 1995
160	YDG616	Volvo B10M-61	Plaxton Paramount 3500 III	C48FT	1987	Ex Ribble, 1995
161	JPU817	Volvo B10M-61	Plaxton Paramount 3500 III	C53F	1987	Ex Wallace Arnold, 1990
162	B162WRN	Leyland Tiger TRCTL11/3RH	Duple Laser 2	C53F	1985	Ex Ribble, 1991
270	L270LHH	Volvo B6-9.9M	Alexander Dash	B40F	1993	
275	L275JAO	Volvo B6-9.9M	Alexander Dash	B40F	1993	
276	L276JAO	Volvo B6-9.9M	Alexander Dash	B40F	1993	
282	L282JAO	Volvo B6-9.9M	Alexander Dash	B40F	1993	

420-437

Bristol VRT/SL3/6LXB Eastern Coach Works H43/31F 1980

420u	FAO420V	424	FAO424V	427	FAO427V	432	KRM432W	435	KRM435W
421u	FAO421V	425	FAO425V	428	FAO428V	433u	KRM433W	436	KRM436W
422	FAO422V	426	FAO426V	431	KRM431W	434	KRM434W	437	KRM437W
423	FAO423V								

505u	LUA273V	Leyland Leopard PSU3F/4R	Plaxton Supreme IV	C51F	1980	Ex Yeowart, Whitehaven, 1988
520u	D520RCK	Mercedes-Benz L608D	Reeve Burgess	DP19F	1986	Ex Ribble, 1989

525-560

Mercedes-Benz L608D Reeve Burgess B20F 1986 Ex Ribble, 1989

525u	D525RCK	529u	D529RCK	531u	D531RCK	534u	D534RCK	559u	D559RCK
528u	D528RCK	530u	D530RCK	533u	D533RCK	558u	D558RCK	560u	D560RCK

569u	LUA275V	Leyland Leopard PSU3E/4R	Plaxton Supreme IV	C51F	1980	Ex Kirkpatrick, Brigham, 1988

699-788

Volvo B10M-55 Alexander PS B49F* 1992-93 *772-788 are DP48F

699	K699ERM	717	K717DAO	735	K735DAO	754	K754DAO	771	K771DAO
700	K700DAO	718	K718DAO	736	K736DAO	755	K755DAO	772	K772DAO
701	K701DAO	719	K719DAO	737	K737DAO	756	K756DAO	773	K773DAO
702	K702DAO	720	K720DAO	738	K738DAO	757	K757DAO	774	K774DAO
703	K703DAO	721	K721DAO	739	K739DAO	758	K758DAO	775	K775DAO
704	K704ERM	722	K722DAO	741	K741DAO	759	K759DAO	776	K776DAO
705	K705DAO	723	K723DAO	742	K742DAO	760	K760DAO	777	K777DAO
706	K706DAO	724	K724DAO	743	K743DAO	761	K761DAO	778	K778DAO
707	K707DAO	725	K725DAO	744	K744DAO	762	K762DAO	779	K779DAO
708	K708DAO	726	K726DAO	745	K745DAO	763	K763DAO	780	K780DAO
709	K709DAO	727	K727DAO	746	K746DAO	764	K764DAO	781	K781DAO
710	K710DAO	728	K728DAO	748	K748DAO	765	K765DAO	783	K783DAO
711	K711DAO	729	K729DAO	749	K749DAO	766	K766DAO	784	K784DAO
712	K712DAO	730	K730DAO	750	K750DAO	767	K767DAO	785	K785DAO
713	K713DAO	731	K731DAO	751	K751DAO	768	K768DAO	786	K786DAO
714	K714DAO	732	K732DAO	752	K752DAO	769	K769DAO	787	K787DAO
715	K715DAO	733	K733DAO	753	K753DAO	770	K770DAO	788	K788DAO
716	K716DAO	734	K734DAO						

789	N789VRM	Volvo B10M-55	Alexander PS	DP48F	1995	
790	N790VRM	Volvo B10M-55	Alexander PS	DP48F	1995	
810	TRN810V	Leyland National 10351B/1R		B44F	1979	Ex Ribble, 1986
1001	URM801Y	Leyland Olympian ONLXB/1R	Eastern Coach Works	DPH45/30F	1982	
1002	URM802Y	Leyland Olympian ONLXB/1R	Eastern Coach Works	H45/32F	1982	

1003-1011

Leyland Olympian ONLXB/2RZ Alexander RL H51/36F 1988

1003	F803FAO	1005	F805FAO	1007	F807FAO	1009	F809FAO	1011	F811FAO
1004	F804FAO	1006	F806FAO	1008	F808FAO	1010	F810FAO		

1012-1019

Leyland Olympian ON2R56G13Z4 Alexander RL H51/34F 1990

1012	H112SAO	1014	H114SAO	1016	H116SAO	1018	H118SAO	1019	H119SAO
1013	H113SAO	1015	H115SAO	1017	H117SAO				

Most of the Volvo B6s new to Cumberland have now been transferred to other fleets, though those used on Lakeland services remain. Allocated to Kendal is 276, L276JAO seen passing the Yewdale Hotel in Coniston village complete with Coniston Rambler lettering. *Tony Wilson*

The two tri-axle Olympians with Cumberland are now based at Barrow where they are used, among other work, on school duties. Seen here is 1202, F202FHH. *Phillip Stephenson*

Cumberland took on the Cumbria-based operations of Ribble in 1989 and four Leyland Olympians moved with the services. Seen working through Grasmere in June 1996 was 2175, C175ECK. This vehicle carries an Eastern Coach Works body fitted with high-back seating. In February 1997 the Lancaster area services are to be established as Stagecoach Lancaster reporting to Cumberland management at Whitehaven. *Tony Wilson*

1020-1027

Leyland Olympian ON2R56G13Z4 Alexander RL   DPH47/27F 1991

1020	J120AAO	1022	J122AAO	1024	J124XHH	1026	J126XHH	1027	J127XHH
1021	J121AAO	1023	J123XHH	1025	J125XHH				

1028-1035

Leyland Olympian ON2R50G13Z4 Alexander RL   DPH43/27F 1992

1028	K128DAO	1030	K130DAO	1032	K132DAO	1034	K134DAO	1035	K135DAO
1029	K129DAO	1031	K131DAO	1033	K133DAO				

1090	C382SAO	Leyland Olympian ONLXB/1RV	Alexander RL	H47/30F	1986	Ex Bluebird, 1991
1091	C383SAO	Leyland Olympian ONLXB/1RV	Alexander RL	H47/30F	1986	Ex Bluebird, 1991
1092	D384XAO	Leyland Olympian ONLXB/1RV	Alexander RL	H47/30F	1987	Ex Bluebird, 1991
1093	D380XRS	Leyland Olympian ONLXB/1RV	Alexander RL	H47/30F	1987	Ex Bluebird, 1992
1094	D381XRS	Leyland Olympian ONLXB/1RV	Alexander RL	H47/30F	1987	Ex Bluebird, 1992
1103	KRN103T	Leyland Leopard PSU3E/4R	Duple Dominant II	C47F	1978	Ex Ribble, 1989
1105	KRN105T	Leyland Leopard PSU3E/4R	Duple Dominant II	C47F	1978	Ex Ribble, 1989
1113	KRN113T	Leyland Leopard PSU3E/4R	Duple Dominant II	C47F	1979	Ex Ribble, 1989
1119	KRN119T	Leyland Leopard PSU3E/4R	Duple Dominant II	C47F	1979	Ex Ribble, 1986
1125u	GRM625V	Leyland Leopard PSU3F/4R	Duple Dominant II	C49F	1980	
1151	B151WRN	Leyland Tiger TRCTL11/2RH	Duple Laser 2	C49F	1985	Ex Ribble, 1991
1153	B153WRN	Leyland Tiger TRCTL11/2RH	Duple Laser 2	C49F	1985	Ex Ribble, 1991
1154	B154WRN	Leyland Tiger TRCTL11/2RH	Duple Laser 2	C49F	1985	Ex Ribble, 1991
1155	B43MAO	Leyland Tiger TRCTL11/3RH	Duple Laser 2	C53F	1985	Ex Ribble, 1991
1162	WLT380	Volvo B10M-61	Plaxton Paramount 3500 II	C48F	1986	Ex Ribble, 1994
1175	MRJ275W	Leyland Leopard PSU5D/4R	Plaxton Supreme IV	C50F	1981	Ex Ribble, 1989
1199	FDV799V	Leyland Leopard PSU3E/4R	Plaxton Supreme IV Express	C49F	1980	Ex Ribble, 1989
1201	F201FHH	Leyland Olympian ONLXCT/3RZ	Alexander RL	DPH55/41F	1989	
1202	F202FHH	Leyland Olympian ONLXCT/3RZ	Alexander RL	DPH55/41F	1989	
1253	HNE253V	Leyland Leopard PSU5C/4R	Duple Dominant II	C53F	1980	Ex Ribble, 1989

1996 saw the painting of Olympian 1017, H117SAO, into the traditional livery of Cumberland. It was photographed outside the Carlisle depot shortly after repaint. The vehicle is presently allocated to West Cumbria workings. *Phillip Stephenson*

2002	CBV2S	Bristol VRT/SL3/501 (6LXB)	Eastern Coach Works	O43/31F	1977	Ex Ribble, 1986
2024	DBV24W	Bristol VRT/SL3/6LXB	Eastern Coach Works	H43/31F	1980	Ex Ribble, 1986
2032	DBV32W	Bristol VRT/SL3/6LXB	Eastern Coach Works	H43/31F	1980	Ex Ribble, 1986
2035	UWV610S	Bristol VRT/SL3/6LXB	Eastern Coach Works	O43/31F	1977	Ex Southdown, 1990
2036	UWV612S	Bristol VRT/SL3/6LXB	Eastern Coach Works	O43/31F	1977	Ex Southdown, 1990
2037	UWV618S	Bristol VRT/SL3/6LXB	Eastern Coach Works	O43/31F	1978	Ex Southdown, 1990
2038	UWV620S	Bristol VRT/SL3/6LXB	Eastern Coach Works	O43/31F	1978	Ex Southdown, 1990
2075	XRR175S	Bristol VRT/SL3/6LXB	Eastern Coach Works	O43/27F	1980	Ex Ribble, 1995
2076	UWV622S	Bristol VRT/SL3/6LXB	Eastern Coach Works	O43/31F	1980	Ex Ribble, 1996
2134	DBV134Y	Leyland Olympian ONLXB/1R	Eastern Coach Works	H45/32F	1983	Ex Ribble, 1989
2175	C175ECK	Leyland Olympian ONLXB/1R	Eastern Coach Works	DPH42/30F	1985	Ex Ribble, 1989
2176	C176ECK	Leyland Olympian ONLXB/1R	Eastern Coach Works	DPH42/30F	1985	Ex Ribble, 1989
2177	C177ECK	Leyland Olympian ONLXB/1R	Eastern Coach Works	DPH42/30F	1986	Ex Ribble, 1989

Stagecoach Lancaster

135	F135SPX	Dennis Javelin 11SDL1914	Duple 300	B63F	1989	Ex Ribble, 1997
136	F136SPX	Dennis Javelin 11SDL1914	Duple 300	B63F	1989	Ex Ribble, 1997
137	F137SPX	Dennis Javelin 11SDL1914	Duple 300	B63F	1989	Ex Ribble, 1997
152	L152BFV	Dennis Javelin 11SDL2133	Plaxton Premiére Interurban	DP47F	1993	Ex Ribble, 1997
154	L154BFV	Dennis Javelin 11SDL2133	Plaxton Premiére Interurban	DP47F	1993	Ex Ribble, 1997
372	HHH372V	Leyland National 2 NL116L11/1R		B52F	1980	Ex Ribble, 1997
373	HHH373V	Leyland National 2 NL116L11/1R		B52F	1980	Ex Ribble, 1997
378	KHH378W	Leyland National 2 NL116L11/1R		B52F	1980	Ex Ribble, 1997
383	RRM383X	Leyland National 2 NL116AL11/1R		DP52F	1982	Ex Ribble, 1997
393	SHH393X	Leyland National 2 NL116AL11/1R		B52F	1982	Ex Ribble, 1997
398	WAO398Y	Leyland National 2 NL116HLXB/1R		B52F	1982	Ex Ribble, 1997
449	K449YCW	Optare MetroRider	Optare	B31F	1992	Ex Ribble, 1997
450	K450YCW	Optare MetroRider	Optare	B31F	1992	Ex Ribble, 1997

In February 1997 the Lancaster and Morecambe operations of Ribble will be reorganised to form a separate unit from Ribble within Stagecoach North West. The new unit will be Stagecoach Lancaster and will operate to the Whitehaven office, with Cumberland responsible for the administration. Shown in the City of Lancaster is former Highland Omnibuses' Leyland Olympian, 2213, A978OST pictured before its transfer to Chorley. Six of the type move to Cumbria.

455-463

Volvo B10M-55 — Alexander PS — B48F — 1995 — Ex Ribble, 1997

455	M455VCW	457	M457VCW	459	M459VCW	461	M461VCW	463	M463VCW
456	M456VCW	458	M458VCW	460	M460VCW	462	M462VCW		

565	G565PHH	Mercedes-Benz 709D	Alexander Sprint	B23F	1990	Ex Ribble, 1997
566	G566PHH	Mercedes-Benz 709D	Alexander Sprint	B23F	1990	Ex Ribble, 1997
567	G567PHH	Mercedes-Benz 709D	Alexander Sprint	DP25F	1990	Ex Ribble, 1997
592	G192PAO	Mercedes-Benz 709D	Alexander Sprint	B23F	1990	Ex Ribble, 1997

597-625

Mercedes-Benz 709D — Alexander Sprint — B25F — 1993 — Ex Ribble, 1997

597	K117XHG	604	L124XHG	607	L127DRN	615	K615UFR	625	K625UFR
602	L122DRN						

645	WAO645Y	Leyland Tiger TRCTL11/2R	Alexander TE	DP47F	1983	Ex Ribble, 1997
834	DBV834W	Leyland National 2 NL106L11/1R		B44F	1980	Ex Ribble, 1997
884	RHG884X	Leyland National 2 NL116AL11/1R		B52F	1982	Ex Ribble, 1997
888	ARN888Y	Leyland National 2 NL116HLXB/1R		B52F	1983	Ex Ribble, 1997
896	CEO721W	Leyland National 2 NL116L11/1R		B49F	1980	Ex Ribble, 1997
900	B900WRN	Leyland Tiger TRCTL11/1R	Duple Dominant	B49F	1984	Ex Ribble, 1997
1160	L160BFV	Dennis Javelin 11SDL2133	Plaxton Premiére Interurban	DP47F	1993	Ex Ribble, 1997
1482	TRN482V	Leyland Atlantean AN68A/1R	Eastern Coach Works	H43/31F	1980	Ex Ribble, 1997
2100	DBV100W	Leyland Olympian B45.02	Eastern Coach Works	H45/33F	1980	Ex Ribble, 1997
2116	OFV16X	Leyland Olympian ONLXB/1R	Eastern Coach Works	H45/32F	1982	Ex Ribble, 1997
2117	OFV17X	Leyland Olympian ONLXB/1R	Eastern Coach Works	H45/32F	1982	Ex Ribble, 1997
2138	A138MRN	Leyland Olympian ONLXB/1R	Eastern Coach Works	H45/32F	1984	Ex Ribble, 1997
2179	C179ECK	Leyland Olympian ONLXB/1R	Eastern Coach Works	DPH41/26F	1985	Ex Ribble, 1997

2180-2189

Leyland Olympian ON2R50G16Z4 — Alexander RL — DPH51/31F — 1989 — Ex Ribble, 1997

2180	G180JHG	2182	G182JHG	2184	G184JHG	2186	G186JHG	2189	G189JHG
2181	G181JHG	2183	G183JHG	2185	G185JHG			

The 1997 Stagecoach Bus Handbook

Pictured passing through the Lancashire town of Great Eccleston in June 1996 was Olympian 2207, J207HFR. Based at Morecambe, it is one the 1991 delivery all of which feature high-back seating for commuter duties. The limited stop service X42, between Morecambe and Blackpool is now operated by Stagecoach Lancaster.
Paul Wigan

2191	H191WFR	Leyland Olympian ON2R50G16Z4 Alexander RL				H47/30F	1990	Ex Ribble, 1997
2192	H192WFR	Leyland Olympian ON2R50G16Z4 Alexander RL				H47/30F	1990	Ex Ribble, 1997
2194	H194WFR	Leyland Olympian ON2R50G16Z4 Alexander RL				H47/30F	1990	Ex Ribble, 1997

2199-2210   Leyland Olympian ON2R56G13Z4 Alexander RL   DPH43/27F* 1991   Ex Ribble, 1997
*2204-6/10 are DPH47/27F

2199	J199HFR	2203	J203HFR	2205	J205HFR	2207	J207HFR	2209	J209HFR
2201	J201HFR	2204	J204HFR	2206	J206HFR	2208	J208HFR	2210	J210HFR
2202	J202HFR								

2211-2223   Leyland Olympian ONLXB/1R   Alexander RL   H45/32F   1984-85 Ex Ribble, 1997

2211	A975OST	2216	B892UAS	2217	B893UAS	2219	B895UAS	2223	B899UAS
2212	A977OST								

Previous Registrations:

109DRM	A101DAO	LJC800	From new
B43MAO	B155WRN, PCK335	LJY145	D205LWX
C382SAO	C473SSO, GSO3V	PCK335	B156WRN
C383SAO	C474SSO, GSO4V	PSU787	C495LJV
D384XAO	D375XRS, GSO5V	TCK841	B107HAO
D560RCK	D561RCK	VRR447	B180RLJ
DSV943	D203LWX	WLT380	C105DWR
JPU817	D207LWX	WLT706	C109OHH
K449YCW	K300LCT	WLT824	C110OHH
K450YCW	K200LCT	YDG616	D206LWX

Livery variations:
Red (Coachline):109/11/4, 153/8/60/1, 1153; white (National Express) 120/1/5-32; apple green and cream (Lakeland Experience) 78, 275/6/82, 520, 810, 2002/35-8/75/6.

Named vehicles: 520 *William Wordsworth*, 558 *John Ruskin*, 560 *Beatrix Potter*.

DEVON

Stagecoach Devon, Belgrave Road, Exeter, EX1 2AJ
Torbay Bayline Ltd, Regents Close, Torquay, Devon

Depots: Belgrave Road, Exeter; Imperial Road, Exmouth and Woolbrook Road, Sidmouth.

201-216   Ford Transit VE6   Mellor   B16F   1987-88

201	D110PTT	204	D113PTT	207	D117PTT	210	D125PTT	214	E825ATT
202	D111PTT	205	D114PTT	208	D118PTT	211	D131PTT	215	E827ATT
203	D112PTT	206	D116PTT	209	D120PTT	212	D134PTT	216	E828ATT

217-227   Ford Transit VE6   Mellor   B16F   1988

217	E200BDV	220	E210BDV	222	E213BDV	224	E223BDV	226	F754FDV
218	E205BDV	221	E211BDV	223	E216BDV	225	F750FDV	227	F755FDV
219	E209BDV								

228-240   Ford Transit VE   Mellor   B16F   1987

228w	D636NOD	231	D640NOD	234	D647NOD	237	D650NOD	239	D655NOD
229	D654NOD	232	D642NOD	235	D648NOD	238	D652NOD	240	D656NOD
230	D639NOD	233	D646NOD	236	D649NOD				

241-271   Ford Transit VE   Mellor   B16F   1987-88

241w	F771FDV	248	D781NDV	255w	D794NDV	261	E800WDV	267	E816WDV
242	F772FDV	249	D784NDV	256w	D795NDV	262	E801WDV	268w	E821WDV
244	D777NDV	250	D785NDV	257	D796NDV	263	E802WDV	269	E822WDV
245	D778NDV	251	D786NDV	258	D797NDV	264	E806WDV	270	E823WDV
246	D779NDV	252	D787NDV	259	D798NDV	265	E810WDV	271w	E824WDV
247	D780NDV	254	D792NDV	260	D799NDV	266	E815WDV		

300-314   Iveco Daily 59.12   Mellor Duet   B21D   1994

300	L929CTT	303	L932CTT	306	L935CTT	309	L938CTT	312	L941CTT
301	L930CTT	304	L933CTT	307	L936CTT	310	L939CTT	313	L942CTT
302	L931CTT	305	L934CTT	308	L937CTT	311	L940CTT	314	L943CTT

315-333   Iveco Daily 59.12   WS Wessex II   B21D   1994

315	M638HDV	319	M639HDV	323	M624HDV	327	M630HDV	331	M194HTT
316	M640HDV	320	M629HDV	324	M628HDV	328	M193HTT	332	M191HTT
317	M637HDV	321	M624HDV	325	M626HDV	329	M627HDV	333	M641HDV
318	M636HDV	322	M623HDV	326	M192HTT	330	M622HDV		

334-364   Iveco Daily 59.12   Mellor Duet   B26D   1993

334	K702UTT	341	K721UTT	347	K730UTT	353	K927VDV	359	K822WFJ
335	K711UTT	342	K722UTT	348	K731UTT	354	K824WFJ	360	K805WFJ
336	K713UTT	343	K913VDV	349	K732UTT	355	K823WFJ	361	K804WFJ
337	K714UTT	344	K725UTT	350	K724UTT	356	K821WFJ	362	K806WFJ
338	K717UTT	345	K726UTT	351	K924VDV	357	K803WFJ	363	K816WFJ
339	K719UTT	346	K727UTT	352	K926VDV	358	K925VDV	364	K620XOD
340	K720UTT								

When Stagecoach took over the Devon operation only one vehicle was not a minibus. Since then there have been many changes to the operation. Six new Plaxton Interurban coaches have been placed on Stagecoach Express services while the summer opentop service has been augmented with two additional buses from Stagecoach South. Here, the upper picture shows 801, P801XTA working service X46 when new, while the lower picture shows Invincible, alias 937, UWV614S, in Torquay. *BWS/Paul Wigan*

While many of the original Ford Transit minibuses have been displaced, the second generation have been receiving repaints. Shown working in Exmouth is 247, D780NDV. *Paul Wigan*

The three opentop VRs working in Torquay are of the convertible model. Proving the versatility is 935, VDV135S seen with an all-white roof attached in Torbay Road, Torquay. *BWS*

365-377 — Iveco Daily 59.12 — Marshall C31 — B26D — 1994

365	L193FDV	368	L197FDV	371	L204FDV	374	L210FDV
366	L194FDV	369	L201FDV	372	L208FDV	375	L211FDV
367	L195FDV	370	L203FDV	373	L209FDV		
				376	L212FDV		
				377	L214FDV		

380	F958HTO	Iveco Daily 49.10	Robin Hood City Nippy	B23F	1988	Ex Red & White, 1996
381	G912KWF	Iveco Daily 49.10	Reeve Burgess Beaver	B25F	1989	Ex Red & White, 1996
382	G919KWF	Iveco Daily 49.10	Reeve Burgess Beaver	B25F	1989	Ex Red & White, 1996
383	G920KWF	Iveco Daily 49.10	Reeve Burgess Beaver	B25F	1989	Ex Red & White, 1996
384	G924KWF	Iveco Daily 49.10	Reeve Burgess Beaver	B25F	1989	Ex Red & White, 1996
385	H370PNY	Iveco Daily 49-10	Carlyle Dailybus 2	B25F	1991	Ex Red & White, 1996

400-434 — Mercedes-Benz 709D — Reeve Burgess Beaver — DP25F — 1988

400	F748FDV	407	F719FDV	414	F730FDV	421	F738FDV
401	E830ATT	408	F720FDV	415	F731FDV	422	F740FDV
402	F714FDV	409	F722FDV	416	F732FDV	423	F741FDV
403	F715FDV	410	F723FDV	417	F733FDV	424	F742FDV
404	F716FDV	411	F726FDV	418	F735FDV	425	F743FDV
405	F717FDV	412	F728FDV	419	F736FDV	426	F744FDV
406	F718FDV	413	F729FDV	420	F737FDV	427	F745FDV
428	F756FDV	429	F757FDV	430	F758FDV	431	F759FDV
432	F760FDV	433	F762FDV	434	F763FDV		

435-443 — Mercedes-Benz 709D — Reeve Burgess Beaver — DP25F — 1989

435	F404KOD	437	F406KOD	439	F408KOD	441	F411KOD
436	F405KOD	438	F407KOD	440	F410KOD	442	F412KOD
443	F413KOD						

444-468 — Mercedes-Benz 709D — Marshall C19 — B21D — 1995

444	M226UTM	449	M231UTM	454	M236UTM	459	M241UTM
445	M227UTM	450	M232UTM	455	M237UTM	460	M242UTM
446	M228UTM	451	M233UTM	456	M238UTM	461	M243UTM
447	M229UTM	452	M234UTM	457	M239UTM	462	M244UTM
448	M230UTM	453	M235UTM	458	M240UTM	463	M245UTM
464	M246UTM	465	M247UTM	466	M248UTM	467	M249UTM
468	M250UTM						

470-487 — Mercedes-Benz 709D — Alexander Sprint — B23F — 1996

470	N978NAP	474	N982NAP	478	N509BJA	482	N513BJA
471	N979NAP	475	N506BJA	479	N510BJA	483	N514BJA
472	N980NAP	476	N507BJA	480	N511BJA	484	N515BJA
473	N981NAP	477	N508BJA	481	N512BJA		
485	N516BJA	486	N517BJA	487	N518BJA		

Stagecoach Devon has been able to speed the replacement of ageing Ford Transits with the transfer of eighteen Mercedes-Benz 709Ds with Reeve Burgess Beaver bodies from Busways. Shown here at work in Exeter with Devon names is 493, D412TFT.
Paul Wigan

488-505 — Mercedes-Benz 709D — Reeve Burgess Beaver — B20F — 1986-87 Ex Busways, 1996

488	D404TFT	492	D409TFT	496	D417TFT	500	E438AFT	503	D413TFT
489	D405TFT	493	D412TFT	497	D418TFT	501	E439AFT	504	D420TFT
490	D407TFT	494	D414TFT	498	E431AFT	502	E446AFT	505	E441AFT
491	D408TFT	495	D416TFT	499	E436AFT				

589-598 — Mercedes-Benz 811D — Alexander Sprint — B28F — 1988 — Ex Selkent, 1996-97 / 597/8 ex Bluebird, 1996

589	F614XMS	591	F619XMS	593	F631XMS	595	F641XMS	597	F609XMS
590	F615XMS	592	F620XMS	594	F616XMS	596	F630XMS	598	F617XMS

599	H889NFS	Mercedes-Benz 814D	PMT Ami	DP33F	1990	Ex Bluebird, 1996

701-714 — Volvo B6LE — Alexander ALX200 — B36F — 1997

701	P701PTA	704	P704PTA	707	P707PTA	710	P710PTA	713	P713PTA
702	P702PTA	705	P705PTA	708	P708PTA	711	P711PTA	714	P714PTA
703	P703PTA	706	P706PTA	709	P709PTA	712	P712PTA		

801-806 — Volvo B10M-62 — Plaxton Premiére Interurban — DP51F — 1996

801	P801XTA	803	P803XTA	804	P804XTA	805	P805XTA	806	P806XTA
802	P802XTA								

935	VDV135S	Bristol VRT/SL3/6LXB	Eastern Coach Works	CO43/31F	1977	Ex Western National, 1983
936	UWV604S	Bristol VRT/SL3/6LXB	Eastern Coach Works	CO43/31F	1977	Ex Stagecoach South, 1996
937	UWV614S	Bristol VRT/SL3/6LXB	Eastern Coach Works	CO43/31F	1978	Ex Stagecoach South, 1996
938	RAH265W	Bristol VRT/SL3/6LXB	Eastern Coach Works	H43/31F	1980	Ex Cambus, 1997
939	RAH268W	Bristol VRT/SL3/6LXB	Eastern Coach Works	H43/31F	1980	Ex Cambus, 1997
940	LWV467V	Bristol VRT/SL3/6LXB	Eastern Coach Works	H43/31F	1980	Ex Cambus, 1997
941	LWV468V	Bristol VRT/SL3/6LXB	Eastern Coach Works	H43/31F	1980	Ex Cambus, 1997
942	PWY45W	Bristol VRT/SL3/6LXB	Eastern Coach Works	H43/31F	1981	Ex Cambus, 1997
943	PWY47W	Bristol VRT/SL3/6LXB	Eastern Coach Works	H43/31F	1981	Ex Cambus, 1997

Named vehicles: 935 Ark Royal; 936 Illustrious; 937 Invincible.

One of the 1996 intake at Devon with less common bodywork is 599, H889NFS. Transferred from Bluebird during 1996, this vehicle carries a PMT-built body and high-back seating on the Mercedes-Benz chassis. The vehicle was photographed in Bampfylde Street in Exeter. *BWS*

EAST LONDON

East London Bus & Coach Company Ltd, 2-4 Clements Road, Ilford,
Essex, IG1 1BA

Depots : Longbridge Road, Barking; Fairfield Road, Bow; High Road, Leyton; North Street, Romford; Waterden Road, Stratford
and Redclyffe Road, Upton Park.

DA10	G684KNW			DAF SB220LC550		Optare Delta		B36D	1989	

DA11-35

DAF SB220LC550 — Optare Delta — B40D — 1992-93 DA13/5 on loan to Stagecoach South

11	J711CYG	16	J716CYG	21	J721CYG	26	J726CYG	31	K631HWX
12	J712CYG	17	J717CYG	22	J722CYG	27	J727CYG	32	K632HWX
13	472YMF	18	J718CYG	23	J723CYG	28	J728CYG	33	K633HWX
14	J714CYG	19	J719CYG	24	J724CYG	29	J729CYG	34	K634HWX
15	YLJ332	20	J720CYG	25	J725CYG	30	K630HWX	35	K635HWX

DAL1-27

Dennis Dart 9.8SDL3054 — Alexander Dash — B36F — 1995

1	N301AMC	7	N307AMC	13	N313AMC	18	N318AMC	23	N323AMC
2	N302AMC	8	N308AMC	14	N314AMC	19	N319AMC	24	N324AMC
3	N303AMC	9	N309AMC	15	N315AMC	20	N320AMC	25	N325AMC
4	N304AMC	10	N310AMC	16	N316AMC	21	N321AMC	26	N326AMC
5	N305AMC	11	N311AMC	17	N317AMC	22	N322AMC	27	N327AMC
6	N306AMC	12	N312AMC						

DRL109-138

Dennis Dart 9SDL3024 — Plaxton Pointer — B34F — 1993

109	K109SRH	115	K115SRH	121	K121SRH	127	K127SRH	133	K133SRH
110	K110SRH	116	K116SRH	122	K122SRH	128	K128SRH	134	K134SRH
111	K211SRH	117	K117SRH	123	K123SRH	129	K129SRH	135	K135SRH
112	K112SRH	118	K118SRH	124	K124SRH	130	K130SRH	136	L136VRH
113	K113SRH	119	K119SRH	125	K125SRH	131	K131SRH	137	L137VRH
114	K114SRH	120	K120SRH	126	K126SRH	132	K132SRH	138	L138VRH

DRL139-146

Dennis Dart 9SDL3034 — Plaxton Pointer — B34F — 1993

139	L139VRH	141	L141VRH	143	L143VRH	145	L145VRH	146	L146VRH
140	L140VRH	142	L142VRH	144	L144VRH				

1716	NFX667	Dennis Dart 9.8SDL3017	Alexander Dash	DP32F	1992	On loan to Stagecoach South
1719	XYK976	Dennis Dart 9.8SDL3017	Alexander Dash	DP32F	1992	On loan to Stagecoach South

East London have
continued to paint
their vehicles in
the smart all-red
livery, clearly
noticeable in
central London.
Pictured in Ilford
while working
service 169 to
Barking is Optare
Delta DA27,
J727CYG.
Malc McDonald

Two of the RMA class have now been prepared for service. As with the other red Routemasters at East London, they carry the fleet name in gold and centrally positioned. Pictured at Marble Arch while working service 15 to Paddington is RMA5, NMY635E. *Malc McDonald*

DWL15-26 — Dennis Dart 9SDL3016 — Wright Handy-bus — B35F — 1993

15	NDZ3015	18	NDZ3018	21	NDZ3021	23	NDZ3023	25	NDZ3025
16	NDZ3016	19	NDZ3019	22	NDZ3022	24	NDZ3024	26	NDZ3026
17	NDZ3017	20	NDZ3020						

DW133-159 — Dennis Dart 8.5SDL3015 — Wright Handy-bus — B29F — 1993

133	NDZ3133	139	NDZ3139	145	NDZ3145	150	NDZ3150	155	NDZ3155
134	NDZ3134	140	NDZ3140	146	NDZ3146	151	NDZ3151	156	NDZ3156
135	NDZ3135	141	NDZ3141	147	NDZ3147	152	NDZ3152	157	NDZ3157
136	NDZ3136	142	NDZ3142	148	NDZ3148	153	NDZ3153	158	NDZ3158
137	NDZ3137	143	NDZ3143	149	NDZ3149	154	NDZ3154	159	NDZ3159
138	NDZ3138	144	NDZ3144						

MR16	D476PON	MCW MetroRider MF150/14	MCW	B23F	1987	
MRL144	H144UUA	Optare MetroRider MR03	Optare	B26F	1990	Ex Selkent, 1996
RMA5	NMY635E	AEC Routemaster R2RH2	Park Royal	H32/24F	1967	
RMA8	NMY640E	AEC Routemaster R2RH2	Park Royal	H32/24F	1967	
RM613	WLT613	AEC Routemaster R2RH	Park Royal	H36/28R	1960	
RML886	WLT886	AEC Routemaster R2RH1	Park Royal	H36/28R	1961	Cummins engine fitted
RML890	XFF814	AEC Routemaster R2RH1	Park Royal	H40/32R	1961	Cummins engine fitted
RML898	XFF813	AEC Routemaster R2RH1	Park Royal	H40/32R	1961	Iveco engine fitted
RMC1456	LFF875	AEC Routemaster R2RH	Park Royal	H32/25RD	1962	
RMC1461	461CLT	AEC Routemaster R2RH	Park Royal	H32/25RD	1962	
RMC1485	485CLT	AEC Routemaster R2RH	Park Royal	H32/25RD	1962	
RM1527	527CLT	AEC Routemaster 2R2RH	Park Royal	H36/28R	1963	

Opposite: **East London had taken several Scania into the fleet prior to its sale to Stagecoach. Shown here are two of the models.** *Top:* **SLW28, RDZ6128, an early, low floor, N113CRL with Wright Pathfinder bodywork and, bottom, S65, K865LMK, a double deck N113DRB with Northern Counties Palatine bodywork.** *Malc McDonald*

Passing St Mary Bow Church on service 8 is Routemaster 2450, JJD450D. Classified as RML, the vehicle is one of many in the East London fleet that have received a repaint. East London introduced an all-red livery to conform to the LRT requirement while also restoring gold fleetnames to the side panels, here showing the Stagecoach East London names.
Les Peters

RML2272-2592

	AEC Routemaster R2RH1			Park Royal		H40/32R	1965-66		
	2272/86/311/445/456/495-581 have Cummins engines; all others have Iveco engines								
2272	CUV272C	2399	JJD399D	2444	JJD444D	2470	JJD470D	2497	JJD497D
2286	CUV286C	2402	JJD402D	2445	JJD445D	2481	JJD481D	2541	JJD541D
2300	CUV300C	2415	JJD415D	2450	JJD450D	2488	JJD488D	2550	JJD550D
2303	CUV303C	2429	JJD429D	2451	JJD451D	2493	JJD493D	2565	JJD565D
2311	CUV311C	2435	JJD435D	2456	JJD456D	2495	JJD495D	2581	JJD581D
2392	JJD392D	2437	JJD437D	2462	JJD462D	2496	JJD496D	2592	JJD592D

RML2607-2760

	AEC Routemaster R2RH1			Park Royal		H40/32R	1967-68		
	2610/6/39-42/61/70/1/96/705/23/43/8 have Cummins engines; all others except 2760 have Iveco engines								
2607	NML607E	2641	NML641E	2665	SMK665F	2705	SMK705F	2743	SMK743F
2610	NML610E	2642	NML642E	2670	SMK670F	2709	SMK709F	2748	SMK748F
2616	NML616E	2657	NML657E	2671	SMK671F	2723	SMK723F	2749	SMK749F
2624	NML624E	2661	SMK661F	2696	SMK696F	2738	SMK738F	2760	SMK760F
2639	NML639E								

S22-29

	Scania N113DRB			Alexander RH		H47/31F	1991		
22	J822HMC	24	J824HMC	26	J826HMC	28	J828HMC	29	J829HMC
23	J823HMC	25	J825HMC	27	J827HMC				

S30	J230XKY	Scania N113DRB	Northern Counties Palatine	H47/33F	1991	
S31	J231XKY	Scania N113DRB	Northern Counties Palatine	H47/33F	1991	

S32-71   Scania N113DRB   Northern Counties Palatine   H41/25D   1991-92

32	J132HMT	40	J140HMT	48	K848LMK	56	K856LMK	64	K864LMK
33	J133HMT	41	J141HMT	49	K849LMK	57	K857LMK	65	K865LMK
34	J134HMT	42	J142HMT	50	K850LMK	58	K858LMK	66	K866LMK
35	J135HMT	43	J143HMT	51	K851LMK	59	K859LMK	67	K867LMK
36	J136HMT	44	J144HMT	52	K852LMK	60	K860LMK	68	K868LMK
37	J137HMT	45	J145HMT	53	K853LMK	61	K861LMK	69	K869LMK
38	J138HMT	46	K846LMK	54	K854LMK	62	K862LMK	70	K870LMK
39	J139HMT	47	K847LMK	55	K855LMK	63	K863LMK	71	K871LMK

SLD1-9   Dennis Dart SLF   Alexander ALX200   B40F   1996

1	P21HMF	3	P23HMF	5	P25HMF	7	P27HMF	9	P29HMF
2	P31HMF	4	P24HMF	6	P26HMF	8	P28HMF		

SLW15-30   Scania N113CRL   Wright Pathfinder 320   B37D   1994

15	RDZ6115	19	RDZ6119	22	RDZ6122	25	RDZ6125	28	RDZ6128
16	RDZ6116	20	RDZ6120	23	RDZ6123	26	RDZ6126	29	RDZ6129
17	RDZ6117	21	RDZ6121	24	RDZ6124	27	RDZ6127	30	RDZ6130
18	RDZ6118								

SP2	K302FYG	DAF DB250WB505	Optare Spectra	H44/23D	1992
SR1	E155CGJ	Mercedes-Benz 811D	Optare StarRider	B26F	1988
SR2	E712LYU	Mercedes-Benz 811D	Optare StarRider	B26F	1988

SR12-119   Mercedes-Benz 811D   Optare StarRider   B26F   1988-89

12	F912YWY	60	F160FWY	72	F172FWY	76	F176FWY	105	G105KUB
13	F913YWY	65	F165FWY	73	F173FWY	78	F178FWY	106	G106KUB
32	F32CWY	66	F166FWY	74	F174FWY	79	F179FWY	107	G107KUB
50	F50CWY	70	F170FWY	75	F175FWY	91	G91KUB	119	G119KUB
56	F156FWY	71	F171FWY						

The latest single-deck deliveries to East London are Dennis Darts with bodywork by Alexander. Delivered before the body style was launched, SLD4, P24HMF, shows much of the ALX200 styling.
Malc McDonald

T1-163

| | | | | | | | | | Leyland Titan TNLXB2RRSp | Park Royal | | H44/26D* | 1978-80 *63/80 are DPH44/26F, many H44/22D |

1	THX401S	11	WYV11T	21	WYV21T	30	WYV30T	35	WYV35T
2	THX402S	12	WYV12T	22	WYV22T	30	WYV30T	36	WYV36T
3	WYV3T	13	WYV13T	23	WYV23T	31	WYV31T	39	WYV39T
4	WYV4T	14	WYV14T	24	WYV24T	32	WYV32T	63	WYV63T
6	WYV6T	15	WYV15T	25	WYV25T	33	WYV33T	80	CUL80V
7	WYV7T	16	WYV16T	28	WYV28T	34	WYV34T	163	CUL163V
8	WYV8T	18	WYV18T						

T260	GYE260W	Leyland Titan TNLXB2RR	Park Royal/Leyland	H44/26D	1981
T261	GYE261W	Leyland Titan TNTL112RR	Park Royal/Leyland	H44/26D	1981
T262	GYE262W	Leyland Titan TNLXB2RR	Park Royal/Leyland	H44/26D	1981
T263	GYE263W	Leyland Titan TNLXB2RR	Park Royal/Leyland	H44/26D	1981

T264-549

Leyland Titan TNLXB2RR Leyland H44/24D* 1981-82
266/85, 311/20/31 are H44/26D; 282 is H44/26F; 512 is O44/24D; 282 ex Selkent, 1995

264	GYE264W	379	KYV379X	458	KYV458X	497	KYV497X	527	KYV527X
266	GYE266W	380	KYV380X	460	KYV460X	498	KYV498X	529	KYV529X
268	GYE268W	386	KYV386X	461	KYV461X	500	KYV500X	531	KYV531X
272	GYE272W	387	KYV387X	462	KYV462X	501	KYV501X	532	KYV532X
282	KYN282X	394	KYV394X	465	KYV465X	502	KYV502X	533	KYV533X
285	KYN285X	395	KYV395X	466	KYV466X	503	KYV503X	535	KYV535X
286	KYN286X	406	KYV406X	467	KYV467X	504	KYV504X	536	KYV536X
298	KYN298X	428	KYV428X	469	KYV469X	505	KYV505X	537	KYV537X
306	KYN306X	434	KYV434X	470	KYV470X	506	KYV506X	539	KYV539X
311	KYV311X	437	KYV437X	471	KYV471X	508	KYV508X	540	KYV540X
318	KYV318X	439	KYV439X	473	KYV473X	512	KYV512X	541	KYV541X
320	KYV320X	441	KYV441X	476	KYV476X	513	KYV513X	542	KYV542X
326	KYV326X	444	KYV444X	480	KYV480X	514	KYV514X	543	KYV543X
331	KYV331X	445	KYV445X	486	KYV486X	515	KYV515X	544	KYV544X
334	KYV334X	446	KYV446X	488	KYV488X	517	KYV517X	545	KYV545X
340	KYV340X	448	KYV448X	490	KYV490X	521	KYV521X	546	KYV546X
360	KYV360X	453	KYV453X	492	KYV492X	522	KYV522X	548	KYV548X
366	KYV366X	454	KYV454X	495	KYV495X	525	KYV525X	549	KYV549X
378	KYV378X	456	KYV456X	496	KYV496X	526	KYV526X		

The mainstay of the East London fleet remains the Leyland Titan. Pictured in Tooley Street while working tourist service LB1 is T666, NUW666Y, a number no longer issued by the DVLA.
Malc McDonald

Opposite: **The corporate livery has been placed on a few of the Leyland Titans in the East London fleet. Low numbered T3 heads for Romford Station in May 1996 on route 128.** *Tony Wilson*

T550-675

		Leyland Titan TNLXB2RR		Leyland		H44/24D		1982-83	
550	NUW550Y	575	NUW575Y	598	NUW598Y	626	NUW626Y	650	NUW650Y
551	NUW551Y	576	NUW576Y	600	NUW600Y	627	NUW627Y	651	NUW651Y
552	NUW552Y	577	NUW577Y	601	NUW601Y	629	NUW629Y	652	NUW652Y
553	NUW553Y	578	NUW578Y	602	NUW602Y	630	NUW630Y	653	NUW653Y
554	NUW554Y	579	NUW579Y	603	NUW603Y	631	NUW631Y	654	NUW654Y
555	NUW555Y	580	NUW580Y	604	NUW604Y	632	NUW632Y	657	NUW657Y
556	NUW556Y	581	NUW581Y	605	NUW605Y	633	NUW633Y	658	NUW658Y
557	NUW557Y	582	NUW582Y	606	NUW606Y	634	NUW634Y	659	NUW659Y
558	NUW558Y	583	NUW583Y	608	NUW608Y	636	NUW636Y	660	NUW660Y
559	NUW559Y	584	NUW584Y	609	NUW609Y	637	NUW637Y	662	NUW662Y
560	NUW560Y	585	NUW585Y	610	NUW610Y	639	NUW639Y	663	NUW663Y
562	NUW562Y	586	NUW586Y	613	NUW613Y	640	NUW640Y	664	NUW664Y
563	NUW563Y	587	NUW587Y	614	NUW614Y	641	NUW641Y	665	NUW665Y
564	NUW564Y	588	NUW588Y	615	NUW615Y	642	NUW642Y	666	NUW666Y
565	NUW565Y	589	NUW589Y	617	NUW617Y	643	NUW643Y	668	NUW668Y
566	NUW566Y	590	NUW590Y	619	NUW619Y	644	NUW644Y	669	NUW669Y
568	NUW568Y	591	NUW591Y	621	NUW621Y	645	NUW645Y	670	NUW670Y
569	NUW569Y	592	NUW592Y	622	NUW622Y	646	NUW646Y	671	NUW671Y
571	NUW571Y	593	NUW593Y	623	NUW623Y	647	NUW647Y	672	NUW672Y
572	NUW572Y	595	NUW595Y	624	NUW624Y	648	NUW648Y	673	NUW673Y
573	NUW573Y	597	NUW597Y	625	NUW625Y	649	NUW649Y	675	NUW675Y
574	NUW574Y								

The latest arrivals with East London are Volvo Olympians and these have started a new VN series. The first 26 of these have single door bodies while the remainder of the order are scheduled to have dual-door configuration for central routes. Seen shortly after delivery is VN2, P802GMU.
Malc McDonald

T686-971

								Leyland Titan TNLXB2RR		Leyland		H44/24D*	1983-84 *802-970 are H44/26D

686	OHV686Y	731	OHV731Y	784	OHV784Y	846	A846SUL	935	A935SYE
688	OHV688Y	738	OHV738Y	789	OHV789Y	849	A849SUL	944	A944SYE
691	OHV691Y	743	OHV743Y	802	OHV802Y	867	A867SUL	945	A945SYE
697	OHV697Y	744	OHV744Y	819	RYK819Y	873	A873SUL	949t	A949SYE
699	OHV699Y	749	OHV749Y	826	A826SUL	902	A902SYE	953t	A953SYE
702	OHV702Y	751	OHV751Y	827	A827SUL	905	A905SYE	960t	A960SYE
719	OHV719Y	759	OHV759Y	832	A832SUL	921	A921SYE	965t	A965SYE
724	OHV724Y	761	OHV761Y	840	A840SUL	922	A922SYE	971t	A971SYE
729	OHV729Y	769	OHV769Y						

T1022	A622THV	Leyland Titan TNLXB2RR	Leyland	H44/24D	1984
T1026	A626THV	Leyland Titan TNLXB2RR	Leyland	H44/24D	1984
T1050	A650THV	Leyland Titan TNLXB2RR	Leyland	H44/24D	1984
T1128	630DYE	Leyland Titan TNLXB1RF	Park Royal	DPH43/29F	1979

VN1-26

			Volvo Olympian YN2RV18Z4		Northern Counties Palatine	H49/31F	1996

1	P801GMU	7	P807GMU	12	P812GMU	17	P817GMU	22	P822GMU
2	P802GMU	8	P808GMU	13	P813GMU	18	P818GMU	23	P823GMU
3	P803GMU	9	P809GMU	14	P814GMU	19	P819GMU	24	P824GMU
4	P804GMU	10	P810GMU	15	P815GMU	20	P820GMU	25	P825GMU
5	P805GMU	11	P811GMU	16	P816GMU	21	P821GMU	26	P826GMU
6	P806GMU								

Three coaches from Wallace Arnold are now operated by East London Coaches. All are Volvo B10Ms with Plaxton Paramount 3500 bodywork. Shown here is VP7, H657UWR. *Phillip Stephenson*

VN27-90   Volvo Olympian YN2RV18Z4   Northern Counties Palatine   H49/27D   1996-97

27	P527HMP	40	P540HMP	53	P 53	66	P 66	79	P 79
28	P528HMP	41	P541HMP	54	P 54	67	P 67	80	P 80
29	P529HMP	42	P542HMP	55	P 55	68	P 68	81	P 81
30	P530HMP	43	P543HMP	56	P 56	69	P 69	82	P 82
31	P531HMP	44	P 44	57	P 57	70	P 70	83	P 83
32	P532HMP	45	P 45	58	P 58	71	P 71	84	P 84
33	P533HMP	46	P 46	59	P 59	72	P 72	85	P 85
34	P534HMP	47	P 47	60	P 60	73	P 73	86	P 86
35	P535HMP	48	P 48	61	P 61	74	P 74	87	P 87
36	P536HMP	49	P 49	62	P 62	75	P 75	88	P 88
37	P537HMP	50	P 50	63	P 63	76	P 76	89	P 89
38	P538HMP	51	P 51	64	P 64	77	P 77	90	P 90
39	P539HMP	52	P 52	65	P 65	78	P 78		

VP4	H654UWR	Volvo B10M-60	Plaxton Paramount 3500 III	C49FT	1991	Ex Wallace Arnold, 1995
VP5	H655UWR	Volvo B10M-60	Plaxton Paramount 3500 III	C49FT	1991	Ex Wallace Arnold, 1995
VP7	H657UWR	Volvo B10M-60	Plaxton Paramount 3500 III	C51F	1991	Ex Wallace Arnold, 1995

Previous Registrations:

461CLT	From new	E155CGJ	E711LYU, WLT461	XFF813	WLT898
472YMF	J713CYG	LFF875	456CLT	XFF814	WLT890
485CLT	From new	NFX667	K716PCN	XYK976	K719PCN
527CLT	From new	WLT613	From new	YLJ332	J715CYG
630DYE	WDA3T, 486CLT	WLT886	From new		

Liveries: Red; green (1962 Green Line) RMC1461; yellow (East London Line): SR12/3/32/50/6/60/70/2-6/91/105-7/19, MRL144; red and silver (East London Coaches) T63, 80, 1128, VP4-7; blue, white red and orange (South West Trains) DA13/5, 1716/9; Corporate T3, T282.

Named Vehicle: RMA5 *King Charles II*

Note: Allvehicles were formerly London Buses, 1994 unless shown otherwise or acquired later. DA13/5, 1716/9 are on loan to Stagecoach South for South West Trains feeder contracts.

EAST MIDLAND

East Midland Motor Services Ltd, Grimsby Cleethorpes Transport Ltd,
Chesterfield Transport Ltd, New Street, Chesterfield, Derbyshire, S40 2LQ

Depots : Stonegravels, Chesterfield ; Flinthouse Garage, Calver ; Victoria Street, Grimsby ; Sutton Road, Mansfield and
Hardy Street, Worksop.

1-9			Dennis Lance 11SDA3106*		East Lancashire EL2000		B45F	1993	1-7 ex Grimsby Cleethorpes, 1993 *5-9 are type 11SDA3111
1	K701NDO	3	K703NDO	5	L705HFU	7	L707HFU	9	L709HFU
2	K702NDO	4	K704NDO	6	L706HFU	8	L708HFU		

12-19			Mercedes-Benz 811D		Alexander Sprint		B31F	1992	Ex Chesterfield, 1995
12	J213AET	15	J215AET	17	J217AET	18	J218AET	19	J219AET
14	J214AET	16	J216AET						

21	EKY21V	Leyland National 2 NL116L11/1R		B52F	1980	Ex Chesterfield, 1995
22	EKY22V	Leyland National 2 NL116L11/1R		B52F	1980	Ex Chesterfield, 1995
23	EKY23V	Leyland National 2 NL116L11/1R		B52F	1981	Ex Chesterfield, 1995

24-29			Leyland National 2 NL106L11/1R				B44F	1980	Ex Chesterfield, 1995
24	EKY24V	25	EKY25V	27	EKY27V	28	EKY28V	29	EKY29V

30-34			Leyland National 2 NL116AL11/1R				B52F	1981	Ex Chesterfield, 1995
30	OWB30X	31	OWB31X	32	OWB32X	33	OWB33X	34	OWB34X

35	SKY31Y	Leyland Tiger TRCTL11/3R	Eastern Coach Works B51	C51F	1983	
36	SKY32Y	Leyland Tiger TRCTL11/3R	Eastern Coach Works B51	C51F	1983	
37w	PJI4316	Leyland Tiger TRCTL11/2R	Duple Dominant IV	C47F	1983	
37	WBN477T	Leyland National 11351A/1R		B49F	1979	Ex Chesterfield, 1995

39-44			Leyland Tiger TRCTL11/2R		Alexander TE		DP45F*	1983-84	*42/3 are DP49F
39	A39XHE	41	A41XHE	42	A42XHE	43w	A43XHE	44	A44XHE

48	B54DWJ	Leyland Tiger TRCTL11/2RH	Alexander TE	DP49F	1985
49w	B49DWE	Leyland Tiger TRCTL11/2RH	Alexander TE	DP49F	1984

A batch of Dennis Lance buses were being delivered to Grimsby Cleethorpes when that undertaking was taken over by Stagecoach. These now take the early numbers in the East Midland fleet and remain based at Grimsby. Pictured on local service is 6, L706HFU.
Malc McDonald

The Leyland Lynx forms a small class of vehicles in the Stagecoach empire. It was the successor to the National, but not built in such numbers. More information on the type can be found in the Leyland Lynx Bus Handbook. Two of the breed remain within the fold at East Midland represented here by 65, E61WDT, at the Meadowhall Interchange bound for its home town. Note the wheel trim which considerably enhances the vehicle's appearance. *Mike Fowler*

50-55		Leyland National 2 NL116HLXCT/1R		B52F	1984	Ex Chesterfield, 1995	
50	B150DHL	**52**	B152DHL	**53**	B153DHL	**54** B154DHL	**55** B155DHL
51	B151DHL						

56	RHL174X	Leyland Tiger TRCTL11/3R	Duple Dominant IV	C53F	1982	Ex Chesterfield, 1995
57	YPD129Y	Leyland Tiger TRCTL11/2R	Duple Dominant IV Express	DP53F	1983	Ex Chesterfield, 1995
58	YPD133Y	Leyland Tiger TRCTL11/2R	Duple Dominant IV Express	DP53F	1983	Ex Chesterfield, 1995
59	B52DWE	Leyland Tiger TRCTL11/2RH	Alexander TE	DP49F	1984	
60	B53DWJ	Leyland Tiger TRCTL11/2RH	Alexander TE	DP49F	1985	
62	AYR322T	Leyland National 10351A/2R		B35D	1979	Ex Haven Coaches, Newhaven, 1993
63	VKU77S	Leyland National 11351A/1R		B49F	1978	Ex Chesterfield, 1995
64	E60WDT	Leyland Lynx LX112TL11ZR1	Leyland Lynx	DP49F	1988	Ex Chesterfield, 1995
65	E61WDT	Leyland Lynx LX112TL11ZR1	Leyland Lynx	DP49F	1988	Ex Chesterfield, 1995
71	A71GEE	Leyland Olympian ONTL11/1R	Eastern Coach Works	H45/31F	1983	Ex Grimsby Cleethorpes, 1993
72	A72GEE	Leyland Olympian ONTL11/1R	Eastern Coach Works	H45/31F	1983	Ex Grimsby Cleethorpes, 1993
73	A73GEE	Leyland Olympian ONTL11/1R	Eastern Coach Works	H47/28D	1983	Ex Grimsby Cleethorpes, 1993
74	A74GEE	Leyland Olympian ONTL11/1R	Eastern Coach Works	H47/28D	1983	Ex Grimsby Cleethorpes, 1993
75	F75TFU	Dennis Dominator DDA1021	Alexander RH	H45/33F	1989	Ex Grimsby Cleethorpes, 1993
76	F76TFU	Dennis Dominator DDA1021	Alexander RH	H45/33F	1989	Ex Grimsby Cleethorpes, 1993
77	F77TFU	Dennis Dominator DDA1021	Alexander RH	H45/33F	1989	Ex Grimsby Cleethorpes, 1993
78	F78TFU	Dennis Dominator DDA1022	Alexander RH	H45/33F	1989	Ex Grimsby Cleethorpes, 1993
79	G79VFW	Dennis Dominator DDA1028	Alexander RH	H45/33F	1990	Ex Grimsby Cleethorpes, 1993
80	G80VFW	Dennis Dominator DDA1028	Alexander RH	H45/33F	1990	Ex Grimsby Cleethorpes, 1993
81	G81VFW	Dennis Dominator DDA1029	Alexander RH	H45/33F	1990	Ex Grimsby Cleethorpes, 1993
82cu	RBU180R	Leyland National 11351A/1R		B49F	1977	Ex Chesterfield, 1995

82-89		Dennis Dominator DDA1034*		East Lancashire	H45/33F	1991-92 Ex Grimsby Cleethorpes, 1993	
						*86-9 are DDA1036	
82	H482BEE	**84**	H484BEE	**86**	J91DJV	**88** J93DJV	**89** J94DJV
83	H483BEE	**85**	H485BEE	**87**	J92DJV		

British seaside towns would not be the same without the open-top bus where passengers can take the bracing air. Cleethorpes is no exception, and two Fleetlines are retained for this purpose. Seen in corporate livery at Cleethorpes Pier is 113, MBE613R.
Andrew Bagshaw

90-98				Mercedes-Benz 709D		Alexander Sprint		B25F*		1988	Ex Chesterfield, 1995
											*97/8 are DP25F
90	E90YWB	92	E92YWB	94	E94YWB	96	E96YWB	98	E98YWB		
91	E91YWB	93	E93YWB	95	E95YWB	97	E97YWB				

99	H257THL			Mercedes-Benz 709D		Reeve Burgess Beaver		B25F		1991	Ex Chesterfield, 1995

101-109				Volvo Olympian YN2RV18Z4		Northern Counties Palatine		H47/29F		1993	
101	K101JWJ	103	K103JWJ	105	K105JWJ	107	K107JWJ	109	L109LHL		
102	K102JWJ	104	K104JWJ	106	K106JWJ	108	L108LHL				

113	MBE613R			Leyland Fleetline FE30AGR		Roe		O45/29D		1976	Ex Grimsby Cleethorpes, 1993
114	BJV103L			Daimler Fleetline CRG6LX		Roe		O45/29D		1973	Ex Grimsby Cleethorpes, 1993

117-129				Leyland Fleetline FE30AGR		Roe		H45/29D		1979-80	Ex Grimsby Cleethorpes, 1993
117	TFU61T	119	WFU467V	125w	XFU125V	126	XFU126V	129	XFU129V		
118	WFU466V	120w	OJV120S								

130-144				Volvo Olympian YN2RV18Z4		Alexander RL		H47/32F		1995	
130	N130AET	133	N133AET	136	N136AET	139	N139AET	142	N142AET		
131	N131AET	134	N134AET	137	N137AET	140	N140AET	143	N143AET		
132	N132AET	135	N135AET	138	N138AET	141	N141AET	144	N144AET		

145-160				Volvo Olympian		Alexander RL		H51/35F		1996-97	
145	P145KWJ	149	P149KWJ	152	P152KWJ	156	P156KWJ	159	P159KAK		
146	P146KWJ	150	P150KWJ	153	P153KWJ	157	P157KWJ	160	P160KAK		
148	P148KWJ	151	P151KWJ	154	P154KWJ	158	P158KWJ				

Opposite, top: **1996 has seen the integration of the Chesterfield operation in core workings after many months of being worked independently. During that time ten Volvo B10Ms with Alexander PS bodywork were allocated to the town operation. These came from Ribble and are represented here by 599, M413RRN.** *M E Lyons*
Opposite, bottom: **Two Volvo B10MAs with Plaxton interurban bodies were planned for East Midland's 909 service. Photographed in early December, 670 has still not had its registration plates fitted when photographed for this publication. The vehicle commenced operation on the Stagecoach Express service from Sheffield to Grimsby, but has since been transferred to Fife.** *Tony Wilson*

146Rw	NKY146R	Leyland Fleetline FE30ALR	Roe		H42/29D	1977	

150R-159R

		Leyland Fleetline FE30AGR	Roe		H42/29D	1978	Ex Chesterfield, 1995
150R	UWA150S	**154R**	UWA154S	**155R**	UWA155S	**157R**	UWA157S	**159R**	UWA159S

172	XGS736S	Leyland Leopard PSU3E/4R	Plaxton Supreme III	C53F	1978	Ex Grimsby Cleethorpes, 1993
173	BHO441V	Leyland Leopard PSU5C/4R	Duple Dominant II	C55F	1980	Ex Grimsby Cleethorpes, 1993
174	MRJ270W	Leyland Leopard PSU5C/4R	Plaxton Supreme IV	C41DL	1980	Ex Grimsby Cleethorpes, 1993
175	EFU935Y	Leyland Leopard PSU5C/4R	Duple Dominant I	C53F	1983	Ex Grimsby Cleethorpes, 1993
176	OJL823Y	Leyland Leopard PSU5C/4R	Duple Dominant III	C53F	1983	Ex Grimsby Cleethorpes, 1993
177	OJL822Y	Leyland Leopard PSU5C/4R	Duple Dominant III	C49F	1983	Ex Grimsby Cleethorpes, 1993
183	PJI4314	Leyland Tiger TRCTL11/2R	Plaxton Paramount 3200 E	C47F	1983	
187	PYE841Y	Leyland Tiger TRCTL11/3R	Duple Laser	C53F	1983	Ex Grimsby Cleethorpes, 1993
188	PYE842Y	Leyland Tiger TRCTL11/3R	Duple Laser	C53F	1983	Ex Grimsby Cleethorpes, 1993
189	PSU764	Leyland Tiger TRCTL11/3R	Duple Laser	C53F	1983	Ex Grimsby Cleethorpes, 1993
190	PSU443	Leyland Tiger TRCTL11/3R	Duple Laser	C53F	1983	Ex Grimsby Cleethorpes, 1993
191	A243YGF	Leyland Tiger TRCTL11/3RH	Duple Laser	C57F	1984	Ex Grimsby Cleethorpes, 1993
192	PS2743	Leyland Tiger TRCTL11/3RH	Duple Laser	C57F	1984	Ex Grimsby Cleethorpes, 1993
201	GOL398N	Leyland National 11351/1R		B49F	1975	Ex Midland Red West, 1990
202	JAO477V	Leyland National 10351A/2R		B44F	1980	Ex Leyland demonstrator, 1984
203	ABA25T	Leyland National 11351A/1R		B49F	1979	Ex GM Buses, 1990
205u	VKU79S	Leyland National 11351A/1R(Volvo)		B49F	1978	Ex Chesterfield, 1995
208	VKU73S	Leyland National 11351A/1R(Volvo)		B49F	1978	Ex Chesterfield, 1995

209-224

		Bristol VRT/SL3/6LXB*	Eastern Coach Works		H43/31F	1980-81 *218 is type 6LXC
209	EWE203V	211	JAK211W	218	KWA218W	223	KWA223W	224	KWA224W
210	EWE206V	214	KWA214W	221	KWA221W				

231	EJV31Y	Dennis Falcon H SDA411	Wadham Stringer Vanguard	B42F	1983	Ex Grimsby Cleethorpes, 1993
232	EJV32Y	Dennis Falcon H SDA411	Wadham Stringer Vanguard	B42F	1983	Ex Grimsby Cleethorpes, 1993
233	EJV33Y	Dennis Falcon H SDA411	Wadham Stringer Vanguard	B42F	1983	Ex Grimsby Cleethorpes, 1993
234	EJV34Y	Dennis Falcon H SDA411	Wadham Stringer Vanguard	B42F	1983	Ex Grimsby Cleethorpes, 1993
259	BFW136W	Ford R1114	Plaxton Supreme IV	C53F	1981	Ex Grimsby Cleethorpes, 1993
299	TWF201Y	Leyland Olympian ONLXB/1R	Roe	H47/29F	1982	Ex Chesterfield, 1995
300	TWF202Y	Leyland Olympian ONLXB/1R	Roe	H47/29F	1982	Ex Chesterfield, 1995

301-325

		Leyland Olympian ONLXB/1R	Eastern Coach Works		H45/32F	1981-84
301	NHL301X	306	SHE306Y	311	SHE311Y	316	A316XWG	321	A321YWJ
302	NHL302X	307	SHE307Y	312	UDT312Y	317	A317XWG	322	A322AKU
303	NHL303X	308	SHE308Y	313	UDT313Y	318	A318XWG	323	A323AKU
304	NHL304X	309	SHE309Y	314	A314XWG	319	A319YWJ	324	A324AKU
305	NHL305X	310	SHE310Y	315	A315XWG	320	A320YWJ	325	A325AKU

326-330

		Leyland Olympian ONLXB/1R	Eastern Coach Works		CH40/32F	1985
326	C326HWJ	327	C327HWJ	328	C328HWJ	329	C329HWJ	330	C330HWJ

331-336

		Leyland Olympian ONLXB/1R	Eastern Coach Works		H45/32F	1986
331	C331HWJ	333	C333HWJ	334	C334HWJ	335	C335HWJ	336	C336HWJ
332	C332HWJ						

337	GSO8V	Leyland Olympian ONLXB/1RV	Alexander RL	H45/32F	1987	Ex United Counties, 1992

339-343

		Leyland Olympian ON6LXB/2RZ	Alexander RL		DPH51/31F	1989
339	G339KKW	340	G340KKW	341	G341KKW	342	G342KKW	343	G343KKW

344-353

		Leyland Olympian ON25R6G13Z4 Alexander RL			DPH51/31F*	1990-91 *349-353 are DPH47/27F
344	H344SWA	346	H346SWA	348	H348SWA	350	J350XET	352	J352XET
345	H345SWA	347	H347SWA	349	J349XET	351	J351XET	353	J353XET

354-358

		Leyland Olympian ON2R50G13Z4 Northern Counties Palatine		H47/29F	1992
354	K354DWJ	355	K355DWJ	356	K356DWJ	357	K357DWJ	358	K358DWJ

The latest delivery of Volvo Olympians to East Midland consist of fourteen intended for Chesterfield where they have displace Daimler Fleetlines. The recent deliveris of Volvo Olympians do not carry chassis type codes, the model now simply known as the Volvo Olympian. Now that the list of options available has been reduced variations within the codes have become less necessary.

359-363
Leyland Olympian ON2R54G13Z4 Alexander RL DPH43/27F 1992

359	K359DWJ	360	K360DWJ	361	K361DWJ	362	K362DWJ	363	K363DWJ

412	DWF22V	Leyland Leopard PSU3E/4R	Duple Dominant(1985)	B55F	1979		
413	DWF23V	Leyland Leopard PSU3E/4R	Duple Dominant(1985)	B51F	1979		
414	DWF24V	Leyland Leopard PSU3E/4R	Alexander P(1985)	B52F	1979		
416	DWF26V	Leyland Leopard PSU3E/4R	Duple Dominant(1985)	B55F	1980		
418	P418KWF	Dennis Dart SFD4	Alexander Dash	B41F	1996		
419	P419KWF	Dennis Dart SFD4	Alexander Dash	B41F	1996		
420	P420KWF	Dennis Dart SFD4	Alexander Dash	B41F	1996		
421	E927PBE	Leyland Tiger TRBLXCT/2RH	Alexander P	DP51F	1987	Ex Grimsby Cleethorpes, 1993	
422	E928PBE	Leyland Tiger TRBLXCT/2RH	Alexander P	DP51F	1987	Ex Grimsby Cleethorpes, 1993	
423	E929PBE	Leyland Tiger TRBLXCT/2RH	Alexander P	DP51F	1987	Ex Grimsby Cleethorpes, 1993	
424	E930PBE	Leyland Tiger TRBLXCT/2RH	Alexander P	DP51F	1987	Ex Grimsby Cleethorpes, 1993	

425-433
Leyland Tiger TRCTL11/2RH Alexander P B52F 1985

425	B625DWF	427	B627DWF	429	B629DWF	431	B631DWF	433	B633DWF
426	B626DWF	428	B628DWF	430	B630DWF	432	B632DWF		

435-453
Volvo B6-9.9M Alexander Dash B40F 1993

435	L435LWA	439	L439LWA	443	L443LWA	448	L448LWA	451	L451LWA
436	L436LWA	440	L440LWA	445	L445LWA	449	L449LWA	452	L452LWA
437	L437LWA	441	L441LWA	446	L446LWA	450	L450LWA	453	L453LHL
438	L438LWA	442	L442LWA	447	L447LWA				

591-600
Volvo B10M-55 Alexander PS DP48F 1994 Ex Ribble, 1995

591	L341KCK	593	L343KCK	595	L339KCK	597	M411RRN	599	M413RRN
592	L342KCK	594	L344KCK	596	L340KCK	598	M412RRN	600	M414RRN

601-609 — Volvo B10M-55, Alexander PS, DP48F, 1995

601	M601VHE	**603**	M603VHE	**605**	M605VHE	**607**	M607VHE	**609**	M609WET
602	M602VHE	**604**	M604VHE	**606**	M606VHE	**608**	M608WET		

614	EKW614V	Leyland National 2 NL106L11/1R	B44F	1980	
615	EKW615V	Leyland National 2 NL106L11/1R	B44F	1980	
616	EKW616V	Leyland National 2 NL106L11/1R	B44F	1980	

617-621 — Leyland National 2 NL116L11/1R, B49F, 1980

617	GWE617V	**618**	GWE618V	**619**	GWE619V	**620**	HWJ620W	**621**	HWJ621W

622	MWG622X	Leyland National 2 NL116AL11/1R	B49F	1981	
623	MWG623X	Leyland National 2 NL116AL11/1R	B49F	1981	
624	MWG624X	Leyland National 2 NL116AL11/1R	B49F	1981	
625	LAG188V	Leyland National 2 NL116L11/1R	B49F	1980	Ex East Yorkshire, 1988
626	LAG189V	Leyland National 2 NL116L11/1R	B49F	1980	Ex East Yorkshire, 1988
627	NRP580V	Leyland National 2 NL116L11/1R	B49F	1980	Ex United Counties, 1992
628	SVV586W	Leyland National 2 NL116L11/1R	B49F	1981	Ex United Counties, 1992
634	VWA34Y	Leyland National 2 NL116HLXB/1R	DP47F	1983	
635	VWA35Y	Leyland National 2 NL116HLXB/1R	DP47F	1983	
636	VWA36Y	Leyland National 2 NL116HLXB/1R	DP47F	1983	

637-643 — Volvo B10M-62, Plaxton Premiére Interurban DP51F, 1993

637	L637LDT	**639**	L639LDT	**641**	L641LDT	**642**	L642LDT	**643**	L643LDT
638	L638LDT	**640**	L640LDT						

652	HSV196	Volvo B10M-61	Plaxton Paramount 3500 III	C53F	1987	Ex Cambus (Premier), 1996
653	HSV195	Volvo B10M-61	Plaxton Paramount 3500 III	C50F	1988	Ex Cambus (Premier), 1996
654	HSV194	Volvo B10M-61	Plaxton Paramount 3500 III	C50F	1988	Ex Cambus (Premier), 1996
655	H402DEG	Volvo B10M-60	Plaxton Paramount 3500 III	C53F	1990	Ex Cambus (Premier), 1996
656	M942TSX	Volvo B10M-60	Plaxton Premiére Interurban	DP51F	1994	Ex Fife Scottish, 1997
657	M943TSX	Volvo B10M-60	Plaxton Premiére Interurban	DP51F	1994	Ex Fife Scottish, 1997
658	K575DFS	Volvo B10M-60	Plaxton Premiére Interurban	DP51F	1993	Ex Western Buses, 1997

700-710 — Mercedes-Benz L608D, Reeve Burgess, B20F*, 1986 — Ex Cumberland, 1995
*702/6/8-10 are DP19F

700u	D34UAO	**702**u	D504RCK	**705**u	D518RCK	**707**u	D522RCK	**709**u	D547RCK
701u	D503RCK	**703**u	D511RCK	**706**u	D519RCK	**708**u	D539RCK	**710**u	D561RCK

720-727 — Mercedes-Benz 811D, Reeve Burgess Beaver, B31F, 1989-90

720	G820KWF	**722**	G822KWF	**724**	G824KWF	**726**	G826KWF	**727**	G827KWF
721	G821KWF	**723**	G823KWF	**725**	G825KWF				

728	E721BVO	Mercedes-Benz 811D	Optare StarRider	B33F	1988	Ex Maun, Mansfield, 1990
729	E880DRA	Mercedes-Benz 811D	Optare StarRider	B33F	1988	Ex Maun, Mansfield, 1990

Volvo 602, M602VHE, is one of a batch of nine Alexander PS-type delivered new to the company. Here the vehicle has just departed from the Sheffield Interchange on the long semi-express route via Chesterfield to Nottingham.
Tony Wilson

Twenty five Mercedes-Benz 709D were added to the East Midland fleet in 1995-96 displacing many of the older minibuses. Pictured in the 1996 summer sunshine in the square at Bakewell is 758, **N758CKU.** *M E Lyons*

731-751

Mercedes-Benz 709D — Alexander Sprint — B25F — 1993

731	L731LWA	735	L735LWA	739	L739LWA	743	L743LWA	748	L748LWA
732	L732LWA	736	L736LWA	740	L740LWA	744	L744LWA	749	L749LWA
733	L733LWA	737	L737LWA	741	L741LWA	745	L745LWA	750	L750LWA
734	L734LWA	738	L738LWA	742	L742LWA	746	L746LWA	751	L751LHL

752-776

Mercedes-Benz 709D — Alexander Sprint — B25F — 1995-96

752	N752CKU	757	N757CKU	762	N762EWG	767	N767EWG	772	N772EWG
753	N753CKU	758	N758CKU	763	N763EWG	768	N768EWG	773	N773EWG
754	N754CKU	759	N759CKU	764	N764EWG	769	N769EWG	774	N774EWG
755	N755CKU	760	N760CKU	765	N765EWG	770	N770EWG	775	N775EWG
756	N756CKU	761	N761CKU	766	N766EWG	771	N771EWG	776	N776EWG

902-906

MCW MetroRider MF150/94 — MCW — B23F — 1988 — Ex Grimsby Cleethorpes, 1993

902	E47HFE	903	E48HFE	904	E49HFE	905	E50HFE	906	E51HFE

907	E56HFE	MCW MetroRider MF150/94	MCW	DP23F	1988	Ex Grimsby Cleethorpes, 1993
908	E57HFE	MCW MetroRider MF150/94	MCW	DP23F	1988	Ex Grimsby Cleethorpes, 1993
909	E58HFE	MCW MetroRider MF150/94	MCW	DP23F	1988	Ex Grimsby Cleethorpes, 1993

Previous Registrations:

A243YGF	A601HVT, PS2045	PJI4316	UHE37Y
GSO8V	D378XRS	PJI4317	UHE38Y
HSV194	E904UNW	PS2743	A602HVT
HSV195	E905UNW	A354BHL	PS3696, A603HVT
HSV196	E315OEG	PSU443	A844SYR
OJL822Y	SSG321Y, PS2945	PSU764	PYE843Y
OJL823Y	EJV419Y, PS2743	RHL174X	OHE278X, 563UM
PJI4314	UWJ33Y		

FIFE SCOTTISH

Fife Scottish Omnibuses Ltd, Esplanade, Kirkcaldy, Fife, KY1 1SP

Depots : Methilhaven Road, Methil (Aberhill); Broad Street, Cowdenbeath; St Leonard's Street, Dunfermline; Flemington Road, Glenrothes; Esplanade, Kirkcaldy and City Road, St Andrews.

| *1-5* | | | Mercedes-Benz 811D | | Carlyle | | B33F* | 1990 | Ex Selkent, 1996 |
| | | | | | | | | | *1 is B28F |

1	F286KGK	2	H882LOX	3	H883LOX	4	H509AGC	5	H885LOX

44	E644KYW	MCW MetroRider MF158/1	MCW	B30F	1988	Ex Western Buses, 1996
56u	F56RFS	MCW MetroRider MF150/98	MCW	B25F	1988	

| *70-76* | | | Mercedes-Benz 709D | | Alexander Sprint | | B25F | 1994 | |

70	M770TFS	72	M772TFS	74	M774TFS	75	M775TFS	76	M776TFS
71	M771TFS	73	M773TFS						

77	VLT77	Mercedes-Benz 811D	Reeve Burgess Beaver	B33F	1989	Ex Selkent, 1994
78	M778TFS	Mercedes-Benz 709D	Alexander Sprint	B25F	1994	
79	M779TFS	Mercedes-Benz 709D	Alexander Sprint	B25F	1994	
80	G280TSL	Mercedes-Benz 709D	Alexander Sprint	B23F	1990	Ex Bluebird, 1992
81	G281TSL	Mercedes-Benz 709D	Alexander Sprint	B23F	1990	Ex Bluebird, 1992
82	M780TFS	Mercedes-Benz 709D	Alexander Sprint	B25F	1994	

| *85-94* | | | Mercedes-Benz 709D | | Alexander Sprint | | B25F | 1993 | |

85	K485FFS	87	K487FFS	89	K489FFS	91	K491FFS	93	K493FFS
86	K486FFS	88	K488FFS	90	K490FFS	92	K492FFS	94	K494FFS

95	N95ALS	Mercedes-Benz 709D	Alexander Sprint	B25F	1996
96	N96ALS	Mercedes-Benz 709D	Alexander Sprint	B25F	1996
97	N97ALS	Mercedes-Benz 709D	Alexander Sprint	B25F	1996

| *139-160* | | | Leyland Leopard PSU3F/4R* | | Alexander AYS | | B53F | 1980-81 | *159/60 are PSU3G/4R |

139	WFS139W	141	WFS141W	150	WFS150W	159	CSF159W	160	CSF160W
140	WFS140W	147	WFS147W	158	CSF158W				

| *180-189* | | | Leyland Leopard PSU3G/4R | | Alexander AYS | | B53F | 1982 | |

180	PSX180Y	182	PSX182Y	184	PSX184Y	186	PSX186Y	188	PSX188Y
181	PSX181Y	183	PSX183Y	185	PSX185Y	187	PSX187Y	189	PSX189Y

200	XMS420Y	Leyland Leopard PSU3G/4R	Alexander AYS	DP49F	1982	Ex Ribble, 1992
261	CSF161W	Leyland Leopard PSU3G/4R	Alexander AYS	DP49F	1981	
262	CSF162W	Leyland Leopard PSU3G/4R	Alexander AYS	DP47F	1981	

| *263-269* | | | Leyland Leopard PSU3F/4R | | Alexander AYS | | DP49F | 1981 | |

263	CSF163W	265	CSF165W	267	CSF167W	268	CSF168W	269	CSF169W
264	CSF164W	266	CSF166W						

| *270-279* | | | Leyland Leopard PSU3G/4R | | Alexander AT | | DP49F | 1982 | |

270	NFS170Y	272	NFS172Y	274	NFS174Y	276	NFS176Y	278	NFS178Y
271	NFS171Y	273	NFS173Y	275	NFS175Y	277	NFS177Y	279	NFS179Y

The Alexander Y-type has played a major part in Scottish bus operations for four decades. Many remain in service though the number in the Fife fleet is decreasing. Photographed at Dunfermline is 158, CFS158W. *Murdoch Currie*

290	RSC190Y	Leyland Leopard PSU3G/4R	Alexander AT	DP49F	1982		
291	RSC191Y	Leyland Leopard PSU3G/4R	Alexander AT	DP49F	1982		
292	RSC192Y	Leyland Leopard PSU3G/4R	Alexander AT	DP49F	1982		
294	RSC194Y	Leyland Leopard PSU3G/4R	Alexander AT	DP49F	1982		

301-310
Volvo B10M-55 — Alexander PS — B49F — 1994

| 301 | L301PSC | 303 | L303PSC | 305 | L305PSC | 307 | L307PSC | 309 | L309PSC |
| 302 | L302PSC | 304 | L304PSC | 306 | L306PSC | 308 | L308PSC | 310 | L310PSC |

314-329
Volvo B10M-55 — Alexander PS — B49F* — 1995-96 *314/5 are DP48F

314	M314PKS	318	N318VMS	321	N321VMS	324	N324VMS	327	N327VMS
315	M315PKS	319	N319VMS	322	N322VMS	325	N325VMS	328	N328VMS
316	N316VMS	320	N320VMS	323	N323VMS	326	N326VMS	329	N329VMS
317	N317VMS								

412-419
Leyland Tiger TRCTL11/3RH — Alexander P — B61F — 1986-87

| 412 | D512CSF | 414 | D614ASG | 416 | D516DSX | 418 | D518DSX | 419 | D519DSX |
| 413 | D713CSC | 415 | D615ASG | 417 | D517DSX | | | | |

420-424
Leyland Tiger TRBTL11/2RH — Alexander P — B57F — 1987

| 420 | D520DSX | 421 | D521DSX | 422 | D522DSX | 423 | D523DSX | 424 | D524DSX |

441-445
Leyland Tiger TRCTL11/2RH — Alexander TC — C47F* — 1985 *442 is DP49F

| 441 | GSU341 | 442 | GSU342 | 443u | B291YSL | 444 | GSU344 | 445 | MSU445 |

466-470
Leyland Tiger TRBTL11/2R — Alexander TE — DP49F — 1983 — Ex Kelvin Central, 1989

| 466 | MNS6Y | 467 | MNS7Y | 468 | MNS8Y | 469 | MNS9Y | 470 | MNS10Y |

477	D277FAS	Leyland Tiger TRCTL11/3RH	Alexander TE	DP53F	1987	Ex Highland Scottish, 1987
478	D278FAS	Leyland Tiger TRCTL11/3RH	Alexander TE	DP53F	1987	Ex Highland Scottish, 1987
479	D279FAS	Leyland Tiger TRCTL11/3RH	Alexander TE	DP53F	1987	Ex Highland Scottish, 1987
499	MSU499	Leyland Tiger TRCTL11/3RZ	Duple 340	C48FT	1987	Ex Kelvin Central, 1990
503	GSU343	Volvo B10M-61	Van Hool Alizée	C46FT	1983	Ex Ribble (Hyndburn), 1996
504	IIL3504	Volvo B10M-61	Van Hool Alizée	C49FT	1988	Ex Rainworth Travel, 1993
506	IIL3506	Volvo B10M-61	Van Hool Alizée	C49FT	1988	Ex Rainworth Travel, 1993
512	M102CCD	Dennis Javelin 11SDL2133	Plaxton Premiere Interurban	DP47F	1994	Ex Stagecoach South, 1995
513	M103CCD	Dennis Javelin 11SDL2133	Plaxton Premiere Interurban	DP47F	1995	Ex Stagecoach South, 1995
514	M104CCD	Dennis Javelin 11SDL2133	Plaxton Premiere Interurban	DP47F	1995	Ex Stagecoach South, 1995

544-556 — Volvo B10M-62 — Plaxton Première Interurban DP51F — 1994

544	M944TSX	547	M947TSX	550	M950TSX	553	M953TSX	555	M955TSX
545	M945TSX	548	M948TSX	551	M951TSX	554	M954TSX	556	M956TSX
546	M946TSX	549	M949TSX	552	M952TSX				

561	N561SJF	Volvo B10MA-55	Jonckheere Mistral 35	AC72F	1996
562	N562SJF	Volvo B10MA-55	Jonckheere Mistral 35	AC72F	1996
563	P563MSX	Volvo B10MA-55	Plaxton Premiere Interurban	AC71F	1996
564	P564MSX	Volvo B10MA-55	Plaxton Premiere Interurban	AC71F	1996

565-569 — Volvo B10M-62 — Plaxton Première Interurban DP51F — 1996

565	P565MSX	566	P566MSX	567	P567MSX	568	P568MSX	569	P569MSX

570	P670EWB	Volvo B10MA-55	Plaxton Premiere Interurban	AC71F	1996	Ex East Midland, 1997
571	P671EWB	Volvo B10MA-55	Plaxton Premiere Interurban	AC71F	1996	

578-590 — Volvo B10M-60 — Plaxton Premiére Interurban DP51F — 1993

578	L578HSG	581	L581HSG	584	L584HSG	587	L587HSG	589	L589HSG
579	L579HSG	582	L582HSG	585	L585HSG	588	L588HSG	590	L590HSG
580	L580HSG	583	L583HSG	586	L586HSG				

601-605 — Dennis Dart 9.8SDL3017 — Alexander Dash — B40F — 1992

601	K601ESH	602	K602ESH	603	K603ESH	604	K604ESH	605	K605ESH

606-613 — Dennis Dart SFD412 — Alexander Dash — B40F — 1996

606	P606CMS	608	P608CMS	610	P610CMS	612	P612CMS	613	P613CMS
607	P607CMS	609	P609CMS	611	P611CMS				

623-628 — Volvo B6-9.9M — Alexander Dash — B40F — 1993 — Ex Ribble, 1994

623	L423MVV	625	L425MVV	626	L426MVV	627	L427MVV	628	L428MVV
624	L424MVV								

The original P-type body from Alexander carried an awkward, angular frontal design which was quickly replaced with the front designed for the Singapore export model, to make the PS-type, which was much more successful. One of the original P-type models is Fife Scottish 422, D522DSX.
Phillip Stephenson

Volvo B6s are frequently used on local services in Dunfermline and the type is represented here by 673, M673SSX. During 1996 Fife operated, on evaluation, a Volvo B10L with Alexander Ultra bodywork. This vehicle has since been returned to Volvo. *Murdoch Currie*

651-659

		Volvo B6-9.9M		Alexander Dash		B40F	1993-94		
651	L651HKS	653	L653HKS	655	L655HKS	657	L657HKS	659	L659HKS
652	L652HKS	654	L654HKS	656	L656HKS	658	L658HKS		

667	L267CCK	Volvo B6-9.9M	Alexander Dash	B40F	1993	Ex Ribble, 1994
668	L268CCK	Volvo B6-9.9M	Alexander Dash	B40F	1993	Ex Ribble, 1994
669	L269CCK	Volvo B6-9.9M	Alexander Dash	B40F	1993	Ex Ribble, 1994
670	M670SSX	Volvo B6-9.9M	Alexander Dash	B40F	1994	
671	M671SSX	Volvo B6-9.9M	Alexander Dash	B40F	1994	
672	M672SSX	Volvo B6-9.9M	Alexander Dash	B40F	1994	
673	M673SSX	Volvo B6-9.9M	Alexander Dash	B40F	1994	

701-725

		Leyland Olympian ON2R50G13Z4 Alexander RL				H47/32F	1992		
701	J801WFS	704	J804WFS	707	J807WFS	720	K720ASC	723	K723ASC
702	J802WFS	705	J805WFS	718	K718ASC	721	K721ASC	724	K724ASC
703	J803WFS	706	J806WFS	719	K719ASC	722	K722ASC	725	K725ASC

737	G337KKW	Leyland Olympian ON2R56G13Z4	Alexander RL	DPH51/31F	1989	Ex East Midland, 1992
738	G338KKW	Leyland Olympian ON2R56G13Z4	Alexander RL	DPH51/31F	1989	Ex East Midland, 1992
760	KYV455X	Leyland Titan TNLXB2RR	Leyland	H44/24D	1981	Ex Selkent, 1997
761	RYK820Y	Leyland Titan TNLXB2RR	Leyland	H44/24D	1982	Ex Selkent, 1997
762	OHV801Y	Leyland Titan TNLXB2RR	Leyland	H44/24D	1981	Ex Selkent, 1997
765	A825FUL	Leyland Titan TNLXB2RR	Leyland	H44/24D	1983	Ex Selkent, 1997
766	A66THX	Leyland Titan TNLXB2RR	Leyland	H44/26F	1984	Ex Selkent, 1997
767	A607THV	Leyland Titan TNLXB2RR	Leyland	H44/24D	1984	Ex Selkent, 1997
816	LSX16P	Ailsa B55-10	Alexander AV	H44/35F	1975	
817	LSX17P	Ailsa B55-10	Alexander AV	H44/35F	1975	
832	LSX32P	Ailsa B55-10	Alexander AV	H44/35F	1975	
834	NSP334R	Ailsa B55-10	Alexander AV	H44/31D	1976	Ex Western Scottish, 1995
836u	NSP336R	Ailsa B55-10	Alexander AV	H44/31D	1976	Ex Western Scottish, 1995
838	LSX38P	Ailsa B55-10	Alexander AV	H44/35F	1975	

847-866 — Ailsa B55-10 MkII — Alexander AV — H44/35F — 1979

847	OSC47V	851	OSC51V	855	OSC55V	861	OSC61V	864	OSC64V
848	OSC48V	852	OSC52V	856	OSC56V	862	OSC62V	865	OSC65V
849	OSC49V	853	OSC53V	857	OSC57V	863	OSC63V	866	OSC66V
850	OSC50V	854	OSC54V	860	OSC60V				

867-874 — Volvo B55-10 MkIII — Alexander RV — H44/37F — 1984

867	A967YSX	869	A969YSX	871	A971YSX	873	A973YSX	874	A974YSX
868	A968YSX	870	A970YSX	872	A972YSX				

875	UFS875R	Ailsa B55-10	Alexander AV	H44/35F	1977
876	UFS876R	Ailsa B55-10	Alexander AV	H44/35F	1977
877	UFS877R	Ailsa B55-10	Alexander AV	H44/35F	1977
878	UFS878R	Ailsa B55-10	Alexander AV	H44/35F	1977

901-920 — Volvo Citybus B10M-50 — Alexander RV — DPH47/33F* — 1985-87 908 ex Volvo demonstrator, 1986 *909/10 are DPH45/35F

901	C801USG	907	C807USG	910	E910KSG	915	C795USG	919	C799USG
905	C805USG	908	B108CCS	914	C794USG	918	C798USG	920	C800USG
906	C806USG	909	E909KSG						

940	F310MYJ	Volvo Citybus B10M-50	Northern Counties	DPH43/33F	1989	Ex Southdown, 1991
941	F311MYJ	Volvo Citybus B10M-50	Northern Counties	DPH43/33F	1989	Ex Southdown, 1991
942	F312MYJ	Volvo Citybus B10M-50	Northern Counties	DPH43/33F	1989	Ex Southdown, 1991

972-997 — Volvo Citybus B10M-50 — Alexander RV — H47/37F — 1985-86

972	C802USG	979	B179FFS	984	B184FFS	988	C788USG	992	C792USG
973	C803USG	980	B180FFS	985	B185FFS	989	C789USG	993	C793USG
974	C804USG	981	B181FFS	986	B186FFS	990	C790USG	996	C796USG
977	B177FFS	982	B182FFS	987	C787USG	991	C791USG	997	C797USG
978	B178FFS	983	B183FFS						

1102	ABV669A	Leyland Atlantean PDR1/1	Metro Cammell	O44/31F	1961	Ex Cumberland, 1992
1107	UWV617S	Bristol VRT/SL3/6LXB	Eastern Coach Works	CO43/31F	1978	Ex Stagecoach South, 1994
1110	OVV850R	Bristol VRT/SL3/501(6LX)	Eastern Coach Works	H43/31F	1976	Ex Stagecoach, 1994
1111	VTV167S	Bristol VRT/SL3/6LXB	Eastern Coach Works	H43/31F	1978	Ex Stagecoach, 1994
1112	RJT153R	Bristol VRT/SL3/6LXB	Eastern Coach Works	H43/31F	1977	Ex Stagecoach, 1994
1113	VPR487S	Bristol VRT/SL3/6LXB	Eastern Coach Works	H43/31F	1978	Ex Stagecoach, 1994

Opposite: **Commuter services into both Glasgow and Edinburgh provide much work for the Fife Scottish fleet, and the success of Stagecoach Express services can be seen with the introduction of articulated coaches as shown on the cover. The upper picture shows Alexander PS-type 314, M314PKS, one of only two of the batch with high-back seating seen in George Street, Edinburgh. The lower picture shows one of the Interurban coaches with Fife Express names working through the village of Culross** *Tony Wilson/Bill Potter*

Fife had built up a double-deck fleet almost entirely based on the Ailsa product and these still form an important part of the operation. Seen in Dundee is mark III 871, A971YSX. This batch have Alexander RV bodies.
Malc McDonald

Pulling out of Dunfermline bus station bound for Edinburgh is Fife's 724, K724ASC, a Leyland Olympian with Alexander RL bodywork. *Malc McDonald*

1114	XAP643S	Bristol VRT/SL3/6LXB	Eastern Coach Works	H43/31F	1978	Ex Stagecoach, 1994
1115	EWE204V	Bristol VRT/SL3/6LXB	Eastern Coach Works	H43/31F	1980	Ex East Midland, 1994
1116	HWG208W	Bristol VRT/SL3/6LXB	Eastern Coach Works	H43/31F	1980	Ex East Midland, 1994
1117	RTH924S	Bristol VRT/SL3/6LXB	Eastern Coach Works	H43/31F	1977	Ex East Midland, 1994
1118	KWA217W	Bristol VRT/SL3/6LXC	Eastern Coach Works	H43/31F	1981	Ex East Midland, 1994
1119	KKY220W	Bristol VRT/SL3/6LXB	Eastern Coach Works	H43/31F	1981	Ex East Midland, 1994
1120	DWF198V	Bristol VRT/SL3/501	Eastern Coach Works	H43/31F	1980	Ex East Midland, 1994
1121	DWF199V	Bristol VRT/SL3/501	Eastern Coach Works	H43/31F	1980	Ex East Midland, 1994
1122	DWF200V	Bristol VRT/SL3/501	Eastern Coach Works	H43/31F	1980	Ex East Midland, 1994
1123	RVB973S	Bristol VRT/SL3/6LXB	Willowbrook	H43/31F	1978	Ex Stagecoach South, 1994
1124	RVB974S	Bristol VRT/SL3/6LXB	Willowbrook	H43/31F	1978	Ex Stagecoach South, 1994
1125	RVB978S	Bristol VRT/SL3/6LXB	Willowbrook	H43/31F	1978	Ex Stagecoach South, 1994
1126	TFN990T	Bristol VRT/SL3/6LXB	Willowbrook	H43/31F	1978	Ex Stagecoach South, 1994
1127	PRU917R	Bristol VRT/SL3/6LXB	Eastern Coach Works	H43/31F	1977	Ex Bluebird, 1994
1128	RPR716R	Bristol VRT/SL3/6LXB	Eastern Coach Works	H43/31F	1977	Ex Bluebird, 1994
1129	WHH415S	Bristol VRT/SL3/501	Eastern Coach Works	H43/31F	1978	Ex Bluebird, 1994
1130	PJJ16S	Bristol VRT/SL3/6LXB	Willowbrook	H43/31F	1977	Ex Stagecoach South, 1996
1136	LEO736Y	Leyland Atlantean AN68D/1R	Northern Counties	H43/32F	1983	Ex Ribble, 1995
1144	SCN244S	Leyland Atlantean AN68A/2R	Alexander AL	H49/37F	1978	Ex Busways, 1995
1157	SCN257S	Leyland Atlantean AN68A/2R	Alexander AL	H49/37F	1978	Ex Busways, 1995
1161	SCN261S	Leyland Atlantean AN68A/2R	Alexander AL	H49/37F	1978	Ex Busways, 1995

Previous Registrations:

ABV669A	927GTA	H509AGC	H884LOX, WLT400
B291YSL	B209FFS, GSU343	IIL3504	E626UNE, GIL2967, E937XSB
F286KGK	F430BOP, WLT491	IIL3506	E624UNE, MIB658, E931XSB
GSU341	B207FFS	MSU445	B211FFS
GSU342	B208FFS	MSU499	D319SGB
GSU343	PGC522Y, 3402FM, SJI5407	VLT77	F396DHL
GSU344	B210FFS		

MANCHESTER

Greater Manchester Buses South Ltd, Charterplan House, 151 Charles Street,
Stockport, Greater Manchester, SK1 3JU

Depots : Charles Street, Stockport; Hyde Road, Manchester; York Street, Glossop; Princess Road, Manchester and Daw Bank, Stockport.

1	ESU913	Scania K92CRB	Van Hool Alizée	C55F	1988	Ex Cambus (Premier), 1996
2	ESU920	Scania K92CRB	Van Hool Alizée	C55F	1988	Ex Cambus (Premier), 1996
7	F947NER	Scania K112CRB	Plaxton Paramount 3500 III	C49F	1988	Ex Cambus (Premier), 1996
8	F948NER	Scania K112CRB	Plaxton Paramount 3500 III	C49F	1988	Ex Cambus (Premier), 1996
10	C310ENA	Leyland Tiger TRCTL11/3RH	Duple 320	C57F	1986	
82	SND82X	Leyland Leopard PSU3B/4R	Duple Dominant IV (1981)	C51F	1975	
240	WBN474T	Leyland National 11351A/1R		B49F	1979	
251	RUF41R	Leyland National 11351A/2R		DP49F	1977	Ex Hogg, Glasgow, 1994
252	JIL8374	Leyland National 1151/1R/0401		B49F	1974	Ex Munro, Uddington, 1994
253	JIL7610	Leyland National 1151/1R/0402		B49F	1973	Ex R & I, Milton Keynes, 1994
255	LIL3317	Leyland National 11351A/1R		B49F	1979	Ex Amberley, Pudsey, 1994
256	SJI2054	Leyland National 11351A/1R		B49F	1979	Ex Amberley, Pudsey, 1994
257	SJI4558	Leyland National 11351A/1R		B49F	1978	Ex Amberley, Pudsey, 1994
258	SJI4559	Leyland National 11351/1R		B49F	1976	Ex Amberley, Pudsey, 1994
259	SJI4560	Leyland National 1151/1R/SC		DP45F	1975	Ex Amberley, Pudsey, 1994
260	JIL5279	Leyland National 1151/1R/0403		B49F	1973	Ex Amberley, Pudsey, 1994
261	TJI2488	Leyland National 11351/1R/SC		DP45F	1975	Ex Golden Coaches, Llantwit Major, 1994
264	KDW342P	Leyland National 11351/1R/SC		B49F	1976	Ex Golden Coaches, Llantwit Major, 1994
265	WFM801K	Leyland National 1151/2R/0403		B49F	1972	Ex Gatwick Handling, 1994
267	LIL4612	Leyland National 1151/2R/0403		B49F	1972	Ex Gatwick Handling, 1994
269	JIL7609	Leyland National 1151/2R/0403		B49F	1972	Ex Gatwick Handling, 1994
271	JIL7608	Leyland National 1151/2R/0403		B49F	1973	Ex Gatwick Handling, 1994
272	JIL7607	Leyland National 1151/2R/0403		B49F	1973	Ex Gatwick Handling, 1994
273	JIL7606	Leyland National 11351/2R		B49F	1974	Ex Gatwick Handling, 1994

Stagecoach Manchester's coaching arm, Charterplan, was sold during 1996 ensuring that the principal activity of the fleet is local bus service operation. However, four Scania coaches have been brought into the fleet from Cambus to operate longer distance services. Shown here is 2, ESU920, with Van Hool Alizée bodywork. It is seen working service 201 from Derby.
Tony Wilson

The first 'Stagecoach' buses for the Manchester fleet were twenty Volvo B6s which were acquired from Busways and East Midland. These where then painted into a livery of white with orange covering the three stripes. Now back in full livery is 306, M746PRS, seen turning into Piccadilly from Oldham Street, Manchester. *Tony Wilson*

301-310

| | | | | | | | | | Volvo B6-9.9M | | Alexander Dash | | B40F | | 1994 | Ex Busways, 1995 |

301	M741PRS	303	M743PRS	305	M745PRS	307	M847PRS	309	M749PRS
302	M742PRS	304	M744PRS	306	M746PRS	308	M748PRS	310	M750PRS

311-320

Volvo B6-9.9M   Alexander Dash   B40F   1994   Ex East Midland, 1995

311	M461VHE	313	M846HDF	315	M455VHE	317	M457VHE	319	M459VHE
312	M462VHE	314	M454VHE	316	M456VHE	318	M458VHE	320	M460VHE

321-357

Volvo B6-9.9M   Alexander ALX200   B40F   1997

321	P321JND	339	P329JND	337	P337JND	344	P344JND	351	P351JND
322	P322JND	330	P330JND	338	P338JND	345	P345JND	352	P352JND
323	P323JND	331	P331JND	339	P339JND	346	P346JND	353	P353JND
324	P324JND	332	P332JND	340	P340JND	347	P347JND	354	P354JND
325	P325JND	334	P334JND	341	P341JND	348	P348JND	355	P355JND
326	P326JND	335	P335JND	342	P342JND	349	P349JND	356	P356JND
327	P327JND	336	P336JND	343	P343JND	350	P350JND	357	P357JND
328	P328JND								

401-430

Mercedes-Benz 811D   Alexander Sprint   B31F   1995-96

401	N401WVR	407	N407WVR	413	N413WVR	419	N419WVR	425	N425WVR
402	N402WVR	408	N408WVR	414	N414WVR	420	N420WVR	426	N426WVR
403	N403WVR	409	N409WVR	415	N415WVR	421	N421WVR	427	N427WVR
404	N404WVR	410	N410WVR	416	N416WVR	422	N422WVR	428	N428WVR
405	N405WVR	411	N411WVR	417	N417WVR	423	N423WVR	429	N429WVR
406	N406WVR	412	N412WVR	418	N418WVR	424	N424WVR	430	N430WVR

Opposite, top: Since Stagecoach took over the south Manchester operation investment in new buses is clearly seen. New double-deck buses have started to arrive with thirty Olympians now in service together with over sixty Volvo B10M single-decks. One of these, 822, P822FVU is seen passing through Piccadilly bus station. *Tony Wilson*
Opposite bottom: Many vehicles have received a repaint into corporate livery, with most types now represented. Pictured in Stockport, shortly after repaint, is 1467, H467GVM, a Scania N113DRB with Northern Counties bodywork. *Cliff Beeton*

501-528   Mercedes-Benz 709D   Alexander Sprint   B25F   1996

501	N645VSS	507	N651VSS	513	N657VSS	519	N663VSS	524	N881AVV
502	N646VSS	508	N652VSS	514	N658VSS	520	N664VSS	525	N882AVV
503	N647VSS	509	N653VSS	515	N659VSS	521	N665VSS	526	N883AVV
504	N648VSS	510	N654VSS	516	N660VSS	522	N879AVV	527	N884AVV
505	N649VSS	511	N655VSS	517	N661VSS	523	N880AVV	528	N885AVV
506	N650VSS	512	N656VSS	518	N662VSS				

601-605   Volvo B10BLE   Northern Counties   B49F   1997

601	P601JBU	602	P602JBU	603	P603JBU	604	P604JBU	605	P605JBU

701-730   Volvo Olympian YN2RC16V3   Alexander RL   H47/32F   1995

701	N325NPN	704	N328NPN	707	N331NPN	710	N334NPN	713	N337NPN
702	N326NPN	705	N329NPN	708	N332NPN	711	N335NPN	714	N338NPN
703	N327NPN	706	N330NPN	709	N333NPN	712	N336NPN	715	N339NPN

716-730   Volvo Olympian   Alexander RL   H51/36F   1996

716	P716GND	719	P719GND	722	P722GND	725	P725GND	728	P728GND
717	P717GND	720	P720GND	723	P723GND	726	P726GND	729	P729GND
718	P718GND	721	P721GND	724	P724GND	727	P727GND	730	P730GND

801-868   Volvo B10M-55   Alexander PS   B49F   1996

801	N801DNE	815	N815DNE	829	P829FVU	843	P843GND	856	P856GND
802	N802DNE	816	N816DNE	830	P830FVU	844	P844GND	857	P857GND
803	N803DNE	817	N817DNE	831	P831FVU	845	P845GND	858	P858GND
804	N804DNE	818	N818DNE	832	P832FVU	846	P846GND	859	P859GND
805	N805DNE	819	P819GNC	833	P833FVU	847	P847GND	860	P860GND
806	N806DNE	820	P820GNC	834	P834FVU	848	P848GND	861	P861GND
807	N807DNE	821	P821FVU	835	P835FVU	849	P849GND	862	P862GND
808	N808DNE	822	P822FVU	836	P836GND	850	P850GND	863	P863GND
809	N809DNE	823	P823FVU	837	P837GND	851	P851GND	864	P864GND
810	N810DNE	824	P824FVU	838	P838GND	852	P852GND	865	P865GND
811	N811DNE	825	P825FVU	839	P839GND	853	P853GND	866	P866GND
812	N812DNE	826	P826FVU	840	P840GND	854	P854GND	867	P867GND
813	N813DNE	827	P827FVU	841	P841GND	855	P855GND	868	P868GND
814	N814DNE	828	P828FVU	842	P842GND				

869-894   Volvo B10M-55   Northern Counties Paladin   B49F   1997

869	P869MNE	874	P874MNE	879	P879MNE	884	P884MNE	890	P890MNE
870	P870MNE	875	P875MNE	880	P880MNE	885	P885MNE	891	P891MNE
871	P871MNE	876	P876MNE	881	P881MNE	886	P886MNE	892	P892MNE
872	P872MNE	877	P877MNE	882	P882MNE	887	P887MNE	893	P893MNE
873	P873MNE	878	P878MNE	883	P883MNE	889	P889MNE	894	P894MNE

1461	FWH461Y	Scania BR112DH	Northern Counties	H43/32F	1983
1462	FWH462Y	Scania BR112DH	Northern Counties	H43/32F	1983

1463-1467   Scania N113DRB   Northern Counties   H47/28F   1991

1463	H463GVM	1464	H464GVM	1465	H465GVM	1466	H466GVM	1467	H467GVM

1471w	A471HNC	Dennis Falcon V	Northern Counties	H47/37F	1984
1472w	A472HNC	Dennis Falcon V	Northern Counties	H47/37F	1984
1473w	A473HNC	Dennis Falcon V	Northern Counties	H47/37F	1984

1601-1680   MCW Metrorider MF151/3   MCW   B23F*   1987   *1639 is DP19F

1601	D601MDB	1632	D632MDB	1645w	D645MDB	1655	D655NNE	1672	D672NNE
1606	D606MDB	1634w	D634MDB	1646	D646MDB	1658w	D658NNE	1673w	D673NNE
1611w	D611MDB	1636	D636MDB	1647	D647MDB	1659	D659NNE	1674	D674NNE
1618	D618MDB	1638	D638MDB	1648	D648MDB	1662	D662NNE	1675	D675NNE
1619	D619MDB	1639	D639MDB	1649	D649MDB	1666	D666NNE	1676	D676NNE
1623w	D623MDB	1640	D640MDB	1650	D650MDB	1667	D667NNE	1677	D677NNE
1624	D624MDB	1641w	D641MDB	1651	D651NNE	1668w	D668NNE	1678	D678NNE
1627	D627MDB	1643	D643MDB	1653	D653NNE	1670	D670NNE	1679	D679NNE
1630	D630MDB	1644	D644MDB	1654	D654NNE	1671	D671NNE	1680	D680NNE

Repaints into Stagecoach corporate livery are progressing well at Manchester, with all types now sporting the scheme. Seen here are two of the less-common double-deck types, both with Northern Counties bodywork, placed into the fleet by the PTE in 1991. Above is 1467, H467GVM, a Scania N113 based at Hyde Road depot and seen in Piccadilly heading for Hattersley. Below is 2040, H140GVM, one of ten Dennis Dominators placed in service in 1991 following thirty supplied in 1985. All forty are based at Princess Road depot. *Tony Wilson*

1721-1728 Renault-Dodge S75 Northern Counties B17FL 1990-91

1721	H721CNC	**1724**	H724CNC	**1726**	H726CNC	**1727**	H727FNC	**1728**	H728FNC

1752-1769 Dennis Domino SDA1201 Northern Counties B24F 1985-86

1752w	C752YBA	**1753**w	C753YBA	**1754**w	C754YBA	**1758**w	C758YBA	**1769**w	C769YBA

2001-2030 Dennis Dominator DDA1003 Northern Counties H43/32F 1985

2001	B901TVR	**2007**	B907TVR	**2013**	B913TVR	**2019**	B919TVR	**2025**	B25TVU
2002	B902TVR	**2008**	B908TVR	**2014**	B914TVR	**2020**	B920TVR	**2026**	B26TVU
2003	B903TVR	**2009**	B909TVR	**2015**	B915TVR	**2021**	B21TVU	**2027**	B27TVU
2004	B904TVR	**2010**	B910TVR	**2016**	B916TVR	**2022**	B22TVU	**2028**	B28TVU
2005	B905TVR	**2011**	B911TVR	**2017**	B917TVR	**2023**	B23TVU	**2029**	B29TVU
2006	B906TVR	**2012**	B912TVR	**2018**	B918TVR	**2024**	B24TVU	**2030**	B30TVU

2031-2040 Dennis Dominator DDA2033 Northern Counties H43/29F 1991

2031	H131GVM	**2033**	H133GVM	**2035**	H135GVM	**2037**	H137GVM	**2039**	H139GVM
2032	H132GVM	**2034**	H134GVM	**2036**	H136GVM	**2038**	H138GVM	**2040**	H140GVM

3001-3010 Leyland Olympian ONTL11/1R Northern Counties H43/30F 1982

3001	ANA1Y	**3003**	ANA3Y	**3006**	ANA6Y	**3008**	ANA8Y	**3010**	ANA10Y
3002	ANA2Y	**3004**	ANA4Y	**3007**	ANA7Y	**3009**	ANA9Y		

3016-3025 Leyland Olympian ONLXCT/1R Northern Counties H43/30F 1983-84

3016	A581HDB	**3018**	A583HDB	**3020**	A585HDB	**3022**	A22HNC	**3024**	A24HNC
3017	A582HDB	**3019**	A584HDB	**3021**	A21HNC	**3023**	A23HNC	**3025**	A25HNC

3026-3035 Leyland Olympian ONLXB/1R Northern Counties H43/30F 1984

3026	A26ORJ	**3028**	A28ORJ	*3030	A30ORJ	**3032**	A32ORJ	**3034**	B34PJA
3027	A27ORJ	**3029**	A29ORJ	**3031**	A31ORJ	**3033**	A33ORJ	**3035**	B35PJA

3036-3236 Leyland Olympian ONLXB/1R Northern Counties H43/30F* 1984-86 *3139/98 and 3213/14 are DPH43/26F

3036	B36PJA	**3086**	B86SJA	**3133**	B133WNB	**3166**	C166YBA	**3197**	C197YBA
3039	B39PJA	**3087**	B87SJA	**3135**	B135WNB	**3167**	C167YBA	**3198**	C198YBA
3049	B49PJA	**3088**	B88SJA	**3137**	B137WNB	**3169**	C169YBA	**3199**	C199YBA
3053	B53PJA	**3089**	B89SJA	**3138**	B138WNB	**3170**	C170YBA	**3205**	C205CBU
3055	B55PJA	**3091**	B91SJA	**3139**	B139WNB	**3172**	C172YBA	**3207**	C207CBU
3056	B56PJA	**3094**	B94SJA	**3143**	B143WNB	**3173**	C173YBA	**3208**	C208CBU
3057	B57PJA	**3095**	B95SJA	**3145**	B145WNB	**3174**	C174YBA	**3210**	C210CBU
3058	B58PJA	**3110**	B110SJA	**3146**	B146XNA	**3175**	C175YBA	**3212**	C212CBU
3060	B60PJA	**3114**	B114SJA	**3147**	B147XNA	**3176**	C176YBA	**3213**	C213CBU
3065	B65PJA	**3117**	B117TVU	**3149**	B149XNA	**3178**	C178YBA	**3214**	C214CBU
3067	B67PJA	**3118**	B118TVU	**3150**	B150XNA	**3179**	C179YBA	**3215**	C215CBU
3069	B69PJA	**3119**	B119TVU	**3153**	B153XNA	**3181**	C181YBA	**3216**	C216CBU
3070	B70PJA	**3121**	B121TVU	**3154**	B154XNA	**3184**	C184YBA	**3221**	C221CBU
3072	B72PJA	**3122**	B122TVU	**3155**	B155XNA	**3185**	C185YBA	**3224**	C224CBU
3074	B74PJA	**3124**	B124TVU	**3156**	C156YBA	**3191**	C191YBA	**3226**	C226ENE
3077	B77PJA	**3125**	B125TVU	**3158**	C158YBA	**3193**	C193YBA	**3230**	C230ENE
3080	B80PJA	**3126**	B126WNB	**3164**	C164YBA	**3195**	C195YBA	**3234**	C234ENE
3082	B82PJA	**3132**	B132WNB	**3165**	C165YBA	**3196**	C196YBA	**3236**	C236EVU
3084	B84PJA								

3255-3277 Leyland Olympian ONLXB/1R Northern Counties DPH43/26F 1986-87

3255	C255FRJ	**3268**	D268JVR	**3269**	D269JVR	**3272**	D272JVR	**3277**	D277JVR
3260	D260JVR								

3282-3304 Leyland Olympian ONLXB/1RZ Northern Counties H43/30F* 1988-89 *3291 is DPH43/25F

3282	F282DRJ	**3289**	F289DRJ	**3295**	F295DRJ	**3298**	F298DRJ	**3301**	F301DRJ
3283	F283DRJ	**3291**	F291DRJ	**3296**	F296DRJ	**3300**	F300DRJ	**3304**	F304DRJ
3285	F285DRJ	**3294**	F294DRJ	**3297**	F297DRJ				

The early Leyland Olympians in the Manchester fleet were kept in batches, with the first ten all working from Stockport. Shown here working service 22 to Bolton is 3007, ANA7Y.
Cliff Beeton

4231-4396

	Leyland Atlantean AN68A/1R		Northern Counties			H43/32F	1979-81	
4231	ANA231T	**4290**w	FVR290V	**4343**w	MNC543W	**4368**	ORJ368W	**4393** ORJ393W
4249	FVR249V	**4291**	FVR291V	**4348**	MNC548W	**4377**	ORJ377W	**4395** ORJ395W
4280	FVR280V	**4332**w	MNC523W	**4362**w	ORJ362W	**4381**	ORJ381W	**4396** ORJ396W

4402-4521

Leyland Atlantean AN68A/1R*   Northern Counties   H43/32F   1981-82
*4465/77, 501-21 are AN68B/1R

4402	MRJ402W	**4421**	SND421X	**4454**	SND454X	**4496**	SND496X	**4513** SND513X
4404	MRJ404W	**4429**	SND429X	**4455**u	SND455X	**4501**	SND501X	**4514** SND514X
4406	MRJ406W	**4430**	SND430X	**4465**	SND465X	**4505**	SND505X	**4518** SND518X
4409	MRJ409W	**4449**	SND440X	**4477**	SND477X	**4506**	SND506X	**4519** SND519X
4412	SND412X	**4450**	SND450X	**4487**	SND487X	**4512**	SND512X	**4521** SND521X
4418	SND418X	**4451**u	SND451X	**4495**	SND495X			

4526-4600

Leyland Atlantean AN68D/1R   Northern Counties   H43/32F   1982

4526	SND526X	**4543**	ANA543Y	**4559**	ANA559Y	**4579**	ANA579Y	**4592** ANA592Y
4527	SND527X	**4545**	ANA544Y	**4564**	ANA564Y	**4582**	ANA582Y	**4593** ANA593Y
4530	SND530X	**4546**	ANA546Y	**4568**	ANA568Y	**4585**	ANA585Y	**4596** ANA596Y
4533	ANA533Y	**4550**	ANA550Y	**4569**	ANA569Y	**4586**	ANA586Y	**4597** ANA597Y
4537	ANA537Y	**4552**	ANA552Y	**4572**	ANA572Y	**4589**	ANA589Y	**4600** ANA600Y
4538	ANA538Y	**4553**	ANA553Y	**4577**	ANA577Y			

4601-4700

Leyland Atlantean AN68D/1R   Northern Counties   H43/32F   1983-84

4601	ANA601Y	**4627**	ANA627Y	**4651**	ANA651Y	**4671**	A671HNB	**4688** A688HNB
4604	ANA604Y	**4630**	ANA630Y	**4653**	ANA653Y	**4674**	A674HNB	**4690** A690HNB
4605	ANA605Y	**4631**	ANA631Y	**4657**	A657HNB	**4675**	A675HNB	**4693** A693HNB
4608	ANA608Y	**4632**	ANA633Y	**4660**	A660HNB	**4678**	A678HNB	**4694** A694HNB
4609	ANA609Y	**4637**	ANA637Y	**4661**	A661HNB	**4679**	A679HNB	**4695** A695HNB
4612	ANA612Y	**4639**	ANA639Y	**4664**	A664HNB	**4680**	A680HNB	**4696** A696HNB
4613	ANA613Y	**4644**	ANA644Y	**4665**	A665HNB	**4683**	A683HNB	**4698** A698HNB
4620	ANA620Y	**4646**	ANA646Y	**4668**	A668HNB	**4684**	A684HNB	**4699** A699HNB
4624	ANA624Y	**4647**	ANA647Y	**4669**	A669HNB	**4687**	A687HNB	**4700** A700HNB
4625	ANA625Y							

4702-4764

Leyland Atlantean AN68D/1R Northern Counties H43/32F* 1984 *4620 is H39/32F

4702	A702LNC	**4714**	A714LNC	**4734**	A734NNA	**4747**	A747NNA
4704	A704LNC	**4715**	A715LNC	**4735**	A735NNA	**4748**	A748NNA
4705	A705LNC	**4719**	A719LNC	**4741**	A741NNA	**4749**	A749NNA
4706	A706LNC	**4722**	A722LNC	**4743**	A743NNA	**4750**	A750NNA
4708	A708LNC	**4725**	A725LNC	**4744**	A744NNA	**4751**	A751NNA
4710	A710LNC	**4726**	A726LNC	**4745**	A745NNA	**4752**	A752NNA
4711	A711LNC	**4730**	A730LNC				

4754	A754NNA
4757	A757NNA
4759	A759NNA
4761	A761NNA
4762	A762NNA
4764	A764NNA

5017-5030

MCW Metrobus DR102/10 MCW H43/30F 1980

5017	GBU17V	**5021**	MNC496W	**5024**	GBU24V	**5027**	GBU27V
5019	MNC495W	**5022**	GBU22V	**5026**	MNC498W	**5028**	GBU28V
5020	GBU20V						

5029	GBU29V
5030	MNC499W

5036-5110

MCW Metrobus DR102/21 MCW H43/30F 1981

5036	MRJ36W	**5046**	MRJ46W	**5067**	MRJ67W	**5078**	ORJ78W	**5095**	ORJ95W
5037	MRJ37W	**5047**	MRJ47W	**5071**	MRJ71W	**5079**	ORJ79W	**5098**	ORJ98W
5038	MRJ38W	**5048**	MRJ48W	**5072**	ORJ72W	**5080**	ORJ80W	**5100**	ORJ100W
5040	MRJ40W	**5051**	MRJ49W	**5073**	ORJ73W	**5081**	ORJ81W	**5106**	SND106X
5041	MRJ41W	**5052**	MRJ51W	**5074**	ORJ74W	**5091**	ORJ91W	**5107**	SND107X
5042	MRJ42W	**5053**	MRJ52W	**5075**	ORJ75W	**5092**	ORJ92W	**5108**	SND108X
5043	MRJ43W	**5054**	MRJ53W	**5076**	ORJ76W	**5093**	ORJ93W	**5109**	SND109X
5044	MRJ44W	**5055**	MRJ54W	**5077**	ORJ77W	**5094**	ORJ94W	**5110**	SND110X
5045	MRJ45W	**5066**	MRJ66W						

5111-5190

MCW Metrobus DR102/23 MCW H43/30F 1981-83

5111	SND111X	**5123**	SND123X	**5145**	SND144X	**5159**	ANA159Y	**5165**	ANA165Y
5116	SND116X	**5124**	SND124X	**5153**	ANA153Y	**5160**	ANA160Y	**5170**	ANA170Y
5117	SND117X	**5125**	SND125X	**5154**	ANA154Y	**5161**	ANA161Y	**5173**	ANA173Y
5118	SND118X	**5132**	SND132X	**5155**	ANA155Y	**5162**	ANA162Y	**5179**	ANA179Y
5119	SND119X	**5141**	SND141X	**5157**	ANA157Y	**5163**	ANA163Y	**5180**	ANA180Y
5120	SND120X	**5143**	SND143X	**5158**	ANA158Y	**5164**	ANA164Y	**5190**	ANA190Y
5121	SND121X	**5144**	SND144X	**5158**	ANA158Y				

7032	VNB132L	Leyland Atlantean AN68/1R	Park Royal	O43/32F	1972
7729	RJA729R	Leyland Atlantean AN68A/1R	Northern Counties	H43/32F	1977

Previous Registrations:

ESU913	F951NER	JIL7609	WFM817L	SJI2054	FNS161T
ESU920	F950NER	JIL7610	NRD140M, RIB5086, DBY717M SJI4558	CFM352S
JIL5279	JHU861L	JIL8374	NTC622M, RIB7003, DBY718M SJI4559	LPR937P
JIL7606	GFJ663N	LIL3317	EUM900T	SJI4560	HMA657N
JIL7607	JHU868L	LIL4612	WFM806L	TJI2488	KDW347P
JIL7608	XRB416L			

Liveries: Blue (Magic Bus) 4639/57/60/8/71/8/9/83/90/3, 4705/25/6/43/7/9/51.

Note: All vehicles were formerly GM Buses in 1993, then GMS Buses 1994 unless shown otherwise or new later.

MIDLAND RED

Midland Red (South) Ltd, Railway Terrace, Rugby, Warwickshire, CV21 3HS

Depots: Canal Street, Banbury; Rowley Drive, Coventry; Station Approach, Leamington Spa; Newtown Road, Nuneaton; Railway Terrace, Rugby and Avenue Farm, Stratford-on-Avon.

1	A75NAC	Leyland Tiger TRCTL11/2R	Plaxton Paramount 3200 E	C47FT	1983	
2	A76NAC	Leyland Tiger TRCTL11/2R	Plaxton Paramount 3200 E	C47FT	1983	
4	230HUE	Leyland Leopard PSU3E/4R	Plaxton Supreme IV Express	C49F	1980	Ex Midland Red North, 1981
5	331HWD	Leyland Leopard PSU3E/4R	Plaxton Supreme IV Express	C49F	1980	Ex Midland Red North, 1981
6	3273AC	Leyland Leopard PSU3E/4R	Plaxton Supreme IV Express	C46FT	1980	Ex Midland Red North, 1981
7	RNV413V	Leyland Leopard PSU3E/4R	Plaxton Supreme IV Express	C49F	1979	Ex Premier Travel, 1991
11	FYX824W	Leyland Leopard PSU3E/4R	Duple Dominant II Express	C49F	1980	Ex Busways, 1996
12	HTY139W	Leyland Leopard PSU3E/4R	Duple Dominant II Express	C49F	1980	Ex Busways, 1996
15	NPA230W	Leyland Leopard PSU3E/4R	Plaxton Supreme IV Express	C53F	1981	Ex East Midland, 1994
16	YBO16T	Leyland Leopard PSU3E/2R	East Lancashire	B51F	1979	Ex G & G, Leamington, 1993
18	YBO18T	Leyland Leopard PSU3E/2R	East Lancashire	B51F	1979	Ex G & G, Leamington, 1993
19	A848VML	Leyland Leopard PSU3E/4R	Duple Dominant IV (1983)	C53F	1979	Ex Grey-Green, 1987
28	NAK28X	Leyland Leopard PSU3F/4R	Duple Dominant IV	C47F	1981	Ex East Midland, 1994
29	NAK29X	Leyland Leopard PSU3F/4R	Duple Dominant IV	C47F	1981	Ex East Midland, 1994
57	ANA435Y	DAF MB200DKTL600	Plaxton Paramount 3200	C51F	1983	Ex David R Grasby, 1995
58	9984PG	DAF MB200DKTL600	Duple Laser	C53F	1985	Ex Grey-Green, 1988
59	A6GGT	DAF SB2305DHTD585	Duple 320	C55F	1988	Ex Gray, Hoyland Common, 1990

60-65		Volvo B10M-60	Plaxton Paramount 3500 III	C48FT	1990	Ex Wallace Arnold, 1993

60	G528LWU	**62**	G530LWU	**63**	G531LWU	**64**	G532LWU	**65**	G535LWU
61	G529LWU								

60	G528LWU	62	G530LWU	63	G531LWU	64	G532LWU	65	G535LWU
61	G529LWU								

66	3063VC	Volvo B10M-60	Plaxton Paramount 3500 III	C49FT	1990	Ex Wallace Arnold, 1993
67	9258VC	Volvo B10M-60	Plaxton Paramount 3500 III	C49FT	1990	Ex Wallace Arnold, 1993
68	WSU293	Volvo B10M-60	Plaxton Paramount 3200 III	C49FT	1990	Ex Cheltenham & Gloucester, 1993
69	4012VC	Volvo B10M-61	Ikarus Blue Danube	C49F	1987	Ex David R Gasby, 1995
70	BIW4977	Leyland Tiger TRCTL11/3R	Plaxton Paramount 3200 E	C49FT	1984	
73	491GAC	Leyland Tiger TRCTL11/3RH	Plaxton Paramount 3200 II	C51F	1984	
74	4828VC	Leyland Tiger TRCTL11/3RH	Plaxton Paramount 3500 II	C51F	1985	Ex Sovereign, 1990
75	9737VC	Leyland Tiger TRCTL11/3R	Plaxton Paramount 3500 II	C51F	1985	Ex Sovereign, 1990
76	6253VC	Leyland Tiger TRCTL11/3RH	Plaxton Paramount 3200 II	C51F	1986	Ex Thames Transit, 1991
87	498FYB	Leyland Tiger TRCTL11/3R	Plaxton Paramount 3200	C50F	1983	Ex Cheltenham & Gloucester, 1993
88	A8GGT	Leyland Tiger TRCTL11/3R	Plaxton Paramount 3200 E	C57F	1983	Ex Cheltenham & Gloucester, 1993
89	A7GGT	Leyland Tiger TRCTL11/3RH	Plaxton Paramount 3200	C51F	1984	
90	552OHU	Leyland Tiger TRCTL11/3R	Plaxton Paramount 3200 E	C57F	1983	Ex Cheltenham & Gloucester, 1990
91	420GAC	Leyland Tiger TRCTL11/3R	Plaxton Paramount 3200 E	C46FT	1983	Ex Cheltenham & Gloucester, 1991

Stagecoach Midland Red have made many changes to the fleet during the last year with further integration of the various operations. Pictured in Stratford is 91, 420GAC, a Leyland Tiger with Plaxton Paramount 3200 bodywork.
Philip Lamb

Sixteen Volvo B10M buses are employed by Midland Red. Shown passing through Warwick is 202, M202LHP, one of the batch fitted with high-back seating. *Philip Lamb*

101-105

						Dennis Dart		Alexander Dash		B40F	1996		
101	P101HNH	102	P102HNH	103	P103HNH	104	P104HNH	105	P105HNH				

201-216

Volvo B10M-55   Alexander PS   DP48F*   1995   206-212 are B49F

201	M201LHP	205	M205LHP	208	N208TDU	211	N211TDU	214	N214TDU
202	M202LHP	206	N206TDU	209	M209LHP	212	N212TDU	215	N215TDU
203	M203LHP	207	N207TDU	210	M210LHP	213	N213TDU	216	N216TDU
204	M204LHP								

217	P217HBD	Volvo B10M-55	Alexander PS	DP48F	1996	
218	P218HBD	Volvo B10M-55	Alexander PS	DP48F	1996	
219	P219HBD	Volvo B10M-55	Alexander PS	DP48F	1996	
220	P220HBD	Volvo B10M-55	Alexander PS	DP48F	1996	
300	E433YHL	Mercedes-Benz 709D	Reeve Burgess Beaver	B25F	1988	Ex Loftys, Bridge Trafford, 1993
301	G301WHP	Mercedes-Benz 709D	PMT	B25F	1989	
302	G302WHP	Mercedes-Benz 709D	PMT	B25F	1989	
303	G303WHP	Mercedes-Benz 709D	PMT	B25F	1989	
304	J304THP	Mercedes-Benz 709D	Alexander AM	B25F	1992	
305	J305THP	Mercedes-Benz 709D	Alexander AM	B25F	1992	
306	K306ARW	Mercedes-Benz 709D	Wright	B25F	1992	
307	L307SKV	Mercedes-Benz 709D	Wright	B25F	1993	

308-330

Mercedes-Benz 709D   Alexander Sprint   B23F   1994

308	L308YDU	313	L313YDU	318	L318YDU	323	L323YDU	327	L327YKV
309	L309YDU	314	L314YDU	319	L319YDU	324	L324YDU	328	L328YKV
310	L310YDU	315	L315YDU	320	L320YDU	325	L325YDU	329	L329YKV
311	L311YDU	316	L316YDU	321	L321YDU	326	L326YKV	330	L330YKV
312	L312YDU	317	L317YDU	322	L322YDU				

331-346

Mercedes-Benz 709D   Alexander Sprint   B23F   1995

331	M331LHP	335	M335LHP	338	M338LHP	341	M341LHP	344	M344LHP
332	M332LHP	336	M336LHP	339	M339LHP	342	M342LHP	345	M345LHP
334	M334LHP	337	M337LHP	340	M340LHP	343	M343LHP	346	M346KWK

As with other operations, the minibus fleet gained further new Mercedes-Benz 709D during 1996. This year will see the first of the new Mercedes-Benz Vario enter service in some fleets. Pictured arriving in Leamington Spa is 342, M342LHP from the 1995 delivery. *Richard Godfrey*

347-372

Mercedes-Benz 709D — Alexander Sprint — B25F — 1996

347	N347AVV	353	N353AVV	358	N358AVV	363	N363AVV	368	N368AVV
348	N348AVV	354	N354AVV	359	N359AVV	364	N364AVV	369	N369AVV
349	N349AVV	355	N355AVV	360	N360AVV	365	N365AVV	370	N370AVV
350	N350AVV	356	N356AVV	361	N361AVV	366	N366AVV	371	N371AVV
351	N351AVV	357	N357AVV	362	N362AVV	367	N367AVV	372	N372AVV
352	N352AVV							

390	C705FKE	Ford Transit 190D	Dormobile	B16F	1986	Ex Stagecoach South, 1994
400	F71LAL	Mercedes-Benz 811D	Alexander AM	DP33F	1988	Ex Skills, Nottingham, 1991

401-418

Mercedes-Benz 811D — Wright — B33F* — 1991 — *402/4/7-12 are DP33F
*401/3/5/6/13/7/8 are B31F

401	H401MRW	405	H405MRW	409	J409PRW	413	J413PRW	416	J416PRW
402	H402MRW	406	H406MRW	410	J410PRW	414	J414PRW	417	J417PRW
403	H403MRW	407	J407PRW	411	J411PRW	415	J415PRW	418	J418PRW
404	H404MRW	408	J408PRW	412	J412PRW				

419	G115OGA	Mercedes-Benz 811D	Alexander AM	DP33F	1988	Ex Beaton, Blantyre, 1992

420-425

Mercedes-Benz 811D — Wright — B31F — 1993

420	K420ARW	422	K422ARW	423	K423ARW	424	K424ARW	425	K425ARW
421	K421ARW							

426	CSV219	Mercedes-Benz 811D	Optare StarRider	C29F	1989	Ex Brents Coaches, Watford, 1993
427	H912XGA	Mercedes-Benz 814D	Reeve Burgess Beaver	DP31F	1990	Ex Loftys, Bridge Trafford, 1993

451-456

Volvo B6-9.9M — Alexander Dash — DP40F — 1994

451	L451YAC	453	L453YAC	454	L454YAC	455	L455YAC	456	L456YAC
452	L452YAC							

502	JOX502P	Leyland National 11351A/1R	B49F	1976	Ex Midland Red, 1981
503	JOX503P	Leyland National 11351A/1R	B49F	1976	Ex Midland Red, 1981
504	JOX504P	Leyland National 11351A/1R	B49DL	1976	Ex Midland Red, 1981
507	XGR728R	Leyland National 11351A/1R (DAF)	B49F	1977	Ex United, 1993
553	NOE553R	Leyland National 11351A/1R	B49F	1977	Ex Midland Red, 1981
554	NOE554R	Leyland National 11351A/1R	B49F	1977	Ex Cheltenham & Gloucester, 1994
571	NOE571R	Leyland National 11351A/1R	B49F	1977	Ex Midland Red, 1981
577	NOE577R	Leyland National 11351A/1R	B49F	1977	Ex Midland Red, 1981
578	NOE578R	Leyland National 11351A/1R	B49F	1977	Ex Midland Red, 1981
581	NOE581R	Leyland National 11351A/1R	B49F	1977	Ex Midland Red, 1981
582	NOE582R	Leyland National 11351A/1R (DAF)	B49F	1977	Ex Midland Red, 1981
586	NOE586R	Leyland National 11351A/1R	B49F	1977	Ex Midland Red, 1981
587	NOE587R	Leyland National 11351A/1R	B49F	1977	Ex Cheltenham & Gloucester, 1994
589	NOE589R	Leyland National 11351A/1R	B49F	1977	Ex Midland Red, 1981
590	NOE590R	Leyland National 11351A/1R	B49DL	1977	Ex Midland Red, 1981
591	YEU446V	Leyland National 10351B/1R	B44F	1981	Ex Cheltenham & Gloucester, 1994
592	NOE551R	Leyland National 11351A/1R	B49F	1976	Ex Midland Red, 1981
593	KHT122P	Leyland National 11351/1R	B52F	1976	Ex Cheltenham & Gloucester, 1994
594	VAE502T	Leyland National 10351B/1R	B44F	1979	Ex Cheltenham & Gloucester, 1994
595	GOL426N	Leyland National 11351/1R	B49F	1975	Ex Cheltenham & Gloucester, 1994
597	HEU122N	Leyland National 11351/1R	B52F	1975	Ex Cheltenham & Gloucester, 1994
598	KHT124P	Leyland National 11351/1R	B52F	1976	Ex Cheltenham & Gloucester, 1994
600	SAE753S	Leyland National 11351A/1R	B52F	1978	Ex Cheltenham & Gloucester, 1994

602-772

Leyland National 11351A/1R(DAF) B49F* 1977-80 Ex Midland Red, 1981
*624, 708 are B52F; 755/6 have LPG engines

602	NOE602R	621	PUK621R	626	PUK626R	708	TOF708S	755	XOV755T
603	NOE603R	622	PUK622R	627	PUK627R	709	TOF709S	756	XOV756T
604	NOE604R	623	PUK623R	628	PUK628R	710	TOF710S	760	XOV760T
605	NOE605R	624	PUK624R	629	PUK629R	753	XOV753T	771	BVP771V
606	NOE606R	625	PUK625R	707	TOF707S	754	XOV754T	772	BVP772V

802	SHH392X	Leyland National 2 NL116AL11/1R	B52F	1982	Ex Cheltenham & Gloucester, 1995
803	TAE639S	Leyland National 11351A/1R(DAF)	B52F	1978	Ex Cheltenham & Gloucester, 1995
808	BVP808V	Leyland National 2 NL116L11/1R	B49F	1980	Ex North Western, 1991
809	SVV589W	Leyland National 2 NL116L11/1R	B49F	1980	Ex Luton & District, 1991
816	BVP816V	Leyland National 2 NL116L11/1R (DAF)	B49F	1980	Ex Midland Red, 1981
817	BVP817V	Leyland National 2 NL116L11/1R (DAF)	B49F	1980	Ex Midland Red, 1981
818	BVP818V	Leyland National 2 NL116L11/1R (DAF)	B49F	1980	Ex Midland Red, 1981

Opposite: **The Midland Red fleet contained many elderly vehicles when the company passed to Stagecoach. Shown here are two of the, then, newer inherited examples. The upper picture shows typical Leyland National, NOE554R while the lower picture shows Leyland Olympian 964, C964XVC, one of three supplied in 1985 and still the newest double-decks operated.**
Les Peters/Phillip Stephenson

Six Volvo B6s were placed in service in 1994, further midibuses being delivered at the end of 1996 in the form of Dennis Darts. Shown her is 455, L455YAC, heading for Stratford-on-Avon on service X18.
Philip Lamb

| 819 | F661PWK | Leyland Lynx LX112L10ZR1R | Leyland | B51F | 1988 | |
| 820 | F660PWK | Leyland Lynx LX112L10ZR1R | Leyland | B51F | 1988 | |

821-830

		Iveco Daily 49.10	Marshall C29	B23F	1993	Ex Selkent, 1995

821	K521EFL	823	K523EFL	825	K525EFL	827	K527EFL	829	K529EFL
822	K522EFL	824	K524EFL	826	K526EFL	828	K528EFL	830	K530EFL

| 832 | N182CMJ | Iveco Daily 59.12 | Alexander | B29F | 1995 | Long term Iveco demonstrator |
| 833 | N183CMJ | Iveco Daily 59.12 | Alexander | B29F | 1996 | Long term Iveco demonstrator |

902-912

		Leyland Olympian ONLXB/1R	Eastern Coach Works	H45/32F	1983-84

902	A542HAC	904	A544HAC	906	A546HAC	910	B910ODU	912	B912ODU
903	A543HAC	905	A545HAC	907	A547HAC	911	B911ODU		

926	OBD842P	Bristol VRT/SL3/6LX	Eastern Coach Works	H43/31F	1976	Ex Circle Line, 1996
927	NHU671R	Bristol VRT/SL3/6LXB	Eastern Coach Works	H43/27D	1979	Ex Cheltenham & Gloucester, 1994
928	LHT725P	Bristol VRT/SL3/501(6LXB)	Eastern Coach Works	H39/31F	1976	Ex Cheltenham & Gloucester, 1994
929	NHU672R	Bristol VRT/SL3/6LXB	Eastern Coach Works	H43/27D	1979	Ex Cheltenham & Gloucester, 1994
931	MAU145P	Bristol VRT/SL3/6LXB	Eastern Coach Works	H43/31F	1976	Ex Bluebird, 1993
932	CBV16S	Bristol VRT/SL3/501(6LXB)	Eastern Coach Works	H43/31F	1977	Ex Ribble, 1994
933	PEU516R	Bristol VRT/SL3/6LXB	Eastern Coach Works	H43/31F	1977	Ex Swindon & District, 1992
936	ONH846P	Bristol VRT/SL3/6LXB	Eastern Coach Works	H43/31F	1976	Ex Bluebird, 1993
937	DWF195V	Bristol VRT/SL3/6LXB	Eastern Coach Works	H43/31F	1979	Ex East Midland, 1994
939	DWF194V	Bristol VRT/SL3/6LXB	Eastern Coach Works	H43/31F	1979	Ex East Midland, 1994
940	PEU511R	Bristol VRT/SL3/6LXB	Eastern Coach Works	DPH43/31F	1977	Ex Badgerline, 1993
941	GTX746W	Bristol VRT/SL3/501	Eastern Coach Works	H43/31F	1980	Ex Red & White, 1993
943	GTX754W	Bristol VRT/SL3/501	Eastern Coach Works	H43/31F	1980	Ex Red & White, 1993
944	HUD475S	Bristol VRT/SL3/6LXB	Eastern Coach Works	H43/31F	1977	Ex Oxford Bus Company, 1993
945	HUD480S	Bristol VRT/SL3/6LXB	Eastern Coach Works	H43/31F	1977	Ex Oxford Bus Company, 1993
946	HUD479S	Bristol VRT/SL3/6LXB	Eastern Coach Works	H43/31F	1977	Ex Oxford Bus Company, 1993
947	AET181T	Bristol VRT/SL3/6LXB	Eastern Coach Works	H43/31F	1979	Ex East Midland, 1994
948	VTV170S	Bristol VRT/SL3/6LXB	Eastern Coach Works	H43/31F	1978	Ex East Midland, 1994
958	WDA994T	Leyland Fleetline FE30AGR	MCW	H43/33F	1979	Ex West Midlands Travel, 1990
960	B960ODU	Leyland Olympian ONLXB/1R	Eastern Coach Works	DPH42/30F	1984	
961	B961ODU	Leyland Olympian ONLXB/1R	Eastern Coach Works	DPH42/30F	1984	
962	C962XVC	Leyland Olympian ONLXB/1RH	Eastern Coach Works	DPH42/29F	1985	
963	C963XVC	Leyland Olympian ONLXB/1RH	Eastern Coach Works	DPH42/29F	1985	
964	C964XVC	Leyland Olympian ONLXB/1RH	Eastern Coach Works	DPH42/29F	1985	

970-988

		Leyland Atlantean AN68A/2R	Alexander AL	H49/37F	1978-80 Ex Busways, 1995-96

970	SCN252S	975	VCU310T	979	SCN281S	983	AVK168V	987	AVK140V
971	SCN253S	976	AVK172V	980	AVK181V	985	AVK167V	988	AVK145V
972	SCN265S	977	EJR106W	981	VCU304T	986	AVK169V	989	AVK143V
974	VCU301T	978	SCN276S	982	AVK174V				

1052	AIB4053	Leyland National 10351A/2R		B22DL	1978	Ex London Buses, 1991
1053	PIB8109	Leyland National 10351A/2R		B22DL	1978	Ex London Buses, 1991
4364	C714FKE	Ford Transit 190D	Dormobile	B16F	1986	Ex East Kent, 1991

Previous Registrations:

3063VC	G543LWU	6253VC	YDK917, JPU817, C472CAP	A848VML	FRA64V
3273AC	BVP788V	9258VC	G554LWU	AIB4053	THX186S
331HWD	BVP787V	9737VC	C212PPE	BIW4977	A70KDU
3669DG	YKV811X	9984PG	FYX815W	CSV219	F846TLU
4012VC	E422GAC, 6267AC, E315NWK	A6GGT	E630KCX	HTY139W	FYX819W, KSU460
420GAC	CDG213Y	A7GGT	B72OKV	KIB8140	THX249S
4828VC	C211PPE	A75NAC	A190GVC, 420GAC	PIB8019	THX119S
491GAC	B73OKV	A76NAC	A191GVC, 491GAC	RNV413V	KUB546V, 4012VC
498FYB	CDG207Y	A8GGT	A202RHT	WSU293	From New
552OHU	A201RHT				

MK METRO

MK Metro Ltd, Snowdon Drive, Winterhill, Milton Keynes, Buckinghamshire, MK6 1AD

This operation is to be divested during the first half of 1997.

01-45   Mercedes-Benz L608D   Robin Hood*   B20F*   1986   *29 is Dormobile(1990) and B25F

01	D101VRP	10	D110VRP	19	D119VRP	28	D128VRP	37	D137VRP
02	D102VRP	11	D111VRP	20	D120VRP	29	D129VRP	38	D138VRP
03	D103VRP	12	D112VRP	21	D121VRP	30	D130VRP	39	D139VRP
04	D104VRP	13	D113VRP	22	D122VRP	31	D131VRP	40	D140VRP
05	D105VRP	14	D114VRP	23	D123VRP	32	D132VRP	41	D141VRP
06	D106VRP	15	D115VRP	24	D124VRP	33	D133VRP	42	D142VRP
07	D107VRP	16	D116VRP	25	D125VRP	34	D134VRP	43	D143VRP
08	D108VRP	17	D117VRP	26	D126VRP	35	D135VRP	44	D144VRP
09	D109VRP	18	D118VRP	27	D127VRP	36	D136VRP	45	D145VRP

47-64   Mercedes-Benz L608D   Alexander AM   DP19F*   1986   *55/6/64 are B20F

47	D147VRP	55	D155VRP	56	D156VRP	64	D164VRP

66-73   Mercedes-Benz 709D   Robin Hood   B25F   1988

66	E66MVV	68	E68MVV	70	E70MVV	72	E72MVV	73	E73MVV
67	E67MVV	69	E69MVV	71	E71MVV				

The **MK Metro** operation, which also uses the Buckinghamshire Road car names came into Stagecoach with the Cambus Holdings aquisition. However, after agreement with the competition authorities the Milton Keynes unit is to be divested during the first half of 1997. Because this was to take place the corporate livery has not been introduced. Pictured in Milton Keynes is 04, D104VRP, a Mercedes-Benz L609D. *Philip Lamb*

77	D177VRP	Mercedes-Benz L608D	Dormobile (1990)	B25F	1986	
81	D181VRP	Mercedes-Benz L608D	Alexander AM	B20F	1986	
83	D183VRP	Mercedes-Benz L608D	Alexander AM	B20F	1986	
92	D192VRP	Mercedes-Benz L608D	Alexander AM	B20F	1986	

93-99

		Mercedes-Benz 709D	Dormobile Routemaker	B29F	1989-90

93	G93ERP	96	G96ERP	97	G97ERP	98	G98NBD	99	G99NBD
94	G94ERP								

100	G100NBD	Mercedes-Benz 709D	Dormobile Routemaker	B29F	1990	
201	J201JRP	Mercedes-Benz 709D	Plaxton Beaver	B27F	1991	
202	J202JRP	Mercedes-Benz 709D	Plaxton Beaver	B27F	1991	
203	J203JRP	Mercedes-Benz 709D	Plaxton Beaver	B27F	1991	
204	J204JRP	Mercedes-Benz 709D	Plaxton Beaver	B27F	1991	
359	F359GKN	Mercedes-Benz 811D	Dormobile Routemaker	B29F	1989	Ex Dormobile demonstrator, 1989
CT419	K419FAV	Mercedes-Benz 709D	Marshall C19	DP18FL	1993	
CT426	K426FAV	Mercedes-Benz 709D	Marshall C19	DP18FL	1993	
CT428	K428FAV	Mercedes-Benz 709D	Marshall C19	DP18FL	1993	
CT447	C447NNV	Renault-Dodge S56	Harrops Wellfair	M16L	1986	
CT448	C448NNV	Renault-Dodge S56	Harrops Wellfair	M16L	1986	
2618	PEX618W	Leyland National 2 NL116L11/1R		B49F	1980	Ex Cambus, 1995
2619	PEX619W	Leyland National 2 NL116L11/1R		B49F	1980	Ex Cambus, 1994
2622	PEX622W	Leyland National 2 NL116L11/1R		B49F	1980	Ex Cambus, 1994
3009	CBV9S	Bristol VRT/SL3/501(6LXB)	Eastern Coach Works	H43/31F	1977	Ex Ribble, 1993
3019	CBV19S	Bristol VRT/SL3/501(6LXB)	Eastern Coach Works	H43/31F	1977	Ex Ribble, 1993
3559	MEL559P	Bristol VRT/SL3/6LXB	Eastern Coach Works	H43/31F	1976	Ex Viscount, 1995
3724	LOD724P	Bristol VRT/SL3/501	Eastern Coach Works	DPH31/29F	1975	Ex Southern National, 1993
3725	LOD725P	Bristol VRT/SL3/501	Eastern Coach Works	DPH31/29F	1975	Ex Southern National, 1993
3937	MCL937P	Bristol VRT/SL3/6LXB	Eastern Coach Works	H43/31F	1976	Ex Cambus, 1994
3942	URP942W	Bristol VRT/SL3/6LXB	Eastern Coach Works	H43/31F	1981	Ex United Counties, 1986

Liveries: Cream and green

Following on from the initial batch of Mercedes-Benz L609s were eight early 709 models and these were fitted with Robin Hood bodywork. Representing the batch is 69, E69MVV seen in its home town. In the early 1990s larger buses were added to the minibus operation, though the numbers of double-deck buses had reduced by the time the fleet passed into Stagecoach control. *Philip Lamb*

RED & WHITE

Red & White Services Ltd; The Valleys Bus Company Ltd; Aberdare Bus Company Ltd,
1 St David's Road, Cwmbran, Torfaen   NP44 1QX

Depots and outstations: **Red & White** - Mill Street, Abergavenny; Bishops Meadow, Brecon; Warwick Road, Brynmawr; Valley Road, Cinderford; Bulwark Road, Chepstow;   Risca Road, Crosskeys;   St David's Road, Cwmbran;   Lydney;   Ross on Wye;   **The Valleys** - Merthyr Industrial Estate, Pant, Merthyr Tydfil; Commercial Street, Pengam; **Aberdare Bus** - Cwmbach New Road, Cwmbach, Aberdare.

301	H301PAX	Mercedes-Benz 709D		PMT Ami		C25F	1991		
302	J302TUH	Mercedes-Benz 709D		PMT Bursley		B25F	1991		
303	J303TUH	Mercedes-Benz 709D		PMT Bursley		B25F	1991		

304-317 Mercedes-Benz 811D   Wright NimBus   B33F   1992

304	J304UKG	**307**	J307UKG	**311**	K311YKG	**314**	K314YKG	**316**	K316YKG
305	J305UKG	**309**	K309YKG	**312**	K312YKG	**315**	K315YKG	**317**	K317YKG
306	J306UKG	**310**	K310YKG	**313**	K313YKG				

318	K318YKG	Mercedes-Benz 709D		Wright NimBus		B25F	1992		
319	K319YKG	Mercedes-Benz 709D		Alexander Sprint		B25F	1992		
320	K320YKG	Mercedes-Benz 709D		Alexander Sprint		B25F	1992		
321	K321YKG	Mercedes-Benz 709D		Alexander Sprint		B25F	1992		
322	K322YKG	Mercedes-Benz 811D		Wright NimBus		B33F	1992		
323	K323YKG	Mercedes-Benz 811D		Wright NimBus		B33F	1992		
324	K324YKG	Mercedes-Benz 811D		Wright NimBus		B33F	1992		
325	K325YKG	Mercedes-Benz 811D		Wright NimBus		B33F	1992		
326	L326CHB	Mercedes-Benz 811D		Marshall C16		B33F	1993		
327	L327CHB	Mercedes-Benz 811D		Marshall C16		B33F	1993		
328	L328CHB	Mercedes-Benz 811D		Marshall C16		B33F	1993		
329	L329CHB	Mercedes-Benz 811D		Marshall C16		B33F	1993		
330	L685CDD	Mercedes-Benz 709D		Alexander Sprint		B25F	1994	Ex Cheltenham & Gloucester, 1994	
331	L331CHB	Mercedes-Benz 811D		Marshall C16		B33F	1993		
332	H556TUG	Mercedes-Benz 709D		Dormobile Routemaker		DP27F	1990	Ex Graham's, Tredegar, 1994	

334-360 Mercedes-Benz 709D   Alexander Sprint   B25F   1994

334	L334FWO	**340**	L340FWO	**346**	M346JBO	**351**	M351JBO	**356**	M356JBO
335	L335FWO	**341**	L341FWO	**347**	M347JBO	**352**	M352JBO	**357**	M357JBO
336	L336FWO	**342**	L342FWO	**348**	M348JBO	**353**	M353JBO	**358**	M358JBO
337	L337FWO	**343**	L343FWO	**349**	M349JBO	**354**	M354JBO	**359**	M359JBO
338	L338FWO	**344**	M344JBO	**350**	M350JBO	**355**	M355JBO	**360**	M360JBO
339	L339FWO	**345**	M345JBO						

361-371 Mercedes-Benz 709D   Alexander Sprint   B25F   1995

361	M361LAX	**364**	M364LAX	**366**	M366LAX	**368**	M368LAX	**370**	M370LAX
362	M362LAX	**365**	M365LAX	**367**	M367LAX	**369**	M369LAX	**371**	M371LAX
363	M363LAX								

372-384 Mercedes-Benz 709D   Alexander Sprint   B25F   1996

372	N372PNY	**375**	N375PNY	**378**	N378PNY	**381**	N381PNY	**383**	N383PNY
373	N373PNY	**376**	N376PNY	**379**	N379PNY	**382**	N382PNY	**384**	N384PNY
374	N374PNY	**377**	N377PNY	**380**	N380PNY				

391	GHB146N	Bristol RESL6L	Eastern Coach Works	B44F	1974	Ex Cynon Valley, 1992
392	HTG354N	Bristol RESL6L	Eastern Coach Works	B44F	1975	Ex Cynon Valley, 1992
393	GHB148N	Bristol RESL6L	Eastern Coach Works	B44F	1974	Ex Cynon Valley, 1992
394	D109NDW	Leyland Lynx LX112TL11ZR1	Leyland Lynx	B48F	1987	Ex Cynon Valley, 1992
395	E113RBO	Leyland Lynx LX112TL11ZR1	Leyland Lynx	B48F	1987	Ex Cynon Valley, 1992
396	E114SDW	Leyland Lynx LX112TL11ZR1	Leyland Lynx	B48F	1987	Ex Cynon Valley, 1992
397	E115SDW	Leyland Lynx LX112TL11ZR1	Leyland Lynx	B48F	1988	Ex Cynon Valley, 1992
398	F74DCW	Leyland Lynx LX2R11C15Z4R	Leyland Lynx 2	DP45F	1989	Ex Cynon Valley, 1992

Red & White and Busways are now the only two operations where Bristol REs are still in use, those in Hartlepool having been withdrawn as part of the fleet upgrade and renumbering. Seen in corporate livery is R&W 391, GHB146N. *Phillip Stephenson*

420	NWO454R	Leyland National 11351A/1R/SC (Volvo)	DP48F	1977	Ex National Welsh, 1991
423	NWO457R	Leyland National 11351A/1R/SC (Volvo)	DP48F	1977	Ex National Welsh, 1991
427	NWO461R	Leyland National 11351A/1R/SC (DAF)	DP48F	1977	Ex National Welsh, 1991
434	NWO468R	Leyland National 11351A/1R/SC (Volvo)	DP48F	1977	Ex National Welsh, 1991
442	UTX726S	Leyland National 10351A/1R	B44F	1978	Ex Cynon Valley, 1992
448	DDW433V	Leyland National 10351A/1R	B44F	1980	Ex Cynon Valley, 1992
449	DDW434V	Leyland National 10351A/1R	B44F	1980	Ex Cynon Valley, 1992
500	YSX934W	Leyland National 2 NL106L11/1R	B44F	1981	Ex Fife Scottish, 1994
501	RSG814V	Leyland National 2 NL116L11/1R	B52F	1980	Ex Fife Scottish, 1994
502	YSX932W	Leyland National 2 NL106L11/1R	B44F	1981	Ex Fife Scottish, 1994
503	YSX933W	Leyland National 2 NL106L11/1R	B44F	1981	Ex Fife Scottish, 1994
504	MSO13W	Leyland National 2 NL116L11/1R	B52F	1980	Ex Fife Scottish, 1994
505	RSG815V	Leyland National 2 NL116L11/1R	B52F	1980	Ex Fife Scottish, 1994
506	WAS765V	Leyland National 2 NL116L11/1R	B52F	1980	Ex Fife Scottish, 1994
507	WAS767V	Leyland National 2 NL116L11/1R	B52F	1980	Ex Fife Scottish, 1994
508	MSO14W	Leyland National 2 NL116L11/1R	B52F	1980	Ex Fife Scottish, 1994
509	YSX926W	Leyland National 2 NL106L11/1R	B44F	1981	Ex Fife Scottish, 1994
510	YSX935W	Leyland National 2 NL106L11/1R	B44F	1981	Ex Fife Scottish, 1994
512	RSG824V	Leyland National 2 NL116L11/1R	B52F	1980	Ex Fife Scottish, 1994
513	RSG825V	Leyland National 2 NL116L11/1R	B52F	1980	Ex Fife Scottish, 1994
514	RSG823V	Leyland National 2 NL116L11/1R	B52F	1980	Ex Fife Scottish, 1995
515	DMS22V	Leyland National 2 NL116L11/1R	B52F	1980	Ex Fife Scottish, 1995
516	NLS987W	Leyland National 2 NL116L11/1R	B52F	1980	Ex Fife Scottish, 1995
517	DMS20V	Leyland National 2 NL116L11/1R	B52F	1980	Ex Fife Scottish, 1995

598-649		Leyland National 11351A/1R		B49F	1977-79 Ex National Welsh, 1991

635/49 are fitted with Volvo engines, 619 DAF.

598	SKG908S	619	SKG923S	635	WUH168T	646	BUH211V	649	BUH214V
609	PKG741R	634	WUH167T						

Opposite: Representing the Red & White fleet are two saloons. The upper picture shows one of the Leyland Lynx, 394, D109NDW that were new to Merthyr Tydfil. The vehicle was photographed in Cardiff and heading for Blaenavon when photographed. The lower picture shows Volvo B10M 753, M753LAX on service 29 to the Prince Charles Hospital in Merthyr. *Les Peters/Cliff Beeton*

The 1997 Stagecoach Bus Handbook

Red & White operate Dennis Javelins on the Newport to Cheltenham service. In 1995 three Duple-bodied examples were transferred from East Midland's Whites operation. Seen lettered for the service is 953, F243OFP. Since this was taken service 73 has been cut back to Gloucester. *Phillip Stephenson*

651	NOE552R	Leyland National 11351A/1R	B49F	1976	Ex Cheltenham & Gloucester, 1991
652	NOE573R	Leyland National 11351A/1R(Volvo)	B49F	1976	Ex Midland Red South, 1992
653	NOE572R	Leyland National 11351A/1R(DAF)	B49F	1977	Ex Midland Red South, 1992
654	NOE576R	Leyland National 11351A/1R	B49F	1976	Ex Midland Red South, 1992
658	BPT903S	Leyland National 11351A/1R	B49F	1978	Ex Go-Ahead Northern, 1992
660	XVV540S	Leyland National 11351A/1R	B49F	1976	Ex City Line, 1993
663	PHW985S	Leyland National 11351A/1R(DAF)	B52F	1978	Ex Cheltenham & Gloucester, 1995

701-708

		Volvo B6-9.9M		Alexander Dash		B40F		1994	
701	L701FWO	703	L703FWO	705	L705FWO	707	L707FWO	708	L708FWO
702	L702FWO	704	L704FWO	706	L706FWO				

750-770

		Volvo B10M-55		Alexander PS		DP48F		1995	
750	M750LAX	755	M755LAX	759	M759LAX	763	M763LAX	767	M767RAX
751	M751LAX	756	M756LAX	760	M760LAX	764	M764LAX	768	M768RAX
752	M752LAX	757	M757LAX	761	M761LAX	765	M765RAX	769	M769RAX
753	M753LAX	758	M758LAX	762	M762LAX	766	M766RAX	770	M770RAX
754	M754LAX								

771	P771TTG	Volvo B10M-62	Plaxton Premiére Interurban	DP51F	1996
772	P772TTG	Volvo B10M-62	Plaxton Premiére Interurban	DP51F	1996
773	P773TTG	Volvo B10M-62	Plaxton Premiére Interurban	DP51F	1996
774	P774TTG	Volvo B10M-62	Plaxton Premiére Interurban	DP51F	1996

825	TWS909T	Bristol VRT/SL3/6LXB	Eastern Coach Works	H43/31F	1979	Ex Cheltenham & Gloucester, 1992
827	A541HAC	Leyland Olympian ONLXB/1R	Eastern Coach Works	H43/31F	1983	Ex Midland Red South, 1993
828	A548HAC	Leyland Olympian ONLXB/1R	Eastern Coach Works	H43/31F	1983	Ex Midland Red South, 1993
829	A549HAC	Leyland Olympian ONLXB/1R	Eastern Coach Works	H43/31F	1983	Ex Midland Red South, 1993
830	AET185T	Bristol VRT/SL3/6LXB	Eastern Coach Works	H43/31F	1979	Ex East Midland, 1993
831	DAK201V	Bristol VRT/SL3/501	Eastern Coach Works	H43/31F	1979	Ex East Midland, 1994
832	CBV6S	Bristol VRT/SL3/501(6LXB)	Eastern Coach Works	H43/31F	1977	Ex Ribble, 1994
833	DBV26W	Bristol VRT/SL3/6LXB	Eastern Coach Works	H43/31F	1980	Ex Ribble, 1994

834-844

		Bristol VRT/SL3/501*	Eastern Coach Works	H43/31F	1980	Ex National Welsh, 1991
						*836 is fitted with a 6LXB engine

834	BUH232V	836	GTX738W	840	GTX747W	843	GTX750W	844	GTX753W
835	BUH237V	838	GTX743W	841	GTX748W				

845	WAX194S	Bristol VRT/SL3/501(6LXB)	Eastern Coach Works	H43/31F	1977	Ex Ribble, 1994
860	KVF248V	Bristol VRT/SL3/6LXB	Eastern Coach Works	H43/31F	1980	Ex Cambus (Viscount), 1997
861	OSR206R	Bristol VRT/LL3/501	Alexander AL	H49/38F	1977	Ex National Welsh, 1991
862	OSR207R	Bristol VRT/LL3/501	Alexander AL	H49/38F	1977	Ex National Welsh, 1991
863w	OSR208R	Bristol VRT/LL3/501	Alexander AL	H49/38F	1977	Ex National Welsh, 1991
864	OSR209R	Bristol VRT/LL3/501	Alexander AL	H49/38F	1977	Ex National Welsh, 1991
865	WDA1T	Leyland Titan TNLXB1RF	Park Royal	H43/29F	1978	Ex Selkent, 1994
866	WDA2T	Leyland Titan TNLXB1RF	Park Royal	H43/29F	1979	Ex Selkent, 1994
867	WDA5T	Leyland Titan TNLXB1RF	Park Royal	H43/29F	1979	Ex Selkent, 1994
868	AVK163V	Leyland Atlantean AN68A/2R	Alexander AL	H49/37F	1980	Ex Busways, 1995
869	AVK166V	Leyland Atlantean AN68A/2R	Alexander AL	H49/37F	1980	Ex Busways, 1995
870	AVK173V	Leyland Atlantean AN68A/2R	Alexander AL	H49/37F	1980	Ex Busways, 1995
871	VBA166S	Leyland Atlantean AN68A/1R	Northern Counties	H43/32F	1978	Ex Stagecoach Manchester, 1996
872	VBA178S	Leyland Atlantean AN68A/1R	Northern Counties	H43/32F	1978	Ex Stagecoach Manchester, 1996
873	VBA188S	Leyland Atlantean AN68A/1R	Northern Counties	H43/32F	1978	Ex Stagecoach Manchester, 1996
874	VBA190S	Leyland Atlantean AN68A/1R	Northern Counties	H43/32F	1978	Ex Stagecoach Manchester, 1996

898-915

		Leyland Tiger TRCTL11/3R	Plaxton Paramount 3200	C51F*	1983	Ex National Welsh, 1991
						*906-14 are C46F; 915 is C53F

898	AAX450A	901	AAX466A	907	AAL575A	911	AAL516A	914	AAX516A
899	AAX451A	902	AAX488A	909	AAL538A	912	AAX489A	915	AAX529A
900	AAX465A	906	AAL544A	910	AAL518A	913	AAX515A		

916	CYJ492Y	Leyland Tiger TRCTL11/3R	Plaxton Paramount 3200	C50F	1983	Ex Stagecoach South, 1994
917	CYJ493Y	Leyland Tiger TRCTL11/3R	Plaxton Paramount 3200	C50F	1983	Ex Stagecoach South, 1994
935	A227MDD	Leyland Tiger TRCTL11/3R	Plaxton Paramount 3200	C51F	1984	Ex Cheltenham & Gloucester, 1994

940-951

		Dennis Javelin 11SDA2133	Plaxton Premiére Interurban DP47F	1994		

940	M940JBO	943	M943JBO	946	M946JBO	948	M948JBO	950	M950JBO
941	M941JBO	944	M944JBO	947	M947JBO	949	M949JBO	951	M951JBO
942	M942JBO	945	M945JBO						

952	H159EJU	Dennis Javelin 12SDA1907	Duple 320	C53FT	1991	Ex Whites of Calver, 1995
953	F243OFP	Dennis Javelin 12SDA1907	Duple 320	C53FT	1991	Ex Whites of Calver, 1995
954	HIL8410	Dennis Javelin 12SDA1907	Duple 320	C53FT	1991	Ex Whites of Calver, 1995
955	M101CCD	Dennis Javelin 11SDL2133	Plaxton Premiere Interurban DP47F	1994	Ex Stagecoach South, 1996
956	M107CCD	Dennis Javelin 11SDL2133	Plaxton Premiere Interurban DP47F	1994	Ex Stagecoach South, 1996

Previous Registrations:

A227MDD	A71KDU, 552OHU, A873MRW, YJV806			
AAL516A	SDW927Y		AAX488A	SDW918Y
AAL518A	SDW926Y		AAX489A	SDW928Y
AAL538A	SDW925Y		AAX515A	SDW929Y
AAL544A	SDW922Y		AAX516A	SDW930Y
AAL575A	SDW923Y		AAX529A	SDW931Y
AAX450A	SDW914Y		CYJ492Y	XUF531Y, 401DCD
AAX451A	SDW915Y		CYJ493Y	XUF532Y, 2880CD, 402DCD
AAX465A	SDW916Y		HIL8410	E759JAY
AAX466A	SDW917Y		WAX194S	CBV8S

RIBBLE

Stagecoach Ribble, Frenchwood Avenue, Preston, Lancashire, PR1 4LU.

Depots : George Street, Blackburn; Goodwin Street, Bolton; Colne Road, Burnley; Eaves Lane, Chorley; Pimlico Road, Clitheroe; Sidings Road, Fleetwood and Selbourne Street, Preston. **Outstations:** Bradley Fold; Cattle Market, Garstang; Ingleton and Cocker Avenue, Poulton-le-Fylde.

101	P973UBV	Volvo B10MA-55	Plaxton Première Interurban AC71F	1996	
102	P974UBV	Volvo B10MA-55	Plaxton Première Interurban AC71F	1996	
103	P975UBV	Volvo B10MA-55	Plaxton Première Interurban AC71F	1996	
104	P976UBV	Volvo B10MA-55	Plaxton Première Interurban AC71F	1996	
105	P977UBV	Volvo B10M-62	Plaxton Première Interurban DP51F	1996	
106	P978UBV	Volvo B10M-62	Plaxton Première Interurban DP51F	1996	
107	P979UBV	Volvo B10M-62	Plaxton Première Interurban DP51F	1996	

138-144
Dennis Javelin 11SDL2129 — Plaxton Première Interurban DP47F — 1993

138	L138BFV	140	L140BFV	142	L142BFV	143	L143BFV	144	L144BFV
139	L139BFV	141	L141BFV						

145-161
Dennis Javelin 11SDL2133 — Plaxton Première Interurban DP47F — 1993

145	L145BFV	149	L149BFV	153	L153BFV	157	L157BFV	159	L159CCW
146	L146BFV	150	L150BFV	155	L155BFV	158	L158BFV	161	L161CCW
148	L148BFV	151	L151BFV	156	L156BFV				

162-168
Dennis Javelin 11SDL2133 — Plaxton Première Interurban DP47F — 1994 — Ex Stagecoach South, 1994

162	L101SDY	164	L104SDY	166	L102SDY	167	L105SDY	168	L107SDY
163	L103SDY	165	L106SDY						

176-180
Dennis Lance SLF 11SDA3201 — Berkhof 2000 — B35F — 1996

176	N176LCK	177	N177LCK	178	N178LCK	179	N179LCK	180	N180LCK

181-196
Dennis Lance 11SDA3101 — Alexander PS — B39D* — 1992 — Ex East London, 1997
*This batch are in the process of being transferred. They are to be converted to single door before they enter service with Ribble.

181	J101WSC	185	J105WSC	188	J108WSC	191	J411WSC	194	J114WSC
182	J102WSC	186	J106WSC	189	J109WSC	192	J112WSC	195	J115WSC
183	J103WSC	187	J107WSC	190	J110WSC	193	J113WSC	196	J116WSC
184	J104WSC								

237-256
Volvo B6-9.9M — Alexander Dash — DP40F — 1993

237	L237CCW	240	L240CCW	251	L251CCK	253	L253CCK	256	L256CCK
239	L239CCW	241	L241CCK	252	L252CCK	255	L255CCK		

257-265
Volvo B6-9.9M — Alexander Dash — DP40F — 1993 — Ex Fife Scottish, 1994

257	L667MSF	259	L669MSF	261	L661MSF	263	L663MSF	265	L665MSF
258	L668MSF	260	L660HKS	262	L662MSF	264	L664MSF		

277-287
Volvo B6-9.9M — Alexander Dash — B40F — 1993 — Ex Cumberland 1994-96

277	L277JAO	279	L279JAO	283	L283JAO	285	L272LHH	287	L274LHH
278	L278JAO	281	L281JAO	284	L271LHH	286	L273LHH		

During 1996 Ribble have taken into stock two interesting batches of vehicles, and these are shown here. The upper picture shows the first of ten Plaxton-bodied articulated B10Ms for the Group. Four were allocated to Ribble and two each to Fife, Western Buses and East Midlands, though the East Midland pair are now with Fife after only the first entered service. Shown at the Blackpool end of the X61 service is 101, P973UBV. The lower picture shows one of five Berkhof-bodied Dennis Lance SLF buses purchased in conjunction with Greater Manchester PTE for the M10 service. Based at Bolton, these buses are dedicated to the route and offer low-floor entry with specific times when these vehicles will operate. Shown on the service is 176, N176LCK. *Paul Wigan/Tony Wilson*

The 1997 Stagecoach Bus Handbook

Most of the remaining Leyland Nationals are allocated to Bolton, the base where many north Manchester operations run. Shown passing Highland House in Victoria Street, Salford - opposite the former bus station - is 394, SHH394X, a Leyland National 2 new to Cumberland. *Tony Wilson*

293	J263KRN	Leyland Swift ST2R44C97A4	Reeve Burgess Harrier	B39F	1991	Ex Hyndburn 1996
294	J264KRN	Leyland Swift ST2R44C97A4	Reeve Burgess Harrier	B39F	1991	Ex Hyndburn 1996
295	G767CDU	Leyland Swift LBM6T/2RA	Reeve Burgess Harrier	B39F	1990	Ex Hyndburn 1996
296	H36YCW	Leyland Swift ST2R44C97A4	Reeve Burgess Harrier	B39F	1990	Ex Hyndburn 1996
297	H37YCW	Leyland Swift ST2R44C97A4	Reeve Burgess Harrier	B39F	1990	Ex Hyndburn 1996
298	H38YCW	Leyland Swift ST2R44C97A4	Reeve Burgess Harrier	B39F	1990	Ex Hyndburn 1996
299	H39YCW	Leyland Swift ST2R44C97A4	Reeve Burgess Harrier	B39F	1990	Ex Hyndburn 1996
301	CHH214T	Leyland National 10351B/1R		B44F	1978	Ex Cumberland, 1993
303	VKU80S	Leyland National 11351A/1R		B49F	1978	Ex East Midland, 1996
311	AHH206T	Leyland National 10351B/1R		B44F	1978	Ex Cumberland, 1993
312	CHH210T	Leyland National 10351B/1R		B44F	1979	Ex Cumberland, 1993
348	NLS988W	Leyland National 2 NL116L11/1R		B52F	1980	Ex Fife Scottish, 1996
357	KHH377W	Leyland National 2 NL116L11/1R		B52F	1980	Ex Cumberland, 1993
359	KHH375W	Leyland National 2 NL116L11/1R		B52F	1980	Ex Cumberland, 1993
370	HHH370V	Leyland National 2 NL116L11/1R		B52F	1980	Ex Cumberland, 1993
375	AHH209T	Leyland National 10351B/1R		B44F	1978	Ex Cumberland, 1993
380	NHH380W	Leyland National 2 NL116AL11/1R		B52F	1981	Ex Cumberland, 1993
384	CHH211T	Leyland National 10351B/1R		B44F	1978	Ex Cumberland, 1993
385	RRM384X	Leyland National 2 NL116AL11/1R		DP52F	1982	Ex Cumberland, 1993

386-394

Leyland National 2 NL116AL11/1R — B52F — 1981-82 Ex Cumberland, 1993

386	RRM386X	387	SHH387X	390	SHH390X	391	SHH391X	394	SHH394X

396	WAO396Y	Leyland National 2 NL116HLXB/1R		B52F	1982	Ex Cumberland, 1993
399	SHH388X	Leyland National 2 NL116AL11/1R		B52F	1982	Ex Cumberland, 1993

428-442

Volvo B10M-55 — Alexander PS — DP48F — 1994-95

428	M782PRS	431	M231TBV	434	M234TBV	437	M794PRS	440	M797PRS
429	M783PRS	432	M232TBV	435	M235TBV	438	M795PRS	441	M798PRS
430	M230TBV	433	M233TBV	436	M236TBV	439	M796PRS	442	M799PRS

The 1997 Stagecoach Bus Handbook

Ribble 434, M234TBV, is one the Volvo B10M/Alexanders displaced from the M10 service by the low floor Dennis Lances. In turn these have been introduced on the Clitheroe to Bolton service 225, recently extended into Manchester as the X25/X26, thus providing a new commuter service for Blackburn and Darwen residents. *Tony Wilson*

451	M451VCW	Volvo B10M-55	Alexander PS	B48F	1995			
452	M452VCW	Volvo B10M-55	Alexander PS	B48F	1995			
453	M453VCW	Volvo B10M-55	Alexander PS	B48F	1995			
454	M454VCW	Volvo B10M-55	Alexander PS	B48F	1995			
464	K740DAO	Volvo B10M-55	Alexander PS	B48F	1994	Ex Cumberland, 1996		

465-472
Volvo B10M-55 — Alexander PS — B49F — 1996

465	P128XCN	**467**	P130XCN	**469**	P132XCN	**471**	P134XCN	**472**	P135XCN
466	P129XCN	**468**	P131XCN	**470**	P133XCN				

568-591
Mercedes-Benz 709D — Alexander Sprint — B23F* — 1990 — 579/80 ex Magicbus, 1990 *568-572 are DP25F

568	G568PRM	**573**	G573PRM	**578**	G578PRM	**583**	G183PAO	**588**	G188PAO
569	G569PRM	**574**	G574PRM	**579**	G179PAO	**584**	G184PAO	**589**	G189PAO
570	G570PRM	**575**	G575PRM	**580**	G180PAO	**585**	G185PAO	**590**	G190PAO
571	G571PRM	**576**	G576PRM	**581**	G181PAO	**586**	G186PAO	**591**	G191PAO
572	G572PRM	**577**	G577PRM	**582**	G182PAO	**587**	G187PAO		

595-608
Mercedes-Benz 709D — Alexander Sprint — B25F — 1993

595	K115XHG	**598**	K118XHG	**600**	K120XHG	**605**	L125DRN	**608**	L128DRN
596	K116XHG	**599**	L119DRN						

610-628
Mercedes-Benz 709D — Alexander Sprint — B23F — 1992-93

610	K610UFR	**613**	K613UFR	**617**	K617UFR	**620**	K620UFR	**627**	K627UFR
611	K611UFR	**614**	K614UFR	**618**	K618UFR	**621**	K621UFR	**628**	K628UFR
612	K612UFR	**616**	K616UFR	**619**	K619UFR	**624**	K624UFR		

595-608 — Mercedes-Benz 709D — Alexander Sprint — B25F — 1993

595	K115XHG	598	K118XHG	600	K120XHG	605	L125DRN	608	L128DRN
596	K116XHG	599	L119DRN						

610-628 — Mercedes-Benz 709D — Alexander Sprint — B23F — 1992-93

610	K610UFR	613	K613UFR	617	K617UFR	620	K620UFR	627	K627UFR
611	K611UFR	614	K614UFR	618	K618UFR	621	K621UFR	628	K628UFR
612	K612UFR	616	K616UFR	619	K619UFR	624	K624UFR		

629-637 — Mercedes-Benz 709D — Alexander Sprint — B25F — 1993

629	L629BFV	631	L631BFV	633	L633BFV	635	L635BFV	637	K112XHG
630	L630BFV	632	L632BFV	634	L634BFV	636	L636BFV		

638-644 — Mercedes-Benz 709D — Alexander Sprint — B25F — 1996

638	N519BJA	640	N451VOD	642	N453VOD	643	N454VOD	644	N455VOD
639	N520BJA	641	N452VOD						

647-659 — Mercedes-Benz 709D — Alexander Sprint — B25F — 1996

647	N456VOD	650	N459VOD	653	N462VOD	656	N465VOD	658	N467VOD
648	N457VOD	651	N460VOD	654	N463VOD	657	N466VOD	659	N468VOD
649	N458VOD	652	N461VOD	655	N464VOD				

660-667 — Mercedes-Benz 709D — Alexander Sprint — B25F — 1996

660	N201LFV	662	N194LFV	664	N196LFV	666	N198LFV	667	N199LFV
661	N202LFV	663	N195LFV	665	N197LFV				

714-722 — Iveco TurboDaily 59.12 — Mellor — B27F — 1996 — Ex Hyndburn, 1996

714	N188GFR	716	N190GFR	718	N464HRN	720	L447FFR	722	L446FFR
715	N189GFR	717	N463HRN	719	L448FFR	721	L445FFR		

723	D860FOT	Iveco Daily 49.10	Robin Hood City Nipper	B19F	1980	Ex Hyndburn, 1996
726u	E26GCK	MCW MetroRider MF151/6	MCW	B23F	1987	Ex Hyndburn, 1996
730	F913HTU	Iveco Daily 49-10	Robin Hood City Nippy	B25F	1989	Ex Hyndburn, 1996
731	F914HTU	Iveco Daily 49-10	Robin Hood City Nippy	B25F	1989	Ex Hyndburn, 1996
732	F882CJC	Iveco Daily 49-10	Robin Hood City Nippy	B25F	1989	Ex Hyndburn, 1996
733	F883CJC	Iveco Daily 49-10	Robin Hood City Nippy	B25F	1989	Ex Hyndburn, 1996
734	G41XBK	Iveco Daily 49-10	Phoenix	B25F	1990	Ex Hyndburn, 1996
740	K740DAO	Volvo B10M-55	Alexander PS	B49F*	1992	Ex Cumberland, 1996
806	TRN806V	Leyland National 10351B/1R		B44F	1979	Ex Cumberland, 1993
812	TRN812V	Leyland National 10351B/1R		B44F	1979	Ex Cumberland, 1993

814-841 — Leyland National 2 NL106L11/1R — B44F — 1980 — 813/4/42 ex Cumberland, 1993

814	YRN814V	820	YRN820V	832	DBV832W	835	DBV835W	839	DBV839W
815	YRN815V	829	DBV829W	833	DBV833W	838	DBV838W	841	DBV841W
817	YRN817V	831	DBV831W						

846-877 — Leyland National 2 NL106AL11/1R — B44F — 1981 — 856/7 ex Cumberland, 1993

846	JCK846W	857	LFR857X	859	LFR859X	868	LFR868X	871	LFR871X
847	JCK847W	858	LFR858X	866	LFR866X	870	LFR870X	877	LFR877X
848	JCK848W								

878	RHG878X	Leyland National 2 NL116AL11/1R		B52F	1982	
879	RHG879X	Leyland National 2 NL116AL11/1R		B52F	1982	
881	RHG881X	Leyland National 2 NL116AL11/1R		B52F	1982	Ex Cumberland, 1993
886	RHG886X	Leyland National 2 NL116AL11/1R		B52F	1982	
889	ARN889Y	Leyland National 2 NL116HLXB/1R		B52F	1983	
890	ARN890Y	Leyland National 2 NL116HLXB/1R		B52F	1983	
895	CEO720W	Leyland National 2 NL116L11/1R		B49F	1980	Ex Cumberland, 1993
901	AFM1W	Leyland National 2 NL116AL11/2R East Lancs Greenway(1992)	B48F		1981	Ex Hyndburn, 1996
902	WPC316X	Leyland National 2 NL116AL11/2R East Lancs Greenway(1992)	B48F		1981	Ex Hyndburn, 1996
903	NOE595R	Leyland National 11351/1R	East Lancs Greenway(1992)	B48F	1981	Ex Hyndburn, 1996
904	CWX669T	Leyland National 2 NL116AL11/2R East Lancs Greenway(1992)	B48F		1981	Ex Hyndburn, 1996

The amalgamation of Hyndburn vehicles into the Ribble fleet is well under way, with re-numbering taking place from November, after the first Hyndburn vehicle had appeared in corporate livery. Shown here is 714, N188GFR, an Iveco TurboDaily 59.12 with locally-built Mellor bodywork. Within a few weeks of the start of 1997 beginning the Hyndburn vehicles will be dispersed to existing Ribble depots as the Accrington property is to be returned to the council within the first half of the year. *Mark Bailey.*

949	GCK49W	Leyland Leopard PSU4E/2R	East Lancashire	DP43F	1981	Ex Hyndburn, 1996
950	A50LHG	Dennis Falcon H SDA413	East Lancashire	DP43F	1984	Ex Hyndburn, 1996
951	B51XFV	Dennis Falcon H SDA413	East Lancashire	DP40F	1985	Ex Hyndburn, 1996
1055	VNH157W	Leyland Leopard PSU3F/4R	Duple Dominant IV Express	C49F	1981	Ex Hyndburn, 1996
1056	YKA8W	Leyland Leopard PSU3E/4R	Duple Dominant II Express	C49F	1981	Ex Hyndburn, 1996
1057	WWM576W	Leyland Leopard PSU3F/4R	Duple Dominant II Express	C49F	1980	Ex Hyndburn, 1996
1122	J122AHH	Volvo B10M-60	Plaxton Expressliner	C46FT	1992	Ex Cumberland, 1995
1123	J123AHH	Volvo B10M-60	Plaxton Expressliner	C46FT	1992	Ex Cumberland, 1995
1124	J124AHH	Volvo B10M-60	Plaxton Expressliner	C46FT	1992	Ex Cumberland, 1995
1145	PSU775	Leyland Tiger TRCTL11/3RZ	Duple Caribbean 2	C48FT	1985	Ex Cumberland, 1995
1149	PSU788	Leyland Tiger TRCTL11/3RZ	Duple Caribbean 2	C48FT	1985	Ex Cumberland, 1995
1152	B152WRN	Leyland Tiger TRCTL11/2R	Duple Laser 2	C49F	1985	
1157	927GTA	Leyland Tiger TRCTL11/3R	Duple Laser 2	C53F	1985	
1158	B158WRN	Leyland Tiger TRCTL11/3R	Duple Laser 2	C53F	1985	
1164	M164SCK	Volvo B10M-62	Plaxton Expressliner 2	C46FT	1994	
1165	M165SCK	Volvo B10M-62	Plaxton Expressliner 2	C46FT	1994	
1200	TCK200X	Leyland Atlantean AN68D/2R	East Lancashire	H50/36F	1982	Ex Lancaster, 1993
1201	SND432X	Leyland Atlantean AN68A/1R	Northern Counties	H43/32F	1981	Stagecoach Manchester, 1996
1202	FVR294V	Leyland Atlantean AN68A/1R	Northern Counties	H43/32F	1981	Stagecoach Manchester, 1996
1205	LFV205X	Leyland Atlantean AN68C/2R	East Lancashire	H50/36F	1981	Ex Lancaster, 1993
1206	LFV206X	Leyland Atlantean AN68C/2R	East Lancashire	H50/36F	1981	Ex Lancaster, 1993
1208	GBV108N	Leyland Atlantean AN68/2R	Alexander AL	H49/35F	1975	Ex Hyndburn, 1996
1209	GBV109N	Leyland Atlantean AN68/2R	Alexander AL	H49/35F	1975	Ex Hyndburn, 1996
1210	GBV110N	Leyland Atlantean AN68/2R	Alexander AL	H49/35F	1975	Ex Hyndburn, 1996
1211	GBV101N	Leyland Atlantean AN68/2R	Alexander AL	H49/35F	1974	Ex Hyndburn, 1996
1212	TCK212X	Leyland Atlantean AN68D/2R	East Lancashire	H50/36F	1982	Ex Lancaster, 1993
1213	WCK213Y	Leyland Atlantean AN68D/2R	East Lancashire	H50/36F	1982	Ex Lancaster, 1993
1214	A214MCK	Leyland Atlantean AN68D/2R	East Lancashire	H50/36F	1984	Ex Lancaster, 1993
1215	WCK215Y	Leyland Atlantean AN68D/2R	East Lancashire	H50/36F	1982	Ex Lancaster, 1993
1221	BFV221Y	Leyland Atlantean AN68D/2R	East Lancashire	DPH45/32F	1983	Ex Lancaster, 1993
1222	BFV222Y	Leyland Atlantean AN68D/2R	East Lancashire	DPH45/32F	1983	Ex Lancaster, 1993
1234	JKW286W	Leyland Atlantean AN68B/1R	Alexander AL	H45/32F	1981	Ex Hyndburn, 1996

1235-1239

		Leyland Atlantean AN68C/1R	East Lancashire	H46/30F	1980-81 Ex Hyndburn, 1996

1235	RGV40W	1236	RBJ36W	1237	RGV37W	1238	RGV38W	1239	RGV39W

1240	WWM920W	Leyland Atlantean AN68B/1R	Willowbrook	H45/33F	1980	Ex Hyndburn, 1996
1241	AFY191X	Leyland Atlantean AN68B/1R	Willowbrook	H45/33F	1982	Ex Hyndburn, 1996
1243	WWM933W	Leyland Atlantean AN68B/1R	Willowbrook	H45/33F	1981	Ex Hyndburn, 1996
1294	KHG194T	Leyland Atlantean AN68A/1R	East Lancashire	H45/33F	1978	Ex Hyndburn, 1996
1296	VCW196V	Leyland Atlantean AN68A/1R	East Lancashire	H45/33F	1979	Ex Hyndburn, 1996
1297	VCW197V	Leyland Atlantean AN68A/1R	East Lancashire	H45/33F	1979	Ex Hyndburn, 1996
1299	DBV199W	Leyland Atlantean AN68B/1R	East Lancashire	H45/33F	1980	Ex Hyndburn, 1996
1476	TRN476V	Leyland Atlantean AN68A/1R	Eastern Coach Works	H43/31F	1980	Ex Cumberland, 1993
1478	TRN478V	Leyland Atlantean AN68A/1R	Eastern Coach Works	H43/31F	1980	Ex Cumberland, 1993
1480	TRN480V	Leyland Atlantean AN68A/1R	Eastern Coach Works	H43/31F	1980	Ex Cumberland, 1993
1481	TRN481V	Leyland Atlantean AN68A/1R	Eastern Coach Works	H43/31F	1980	Ex Cumberland, 1993
2021	CBV21S	Bristol VRT/SL3/501(6LXB)	Eastern Coach Works	H43/31F	1977	
2030	DBV30W	Bristol VRT/SL3/6LXB	Eastern Coach Works	H43/31F	1980	
2034	URF662S	Bristol VRT/SL3/501(6LXB)	Eastern Coach Works	H43/31F	1977	Ex Potteries, 1982
2040	FDV813V	Bristol VRT/SL3/6LXB	Eastern Coach Works	H43/31F	1980	Ex Magicbus, 1990
2042	RRP858R	Bristol VRT/SL3/501	Eastern Coach Works	H43/31F	1977	Ex United Counties, 1990
2043	FDV817V	Bristol VRT/SL3/6LXB	Eastern Coach Works	H43/31F	1980	Ex Magicbus, 1990
2044	FDV833V	Bristol VRT/SL3/6LXB	Eastern Coach Works	H43/31F	1980	Ex Magicbus, 1990
2045	FDV784V	Bristol VRT/SL3/6LXB	Eastern Coach Works	H43/31F	1980	Ex Magicbus, 1990
2051	LFJ882W	Bristol VRT/SL3/6LXC	Eastern Coach Works	H43/31F	1980	Ex United Counties, 1993
2052	LFJ883W	Bristol VRT/SL3/6LXC	Eastern Coach Works	H43/31F	1980	Ex United Counties, 1993
2053	LFJ858W	Bristol VRT/SL3/6LXB	Eastern Coach Works	H43/31F	1980	Ex United Counties, 1993
2054	LFJ859W	Bristol VRT/SL3/6LXB	Eastern Coach Works	H43/31F	1980	Ex United Counties, 1993
2055	LFJ885W	Bristol VRT/SL3/6LXC	Eastern Coach Works	H43/31F	1980	Ex United Counties, 1993
2056	LFJ866W	Bristol VRT/SL3/6LXB	Eastern Coach Works	H43/31F	1980	Ex United Counties, 1993
2057	LFJ861W	Bristol VRT/SL3/6LXB	Eastern Coach Works	H43/31F	1980	Ex United Counties, 1993
2058	LFJ884W	Bristol VRT/SL3/6LXC	Eastern Coach Works	H43/31F	1980	Ex United Counties, 1993
2076	UWV622S	Bristol VRT/SL3/6LXB	Eastern Coach Works	O43/31F	1980	Ex East Kent, 1994

2101-2132

		Leyland Olympian ONLXB/1R*	Eastern Coach Works	H45/32F	1981-83 *2124-30 are ONLXBT/1R

2101	GFR101W	2107	JFR7W	2113	JFR13W	2121	OFV21X	2127	VRN827Y
2102	JFR2W	2108	JFR8W	2114	OFV14X	2122	OFV22X	2128	VRN828Y
2103	JFR3W	2109	JFR9W	2115	OFV15X	2123	OFV23X	2129	VRN829Y
2104	JFR4W	2110	JFR10W	2118	OFV18X	2124	SCK224X	2130	VRN830Y
2105	JFR5W	2111	JFR11W	2119	OFV19X	2125	SCK225X	2131	DBV131Y
2106	JFR6W	2112	JFR12W	2120	OFV20X	2126	SCK226X	2132	DBV132Y

2135	CWR525Y	Leyland Olympian ONLXB/1R	Eastern Coach Works	H45/32F	1983	Ex Hyndburn, 1996
2136	CWR526Y	Leyland Olympian ONLXB/1R	Eastern Coach Works	H45/32F	1983	Ex Hyndburn, 1996

2137-2152

		Leyland Olympian ONLXB/1R	Eastern Coach Works	H45/32F	1983-84

2137	DBV137Y	2142	A142MRN	2143	A143MRN	2145	A145MRN	2152	B152TRN

2156-2178

		Leyland Olympian ONLXB/1R	Eastern Coach Works	DPH41/26F	1984-85

2156	A156OFR	2158	A158OFR	2171	C171ECK	2173	C173ECK	2178	C178ECK
2157	A157OFR	2159	A159OFR	2172	C172ECK				

2187-2197

		Leyland Olympian ON2R50G16Z4 Alexander RL	H47/30F	1989-90 *2187/8 are DPH51/31F

2187	G187JHG	2193	H193WFR	2195	H195WFR	2196	H196WFR	2197	H197WFR
2188	G188JHG								

2198	J198HFR	Leyland Olympian ON2R56G13Z4 Alexander RL	DPH43/27F	1991

2213-2222

		Leyland Olympian ONLXB/1R	Alexander RL	H45/32F	1984-85 Ex Highland Scottish, 1991

2213	A978OST	2215	B891UAS	2220	B896UAS	2221	B897UAS	2222	B898UAS
2214	A979OST	2218	B894UAS						

The 1997 Stagecoach Bus Handbook

2224-2235 — Volvo Olympian YN2RV18Z4, Northern Counties Palatine, H49/33F, 1996

2224	P224VCK	2227	P227VCK	2230	P230VCK	2232	P232VCK	2234	P234VCK
2225	P225VCK	2228	P228VCK	2231	P231VCK	2233	P233VCK	2235	P235VCK
2226	P226VCK	2229	P229VCK						

2236-2245 — Volvo Olympian YN2RV18Z4, Alexander RL, H45/27F, 1996 — 2240-2245 on loan from Stagecoach South

2236	P260VPN	2238	P262VPN	2240	P270VPN	2242	P272VPN	2244	P274VPN
2237	P261VPN	2239	P263VPN	2241	P271VPN	2243	P273VPN	2245	P275VPN

Previous Registrations:

927GTA	B157WRN		PSU775	B148ACK		PSU788	B146ACK

Livery: National Express 1122-4/64/5

Two pictures of different double-deck buses from the Ribble fleet. The upper picture is of Leyland Atlantean 1214, A214MCK, which carries an interesting and relevant advert as the vehicle sets out from Blackpool for Blackburn. The East Lancashire-bodied vehicle joined Ribble from Lancaster. 1997 sees the transfer of Lancaster-based operations from Ribble to Cumberland Management. The lower picture is of newly repainted Bristol VR 2042, RRP858R, based at Clitheroe. It is seen leaving Blackburn bus station bound for Preston.
David Cole/Malc McDonald

SELKENT

South East London and Kent Bus Company, 180 Bromley Road,
Catford, London SE6 2XA

Depots : Hastings Road, Bromley; Bromley Road, Catford and Pettman Crescent, Plumstead.

DT28-55

						Dennis Dart 8.5SDL3003	Carlyle Dartline		B28F*		1990		*28/30/1/55 are DP28F	

28	49CLT	32	VLT240	35	G35TGW	38	G38TGW	40	G40TGW
30	G30TGW	33	G33TGW	36	G36TGW	39	G39TGW	55	WLT575
31	G31TGW	34	G34TGW	37	G37TGW				

DW59-71

Dennis Dart 8.5SDL3003   Wright Handy-bus   B28F   1991

59	JDZ2359	61	JDZ2361	63	JDZ2363	65	JDZ2365	71	JDZ2371
60	JDZ2360	62	JDZ2362	64	JDZ2364				

601-640

Dennis Dart 9.8SDL3054   Alexander Dash   B40F   1995-96

601	N601KGF	609	N609KGF	617	P617PGP	625	P625PGP	633	P633PGP
602	N602KGF	610	N610KGF	618	P618PGP	626	P626PGP	634	P634PGP
603	N603KGF	611	N611LGC	619	P619PGP	627	P627PGP	636	P636PGP
604	N604KGF	612	N612LGC	620	P620PGP	628	P628PGP	637	P637PGP
605	N605KGF	613	N613LGC	621	P621PGP	629	P629PGP	638	P638PGP
606	N606KGF	614	N614LGC	622	P622PGP	630	P630PGP	639	P639PGP
607	N607KGF	615	P615PGP	623	P623PGP	631	P631PGP	640	P640PGP
608	N608KGF	616	P616PGP	624	P624PGP	632	P632PGP		

While the Dennis Lances with East London are moving out, those with Selkent remain. These have bodywork by Plaxton to the Verde design and are designated LV class (Lance Verde). Pictured working the 208 LRT service is LV11, L211YAG. The lower picture shows one of the diminishing number of Leyland Titans, which are being displaced by new Volvo Olympians. T1036, A636THV was photographed working LRT service 166 and is one of the Titans Leyland built at Workington. The factory where the first thirteen Titans were built by Leyland - from Park Royal kits - is now the site of Cumberland's West Cumbria depot.

Some thirty-nine Alexander-bodied Dennis Darts now operate for Selkent, of which 631, P631PGP is seen at Catford heading for Crystal Palace on route 202. This batch of Dash bodies does not have the 'v' formation of windscreen previously supplied and marks the transitional phase before the introduction of the ALX200 body style.
Malc McDonald

During 1996 the management of Selkent changed with East London now performing the support function. Pictured near The Oval is Leyland Olympian L98, C98CHM. This batch were one of the last to be bodied by Eastern Coach Works. *Malc McDonald*

L7-145

		Leyland Olympian ONLXB/1RH		Eastern Coach Works		H42/26D		1986		
7	C807BYY	53	C53CHM	76	C76CHM	107	C107CHM	125	D125FYM
9	C809BYY	54	C54CHM	77	C77CHM	108	C108CHM	126	D126FYM
10	C810BYY	55	C55CHM	80	C80CHM	109	C109CHM	127	D127FYM
11	C811BYY	57	C57CHM	81	C81CHM	110	C110CHM	128	D128FYM
12	C812BYY	60	C60CHM	82	C82CHM	111	C111CHM	129	D129FYM
15	C815BYY	61	C61CHM	83	C83CHM	112	C112CHM	130	D130FYM
18	C818BYY	62	C62CHM	86	C86CHM	114	C114CHM	131	D131FYM
19	C819BYY	64	C64CHM	87	C87CHM	115	C115CHM	132	D132FYM
23	C23CHM	67	C67CHM	91	WLT491	116	C116CHM	133	D133FYM
28	C28CHM	68	C68CHM	92	C92CHM	117	C117CHM	134	D134FYM
29	C29CHM	69	C69CHM	94	C94CHM	118	C118CHM	136	D136FYM
30	C30CHM	70	C70CHM	97	C97CHM	119	C119CHM	137	D137FYM
42	C42CHM	71	C71CHM	98	C98CHM	120	C120CHM	141	D141FYM
43	C43CHM	72	C72CHM	103	C103CHM	121	C121CHM	142	D142FYM
44	C44CHM	73	C73CHM	104	C104CHM	122	C122CHM	144	D144FYM
48	C45CHM	74	C74CHM	105	C105CHM	123	D123FYM	145	D145FYM
51	C51CHM	75	C75CHM	106	C106CHM	124	D124FYM		

L260	VLT20	Leyland Olympian ONLXB/1RH	Eastern Coach Works	DPH42/26D	1986
L262	VLT14	Leyland Olympian ONLXB/1RH	Eastern Coach Works	DPH42/26D	1986
L263	D367JJD	Leyland Olympian ONLXB/1RH	Eastern Coach Works	DPH42/26D	1986

Fifty two Volvo Olympians joined the Selkent fleet in 1995 and these carry Northern Counties Palatine bodywork. Photographed outside County Hall is 321, N321HGK. Imaginatively, the company were able to utilise N353HGK to fill the gap left by N333HGK being unavailable. *Richard Godfrey*

301-352   Volvo Olympian YN2RV18Z4   Northern Counties Palatine I H45/23D   1995

301	M301DGP	312	M312DGP	323	N323HGK	333	N353HGK	343	N343HGK
302	M302DGP	313	M313DGP	324	N324HGK	334	N334HGK	344	N344HGK
303	M303DGP	314	M314DGP	325	N325HGK	335	N335HGK	345	N345HGK
304	M304DGP	315	M315DGP	326	N326HGK	336	N336HGK	346	N346HGK
305	M305DGP	316	M316DGP	327	N327HGK	337	N337HGK	347	N347HGK
306	M306DGP	317	M317DGP	328	N328HGK	338	N338HGK	348	N348HGK
307	M307DGP	318	M318DGP	329	N329HGK	339	N339HGK	349	N349HGK
308	M308DGP	319	M319DGP	330	N330HGK	340	N340HGK	350	N350HGK
309	M309DGP	320	M320DGP	331	N331HGK	341	N341HGK	351	N351HGK
310	M310DGP	321	N321HGK	332	N332HGK	342	N342HGK	352	N352HGK
311	M311DGP	322	N322HGK						

LV1-12   Dennis Lance 11SDA3112   Plaxton Verde   B42D   1994

1	L201YAG	4	L204YAG	7	L207YAG	9	L209YAG	11	L211YAG
2	L202YAG	5	L205YAG	8	L208YAG	10	L210YAG	12	WLT461
3	L203YAG	6	L206YAG						

MRL141-176   Optare MetroRider MR03   Optare   B26F   1990-91

141	H141UUA	148	H148UUA	154	H154UUA	165	H165WWT	171	H171WWT
142	H142UUA	149	H149UUA	160	H160WWT	166	H166WWT	172	H172WWT
143	H143UUA	150	H150UUA	161	H161WWT	167	H167WWT	173	H173WWT
145	H145UUA	151	H151UUA	162	H162WWT	168	H168WWT	174	H174WWT
146	H146UUA	152	H152UUA	163	H163WWT	169	H169WWT	175	H175WWT
147	H147UUA	153	H153UUA	164	H564WWR	170	H170WWT	176	H176WWT

MT4t	F394DHL	Mercedes-Benz 709D		Reeve Burgess Beaver	B23F	1988		
MW2	HDZ2602	Mercedes-Benz 811D		Wright NimBus	B19FL	1989		
MW8	HDZ2608	Mercedes-Benz 811D		Wright NimBus	B19FL	1989		
MW14	HDZ2614	Mercedes-Benz 811D		Wright NimBus	B19FL	1989		

T9-230

Leyland Titan TNLXB2RRSp — Park Royal — H44/26D* — 1978-80 * Several are H44/22D
Ex East London, 1996

9	WYV9T	20	WYV20T	38	WYV38T	140	CUL140V	214	CUL214V
10	WYV10T	26	WYV26T	40	WYV40T	175	CUL175V	222	CUL222V
17	WYV17T	37	WYV37T	66	WYV66T	193	CUL193V	223	CUL223V
19	WYV19T								

T230	EYE230V	Leyland Titan TNLXB2RR	Park Royal	H44/26D	1981	Ex East London, 1996
T267	GYE267W	Leyland Titan TNLXB2RR	Park Royal/Leyland	H44/26D	1981	

T368-822

Leyland Titan TNLXB2RR — Leyland — H44/24D — 1981-82

368	KYV368X	740	OHV740Y	785	OHV785Y	810	OHV810Y	816	RYK816Y
447	KYV447X	748	OHV748Y	791	OHV791Y	812	OHV812Y	818	RYK818Y
616	NUW616Y	770	OHV770Y	797	OHV797Y	813	OHV813Y	821	RYK821Y
680	OHV680Y	771	OHV771Y	804	OHV804Y	814	OHV814Y	822	RYK822Y
721	OHV721Y	772	OHV772Y	805	OHV805Y	815	RYK815Y		

T828-999

Leyland Titan TNLXB2RR* — Leyland — H44/24D — 1983-84 *T877/80 are TNTL112RR;
T881/2/3/5 are TNL112RR

828	A828SUL	842	A842SUL	856	A856SUL	880	A880SUL	950	A950SYE
829	A829SUL	843	A843SUL	857	A857SUL	881	A881SUL	951	A951SYE
830	A830SUL	845	A845SUL	858	A858SUL	882	A882SUL	961	A961SYE
834	A834SUL	847	A847SUL	859	A859SUL	883	A883SUL	976	A976SYE
836	A836SUL	848	A848SUL	866	A866SUL	885	A885SUL	978	A978SYE
837	A837SUL	850	A850SUL	868	A868SUL	918	A918SYE	988	A988SYE
838	A838SUL	854	A854SUL	874	A874SUL	925	A925SYE	996	A996SYE
841	A841SUL	855	A855SUL	877	A877SUL	926	A926SYE	999	A999SYE

T1003-1077

Leyland Titan TNLXB2RR — Leyland — H44/24D — 1984

1003	A603THV	1028	A628THV	1032	A632THV	1045	A645THV	1067	A67THX
1013	A613THV	1029	A629THV	1034	A634THV	1048	A648THV	1076	A76THX
1025	A625THV	1030	A630THV	1035	A635THV	1052	A652THV	1077	A77THX
1027	A627THV	1031	A631THV	1036	A636THV	1065	A65THX		

T1079-1125

Leyland Titan TNLXB2RR — Leyland — H44/24D — 1984

1079	B79WUV	1092	B92WUV	1101	B101WUV	1113	B113WUV	1119	B119WUV
1081	B81WUV	1093	B93WUV	1103	B103WUV	1114	B114WUV	1121	B121WUV
1083	B83WUV	1096	B96WUV	1106	B106WUV	1115	B115WUV	1122	B122WUV
1084	B84WUV	1097	B97WUV	1108	B108WUV	1116	B116WUV	1124	B124WUV
1089	B89WUV	1099	B99WUV	1110	B110WUV	1117	B117WUV	1125	B125WUV
1091	B91WUV	1100	B100WUV	1112	B112WUV	1118	B118WUV		

3001-3008

Leyland Titan TNLXB2RRSp — Park Royal — H44/26D — 1979-80

3001	CUL137V	3003	CUL114V	3005	CUL86V	3007	CUL120V	3008	CUL130V
3002	CUL98V	3004	CUL224V	3006	CUL142V				

Previous Registrations:

49CLT	G29TGW	VLT20	D260FYM	WLT491	C91CHM
D367JJD	D263FYL, VLT9	VLT240	G32TGW	WLT575	G41TGW
VLT14	D262FYL	WLT461	L212YAG		

Note: All vehicles were formerly London Buses, 1994 unless indicated otherwise or new later.

Livery: Red; corporate livery: MT4, 3001-8.

STAGECOACH SOUTH

Stagecoach (South) Ltd, Lewes Enterprise Centre, 112 Malling Street,
Lewes, East Sussex, BN7 2RB

Depots and outstations:
Hampshire Bus: Mill Lane, Alton; Livingstone Road, Andover; New Market Square, Basingstoke; Abbey Mill, Bishops Waltham; Marlborough; Bedford Road, Petersfield; Hazeldown Farm, Stockbridge, The Broadway, Winchester.
Hants & Surrey: Halimote Road, Aldershot; Guildford; Haselmere; Lindford; Bedford Road, Petersfield.
Sussex Coastline: Southgate, Chichester; Henfield; Littlehampton; Langstone Point, Portsmouth; Library Place, Worthing.
South Coast Buses: Cavendish Place, Eastbourne; Beaufort Road, Silverhill, St Leonards; Eastgate Street, Lewes; Littlestone Road, New Romney; Rye; Claremont Road, Seaford; Bell Lane, Uckfield.
East Kent: Brunswick Road, Ashford; St George's Lane, Canterbury; South Street, Deal; Russell Street, Dover; Kent Road, Cheriton, Folkestone; High Street, Herne Bay; Littlestone Road, New Romney; Margate Road, Westwood, Thanet.
Sussex Bus: Southgate, Chichester.

1u	H101EKR	Iveco Daily 49.10	Phoenix	B23F	1991	Ex East Kent, 1993
3	H103EKR	Iveco Daily 49.10	Phoenix	B23F	1991	Ex East Kent, 1993
4u	H104EKR	Iveco Daily 49.10	Phoenix	B23F	1991	Ex East Kent, 1993
12u	J112LKO	Iveco Daily 49.10	Carlyle Dailybus 2	B23F	1991	Ex East Kent, 1993
25w	F25PSL	Iveco Daily 49.10	Robin Hood City Nippy	B23F	1989	Ex Stagecoach, 1990
30w	G30PSR	Iveco Daily 49.10	Phoenix	B23F	1989	Ex Stagecoach, 1990
37w	G37SSR	Iveco Daily 49.10	Phoenix	B23F	1989	Ex Stagecoach, 1990
39w	G39SSR	Iveco Daily 49.10	Phoenix	B23F	1989	Ex Stagecoach, 1990

100-118		Leyland National 11351A/1R		B52F	1979	

100	AYJ100T	103	AYJ103T	110	ENJ910V	113	ENJ913V	116	ENJ916V
101	AYJ101T	107	AYJ107T	111	ENJ911V	114	ENJ914V	117	ENJ917V
102	AYJ102T	109	ENJ909V	112	ENJ912V	115	ENJ915V	118	ENJ918V

The East Kent operation of Stagecoach South now run the remaining Iveco minibuses though less than a hand-full remain. One of these is 3, H103EKR, seen in Ashford while heading for the Town Centre.
Malc McDonald

119-126   Leyland National 2 NL116L11/1R   B52F   1980   124 fitted with TL11 engine

119	GYJ919V	121	GYJ921V	123	HFG923V	125	OUF262W	126	SYC852
120	GYJ920V	122	GYJ922V	124	JNJ194V				

127	FDV830V	Leyland National 2 NL116L11/1R		B52F	1980
128	FDV831V	Leyland National 2 NL116L11/1R		B52F	1980

129-138   Leyland National 2 NL116AL11/1R   B49F*   1982   *129 is B45F
130 is fitted with TL11 engine

129	HUF603X	131	HUF625X	133	HUF639X	135	HUF604X	137	HUF592X
130	HUF579X	132	PMT199X	134	HUF451X	136	HUF593X	138	HUF626X

139	FDV829V	Leyland National 2 NL116L11/1R	B48F	1980	
140	CPO98W	Leyland National 2 NL106L11/1R	B41F	1980	Ex Portsmouth, 1990
142	CPO100W	Leyland National 2 NL106L11/1R	DP40F	1980	Ex Portsmouth, 1990
143	ERV115W	Leyland National 2 NL106AL11/1R	B41F	1981	Ex Portsmouth, 1990
144	ERV116W	Leyland National 2 NL106AL11/1R	B41F	1981	Ex Portsmouth, 1990
145	ERV117W	Leyland National 2 NL106AL11/1R	B41F	1981	Ex Portsmouth, 1990
146	ERV118W	Leyland National 2 NL106AL11/1R	B41F	1981	Ex Portsmouth, 1990
147	BCW827V	Leyland National 2 NL106L11/1R	B44F	1980	Ex Ribble, 1994
148	UFG48S	Leyland National 11351A/2R	B52F	1977	
149	JCK849W	Leyland National 2 NL106AL11/1R	B44F	1981	Ex Ribble, 1994
152	WPR152S	Leyland National 11351A/1R	B49F	1978	
154	VOD604S	Leyland National 11351A/1R	B52F	1978	Ex Devon General, 1987
155	VOD605S	Leyland National 11351A/1R	B52F	1978	Ex Devon General, 1987
157	UHG757R	Leyland National 11351A/1R	B49F	1977	Ex Ribble, 1986
159	YRN816V	Leyland National 2 NL106L11/1R	B44F	1980	Ex Ribble, 1994
160	YRN821V	Leyland National 2 NL106L11/1R	B44F	1980	Ex Ribble, 1994
162	FPR62V	Leyland National 11351A/1R	B49F	1980	
163	PCD73R	Leyland National 11351A/1R	B49F	1976	
164	VFX984S	Leyland National 11351A/1R	B49F	1978	
169	WYJ169S	Leyland National 11351A/2R(DAF)	B48F	1978	
173	YCD73T	Leyland National 11351A/2R	B52F	1978	
174	YCD74T	Leyland National 11351A/2R	B48F	1978	
176	YCD76T	Leyland National 11351A/2R	B48F	1978	
177	YCD77T	Leyland National 11351A/2R	B48F	1978	
179	PCD79R	Leyland National 11351A/1R	B49F	1977	
180	PCD80R	Leyland National 11351A/1R	B49F	1977	

The number of Leyland Nationals with Stagecoach South has reduced to less than a hundred as new vehicles enter service. Shown in Hastings is 142, CPO100W, one of 31 National 2s in service. This vehicle joined the fleet from Portsmouth Transport in 1990. *Malc McDonald*

182	YCD82T	Leyland National 11351A/2R		B48F	1978	
186	CBV776S	Leyland National 11351A/1R		B49F	1978	Ex Ribble, 1986
189	AYJ89T	Leyland National 11351A/1R		B52F	1979	
190	TEL490R	Leyland National 11351A/1R		DP48F	1977	
191	AYJ91T	Leyland National 11351A/1R		B52F	1979	
192	AYJ92T	Leyland National 11351A/1R		B52F	1979	
195	AYJ95T	Leyland National 11351A/1R		B52F	1979	
196	RJT146R	Leyland National 11351A/1R		B49F	1977	
197	AYJ97T	Leyland National 11351A/1R		B52F	1979	

201-206 Leyland Olympian ON2R56G13Z4 Alexander RL   H51/36F 1988

201	F601MSL	203	F603MSL	204	F604MSL	205	F605MSL	206	F606MSL
202	F602MSL								

207-214 Leyland Olympian ON2R56G13Z4 Alexander RL   DPH51/31F 1989

207	G807RTS	209	G809RTS	211	G211SSL	213	G213SSL	214	G214SSL
208	G808RTS	210	G210SSL	212	G212SSL				

215-219 Leyland Olympian ON2R56G13Z4 Alexander RL   H51/34F 1990

215	H815CBP	216	H816CBP	217	H817CBP	218	H818CBP	219	H819CBP

220	J720GAP	Leyland Olympian ON2R56G13Z4 Alexander RL	DPH47/27F	1992	
221	J721GAP	Leyland Olympian ON2R56G13Z4 Alexander RL	DPH47/27F	1992	
222	J722GAP	Leyland Olympian ON2R56G13Z4 Alexander RL	DPH47/27F	1992	
223	J623GCR	Leyland Olympian ON2R56G13Z4 Alexander RL	H47/30F	1991	
224	J624GCR	Leyland Olympian ON2R56G13Z4 Alexander RL	H47/30F	1991	

225-234 Leyland Olympian ON2R56G13Z4 Alexander RL   H51/34F 1990

225	G705TCD	227	G707TCD	229	G709TCD	231	G701TCD	233	G703TCD
226	G706TCD	228	G708TCD	230	G710TCD	232	G702TCD	234	G704TCD

235-240 Leyland Olympian ON2R50G13Z4 Alexander RL   DPH43/27F 1992

235	K235NHC	237	K237NHC	238	K238NHC	239	K239NHC	240	K240NHC
236	K236NHC								

241-250 Volvo Olympian YN2RV18Z4 Northern Counties Palatine II DPH43/25F 1993

241	L241SDY	243	L243SDY	245	L245SDY	247	L247SDY	249	L249SDY
242	L242SDY	244	L244SDY	246	L246SDY	248	L248SDY	250	L250SDY

254	K714ASC	Leyland Olympian ON2R50G13Z4 Alexander RL	H47/32F	1992	Ex Fife Scottish, 1994
255	K715ASC	Leyland Olympian ON2R50G13Z4 Alexander RL	H47/32F	1992	Ex Fife Scottish, 1994
256	K716ASC	Leyland Olympian ON2R50G13Z4 Alexander RL	H47/32F	1992	Ex Fife Scottish, 1994
257	K717ASC	Leyland Olympian ON2R50G13Z4 Alexander RL	H47/32F	1992	Ex Fife Scottish, 1994

264-275 Volvo Olympian Alexander RL   H51/36F 1996-97 270-275 are on loan to Ribble

264	P264VPN	267	P267VPN	270	P270VPN	272	P272VPN	274	P274VPN
265	P265VPN	268	P268VPN	271	P271VPN	273	P273VPN	275	P275VPN
266	P266VPN	269	P269VPN						

341-359 Volvo Olympian YN2RC16V3 Alexander RL   DPH47/28F 1996

341	N341MPN	345	N345MPN	349	N349MPN	353	N353MPN	357	N357MPN
342	N342MPN	346	N346MPN	350	N350MPN	354	N354MPN	358	N358MPN
343	N343MPN	347	N347MPN	351	N351MPN	355	N355MPN	359	N359MPN
344	N344MPN	348	N348MPN	352	N352MPN	356	N356MPN		

360-380 Volvo Olympian YN2RC16V3 Alexander RL   H47/32F 1995

360	N360LPN	365	N365LPN	369	N369LPN	373	N373LPN	377	N377LPN
361	N361LPN	366	N366LPN	370	N370LPN	374	N374LPN	378	N378LPN
362	N362LPN	367	N367LPN	371	N371LPN	375	N375LPN	379	N379LPN
363	N363LPN	368	N368LPN	372	N372LPN	376	N376LPN	380	N380LPN
364	N364LPN								

381-399 — Volvo Olympian YN2RC16V3 — Alexander RL — DPH47/28F — 1995-96

381	N381LPN	385	N385LPN	389	N389LPN	393	N393LPN	397	N397LPN
382	N382LPN	386	N386LPN	390	N390LPN	394	N394LPN	398	N398LPN
383	N383LPN	387	N387LPN	391	N391LPN	395	N395LPN	399	N399LPN
384	N384LPN	388	N388LPN	392	N392LPN	396	N396LPN		

400	400DCD	Volvo B6-9.9M	Alexander Dash	DP35F	1994
401	401DCD	Volvo B6-9.9M	Alexander Dash	DP35F	1994
402	402DCD	Volvo B6-9.9M	Alexander Dash	DP35F	1994
403	403DCD	Volvo B6-9.9M	Alexander Dash	DP31F	1994

422-450 — Bristol VRT/SL3/6LXB — Eastern Coach Works — H43/31F — 1979-81

422	FDV818V	438	KRU838W	446	LFJ874W	448	LFJ870W	450	LFJ880W
435	FDV839V	444	KRU844W	447	LFJ881W	449	LFJ875W		

451-455 — Dennis Dart SFD412 — Alexander Dash — DP40F — 1996

451	N451PAP	452	N452PAP	453	N453PAP	454	N454PAP	455	N455PAP

456-467 — Dennis Dart SFD412 — Alexander Dash — B40F — 1996

456	N456PAP	459	N459PAP	462	N462PAP	464	N464PAP	466	N466PAP
457	N457PAP	460	N460PAP	463u	N463PAP	465	N465PAP	467	N467PAP
458	N458PAP	461	N461PAP						

473w	D473WPM	Iveco Daily 49.10	Robin Hood City Nippy	B25F	1987	Ex Alder Valley, 1992
477w	E201EPB	Iveco Daily 49.10	Robin Hood City Nippy	B25F	1987	Ex Alder Valley, 1992
479w	E203EPB	Iveco Daily 49.10	Robin Hood City Nippy	B25F	1987	Ex Alder Valley, 1992
485w	F695OPA	Iveco Daily 49.10	Carlyle Dailybus 2	B23F	1988	Ex Alder Valley, 1992
491w	G421RYJ	Iveco Daily 49.10	Phoenix	B23F	1990	
494w	G864BPD	Iveco Daily 49.10	Carlyle Dailybus 2	B23F	1989	Ex Alder Valley, 1992

501-580 — Dennis Dart 9.8SDL3017 — Alexander Dash — B41F* — 1991-92 — *535-80 are B40F

501	J501GCD	517	J517GCD	533	J533GCD	549	J549GCD	565	K565NHC
502	J502GCD	518	J518GCD	534	J534GCD	550	J550GCD	566	K566NHC
503	J503GCD	519	J519GCD	535	J535GCD	551	J551GCD	567	K567NHC
504	J504GCD	520	J520GCD	536	J536GCD	552	J552GCD	568	K568NHC
505	J505GCD	521	J521GCD	537	J537GCD	553	K553NHC	569	K569NHC
506	J506GCD	522	J522GCD	538	J538GCD	554	K554NHC	570	K570NHC
507	J507GCD	523	J523GCD	539	J539GCD	555	K655NHC	571	K571NHC
508	J508GCD	524	J524GCD	540	J540GCD	556	K556NHC	572	K572NHC
509	J509GCD	525	J525GCD	541	J541GCD	557	K557NHC	573	K573NHC
510	J510GCD	526	J526GCD	542	J542GCD	558	K558NHC	574	K574NHC
511	J511GCD	527	J527GCD	543	J543GCD	559	K559NHC	575	K575NHC
512	J512GCD	528	J528GCD	544	J544GCD	560	K660NHC	576	K576NHC
513	J513GCD	529	J529GCD	545	J545GCD	561	K561NHC	577	K577NHC
514	J514GCD	530	J530GCD	546	J546GCD	562	K562NHC	578	K578NHC
515	J515GCD	531	J531GCD	547	J547GCD	563	K563NHC	579	K579NHC
516	J516GCD	532	J532GCD	548	J548GCD	564	K564NHC	580	K580NHC

581	J701YRM	Dennis Dart 9.8DL3017	Alexander Dash	B41F	1991	Ex Cumberland, 1992
582	J702YRM	Dennis Dart 9.8DL3017	Alexander Dash	B41F	1991	Ex Cumberland, 1992
583	J703YRM	Dennis Dart 9.8DL3017	Alexander Dash	B41F	1992	Ex Cumberland, 1992

584-588 — Dennis Dart 9.8DL3017 — Alexander Dash — B40F — 1992

584	K584ODY	585	K585ODY	586	K586ODY	587	K587ODY	588	K588ODY

601-605 — Volvo B10M-55 — Northern Counties Paladin — DP49F — 1994

601	L601VCD	602	L602VCD	603	L603VCD	604	404DCD	605	405DCD

A sparkling example of the standard Volvo B10M is Eastbourne's 638, M638BCD. One of fifteen of the Alexander-bodied models, it is seen working the coastal service 728 to Brighton.
Phillip Stephenson

606-635

Volvo B10M-55   Alexander PS   DP48F   1994

606	406DCD	612	412DCD	618	L618TDY	624	L624TDY	630	L630TDY
607	407DCD	613	413DCD	619	419DCD	625	L625TDY	631	L631TDY
608	408DCD	614	414DCD	620	420DCD	626	L626TDY	632	L632TDY
609	L609TDY	615	M615APN	621	421DCD	627	L627TDY	633	L633TDY
610	410DCD	616	L616TDY	622	422DCD	628	L628TDY	634	L634TDY
611	411DCD	617	L617TDY	623	423DCD	629	L629TDY	635	L635TDY

636-652

Volvo B10M-55   Alexander PS   DP48F   1995

636	M636BCD	639	M639BCD	642	N642LPN	645	N645LPN	651	M651BCD
637	M637BCD	640	N640LPN	643	N643LPN	650	M650BCD	652	M652BCD
638	M638BCD	641	N641LPN	644	N644LPN				

655	415DCD	Volvo B10M-55	Alexander PS	DP48F	1994	Ex Ribble, 1994
656	416DCD	Volvo B10M-55	Alexander PS	DP48F	1994	Ex Ribble, 1994
657	417DCD	Volvo B10M-55	Alexander PS	DP48F	1994	Ex Ribble, 1994
658	418DCD	Volvo B10M-55	Alexander PS	DP48F	1994	Ex Ribble, 1994
659	K789DAO	Volvo B10M-55	Alexander PS	DP48F	1993	Ex Cumberland, 1994
660	K790DAO	Volvo B10M-55	Alexander PS	DP48F	1993	Ex Cumberland, 1994
661	K791DAO	Volvo B10M-55	Alexander PS	DP48F	1993	Ex Cumberland, 1994

662-670

Volvo B10M-55   Northern Counties Paladin   DP47F   1995

662	M662ECD	664	M664ECD	667	M667ECD	669	M669ECD	670	M670ECD
663	M663ECD	665	M665ECD	668	M668ECD				

671	M311YSC	Volvo B10M-55	Alexander PS	DP48F	1995	Ex Fife Scottish, 1995
672	M312YSC	Volvo B10M-55	Alexander PS	DP48F	1995	Ex Fife Scottish, 1995
673	M313YSC	Volvo B10M-55	Alexander PS	DP48F	1995	Ex Fife Scottish, 1995

678-692 — Bristol VRT/SL3/6LXB — Eastern Coach Works — H43/31F — 1979-80

678	EAP978V	685	EAP985V	687	EAP987V	690	EAP990V	692	EAP992V
684	EAP984V	686	EAP986V	688	EAP988V	691	EAP991V		

749	BKE849T	Bristol VRT/SL3/6LXB	Eastern Coach Works	H43/31F	1979	Ex Hastings & District, 1989
750w	BKE850T	Bristol VRT/SL3/6LXB	Eastern Coach Works	H43/31F	1979	Ex Hastings & District, 1989
759	BKE859T	Bristol VRT/SL3/6LXB	Eastern Coach Works	H43/31F	1979	Ex Hastings & District, 1989
768w	AAP668T	Bristol VRT/SL3/6LXB	Eastern Coach Works	H43/28F	1979	
780	BAU180T	Bristol VRT/SL3/6LXB	Eastern Coach Works	H43/31F	1978	Ex East Midland, 1993
782	AET182T	Bristol VRT/SL3/6LXB	Eastern Coach Works	H43/31F	1979	Ex East Midland, 1993
787	AET187T	Bristol VRT/SL3/6LXB	Eastern Coach Works	H43/31F	1979	Ex East Midland, 1993

841-850 — Mercedes-Benz 709D — Alexander Sprint — B23F* — 1990 — *841-3 are DP25F

841	G71APO	843	G73APO	845	G975ARV	847	G977ARV	849	H679BTP
842	G72APO	844	G974ARV	846	G976ARV	848	G978ARV	850	H680BTP

853-888 — Mercedes-Benz 709D — Alexander Sprint — B25F — 1993

853	K853ODY	861	K861ODY	868	K868ODY	875	K875ODY	882	L882SDY
854	K854ODY	862	K862ODY	869	K869ODY	876	K876ODY	883	L883SDY
855	K855ODY	863	K863ODY	870	K870ODY	877	K877ODY	884	L884SDY
856	K856ODY	864	K864ODY	871	K871ODY	878	K878ODY	885	L885SDY
857	K857ODY	865	K865ODY	872	K872ODY	879	K879ODY	886	L886SDY
858	K858ODY	866	K866ODY	873	K873ODY	880	K880ODY	887	L887SDY
859	K859ODY	867	K867ODY	874	K874ODY	881	L881SDY	888	L188SDY
860	K860ODY								

889-904 — Mercedes-Benz 709D — Alexander Sprint — B25F* — 1995 — *894-904 are B23F

889	M889ECD	892	N192LPN	895	N195LPN	898	N198LPN	902	N202LPN
890	M890ECD	893	N193LPN	896	N196LPN	899	N199LPN	903	N203LPN
891	N191LPN	894	N194LPN	897	N197LPN	901	N201LPN	904	N204LPN

905-977 — Mercedes-Benz 709D — Alexander Sprint — B25F* — 1996 — *924-77 are B23F

905	N905NAP	920	N920NAP	935	N935NAP	950	N950NAP	964	N964NAP
906	N906NAP	921	N921NAP	936	N936NAP	951	N951NAP	965	N965NAP
907	N907NAP	922	N922NAP	937	N937NAP	952	N952NAP	966	N966NAP
908	N908NAP	923	N923NAP	938	N938NAP	953	N953NAP	967	N967NAP
909	N909NAP	924	N924NAP	939	N939NAP	954	N954NAP	968	N968NAP
910	N910NAP	925	N925NAP	940	N940NAP	955	N955NAP	969	N969NAP
911	N911NAP	926	N926NAP	941	N941NAP	956	N956NAP	970	N970NAP
912	N912NAP	927	N927NAP	942	N942NAP	957	N957NAP	971	N971NAP
913	N913NAP	928	N928NAP	943	N943NAP	958	N958NAP	972	N972NAP
914	N914NAP	929	N929NAP	944	N944NAP	959	N959NAP	973	N973NAP
915	N915NAP	930	N930NAP	945	N945NAP	960	N960NAP	974	N974NAP
916	N916NAP	931	N931NAP	946	N946NAP	961	N961NAP	975	N975NAP
917	N917NAP	932	N932NAP	947	N947NAP	962	N962NAP	976	N976NAP
918	N918NAP	933	N933NAP	948	N948NAP	963	N963NAP	977	N977NAP
919	N919NAP	934	N934NAP	949	N949NAP				

1064	VSV564	Leyland Tiger TRCTL11/3R	Plaxton Paramount 3200 E	C49F	1983	Ex Hastings & District, 1989
1072	USV672	Leyland Tiger TRCTL11/3R	Plaxton Paramount 3200 E	C49F	1983	Ex Hastings & District, 1989
1094	GPJ894N	Leyland National 11351/1R		B49F	1975	Ex Alder Valley, 1992
1105	M105CCD	Dennis Javelin 11SDL2133	Plaxton Premiere Interurban	DP47F	1995	
1106	M106CCD	Dennis Javelin 11SDL2133	Plaxton Premiere Interurban	DP47F	1995	
1108	M108CCD	Dennis Javelin 11SDL2133	Plaxton Premiere Interurban	DP47F	1995	
1115	MFN115R	Leyland National 11351A/1R		B49F	1976	Ex East Kent, 1993
1176	NPJ476R	Leyland National 11351A/1R		B49F	1976	Ex Alder Valley, 1992
1180	UMO180N	Leyland National 11351/1R		B49F	1974	Ex Alder Valley, 1992
1181	NFN81R	Leyland National 11351A/1R		DP48F	1977	Ex East Kent, 1993
1188	NFN88R	Leyland National 11351A/1R		DP48F	1977	Ex East Kent, 1993
1201	HPK503N	Leyland National 11351/1R		B49F	1975	Ex Alder Valley, 1992
1203	HPK505N	Leyland National 11351/1R		B49F	1975	Ex Alder Valley, 1992
1215	KPA366P	Leyland National 11351/1R		B49F	1975	Ex Alder Valley, 1992
1218	KPA369P	Leyland National 11351/1R		B49F	1975	Ex Alder Valley, 1992
1223	KPA374P	Leyland National 11351/1R		B49F	1975	Ex Alder Valley, 1992
1228	KPA379P	Leyland National 11351/1R		B49F	1975	Ex Alder Valley, 1992
1236	KPA387P	Leyland National 11351A/1R		B49F	1976	Ex Alder Valley, 1992
1237	KPA388P	Leyland National 11351A/1R		B49F	1976	Ex Alder Valley, 1992
1238	KPA389P	Leyland National 11351A/1R		B49F	1976	Ex Alder Valley, 1992

1247	LPF605P	Leyland National 11351/1R/SC		B49F	1976	Ex Alder Valley, 1992

1256-1272

		Leyland National 11351A/1R		B49F	1976-77	Ex Alder Valley, 1992
1256	NPJ477R	1259	NPJ480R	1261	NPJ482R	1271	TPE148S	1272	TPE149S

1256	NPJ477R	1259 NPJ480R	1261 NPJ482R	1271 TPE148S	1272 TPE149S

1298w	SGS504W	Leyland Tiger TRCTL11/3R	Plaxton Supreme IV	C50F	1981	Ex Alder Valley, 1992
1299w	XGS762X	Leyland Tiger TRCTL11/3R	Plaxton Supreme IV	C51F	1981	Ex Alder Valley, 1992
1344	PJJ344S	Leyland National 10351A/1R		B41F	1977	Ex East Kent, 1993
1345w	PJJ345S	Leyland National 10351A/1R		B41F	1977	Ex East Kent, 1993
1346w	PJJ346S	Leyland National 10351A/1R		B41F	1977	Ex East Kent, 1993

1401	J401LKO	DAF SB220LC550	Optare Delta	B49F	1991	Ex East Kent, 1993
1402	J402LKO	DAF SB220LC550	Optare Delta	B49F	1991	Ex East Kent, 1993
1403	J403LKO	DAF SB220LC550	Optare Delta	B49F	1991	Ex East Kent, 1993

1404-1408

		Dennis Lance SLF 11SDA3201	Berkhof 2000	B40F	1994	
1404	M404OKM	1405	M405OKM	1406	M406OKM	1407	M407OKM	1408	M408OKM

1404	M404OKM	1405 M405OKM	1406 M406OKM	1407 M407OKM	1408 M408OKM

1546	GFN546N	Leyland National 10351/1R		B40F	1975	Ex East Kent, 1993
1890	JJG890P	Leyland National 11351A/1R		B49F	1976	Ex East Kent, 1993
1898	JJG898P	Leyland National 11351A/1R		B49F	1976	Ex East Kent, 1993

2136	N136MPN	OCC Omni	OCC	B21F	1995	Ex Sussex Bus, 1996
2402	H402KPY	CVE Omni	CVE	B23F	1990	Ex Sussex Bus, 1996
2586	XIA586	Leyland National 11351A/1R (Urban Bus)		B62F	1977	Ex Sussex Bus, 1996
2612	XSU612	Leyland Leopard PSU3F/4R	Willowbrook Warrior (1990)	B48F	1981	Ex Sussex Bus, 1996
2646	G646DBG	CVE Omni	CVE	B23F	1989	Ex Sussex Bus, 1996
2651	F651RBP	Iveco Daily 49.10	Robin Hood City Nippy	B25F	1989	Ex Sussex Bus, 1996
2682	XSU682	Leyland Leopard PSU3B/4R	Willowbrook Warrior (1990)	B49F	1973	Ex Sussex Bus, 1996
2705	E705LYU	MCW MetroRider MF150	MCW	DP33F	1988	Ex Sussex Bus, 1996
2857	XIA857	Leyland National 11351A/1R		B48F	1976	Ex Sussex Bus, 1996
2978	CSU978	Leyland Leopard PSU3B/4R	Willowbrook Warrior (1988)	B53F	1975	Ex Sussex Bus, 1996
2992	CSU992	Leyland Leopard PSU3E/4R	Willowbrook Warrior (1990)	DP60F	1979	Ex Sussex Bus, 1996

5001	472YMF	DAF SB220LC550	Optare Delta	B40D	1992	On Loan from East London
5002	YLJ332	DAF SB220LC550	Optare Delta	B40D	1992	On Loan from East London
5003	NFX667	Dennis Dart 9.8SDL3017	Alexander Dash	DP32F	1992	On Loan from East London
5004	XYK976	Dennis Dart 9.8SDL3017	Alexander Dash	DP32F	1992	On Loan from East London

East London provide four vehicles for South West Trains connection services and these are operated by Stagecoach South. Numbered in the latter fleet 5001-5004, they also have numbers allocated by East London. These carry a livery similar to that initially used for the train service. Shown heading for Tiphook rail station is 5004, XYK976.
Philip Lamb

7201	KYV511X	Leyland Titan TNLXB2RR	Leyland	H44/24F	1982	Ex Selkent, 1995	
7203	A823SUL	Leyland Titan TNLXB2RR	Leyland	H44/26F	1983	Ex Selkent, 1995	
7205	KYN305X	Leyland Titan TNLXB2RR	Leyland	H44/24F	1981	Ex Selkent, 1995	
7211	NUW611Y	Leyland Titan TNLXB2RR	Leyland	H44/24F	1982	Ex Selkent, 1995	
7215	CUL215V	Leyland Titan TNLXB2RRSp	Park Royal	H44/26F	1980	Ex Selkent, 1995	
7220	KYV420X	Leyland Titan TNLXB2RR	Leyland	H44/24F	1982	Ex Selkent, 1995	
7223	KYV523X	Leyland Titan TNLXB2RR	Leyland	H44/26F	1982	Ex Selkent, 1995	
7225	CUL225V	Leyland Titan TNLXB2RRSp	Park Royal	H44/24F	1980	Ex Selkent, 1995	
7229	EYE229V	Leyland Titan TNLXB2RRSp	Park Royal	H44/26F	1980	Ex Selkent, 1995	
7233	EYE233V	Leyland Titan TNLXB2RRSp	Park Royal	H44/26F	1980	Ex Selkent, 1995	
7237	EYE237V	Leyland Titan TNLXB2RRSp	Park Royal	H44/26F	1980	Ex Selkent, 1995	
7240	EYE240V	Leyland Titan TNLXB2RRSp	Park Royal	H44/26F	1980	Ex Selkent, 1995	
7242	KYV442X	Leyland Titan TNLXB2RR	Leyland	H44/24F	1982	Ex Selkent, 1995	
7244	EYE244V	Leyland Titan TNLXB2RRSp	Park Royal	H44/26F	1980	Ex Selkent, 1995	
7245	KYV345X	Leyland Titan TNTL112RR	Leyland	H44/26F	1981	Ex Selkent, 1995	
7248	KYV348X	Leyland Titan TNLXB2RR	Leyland	H44/24F	1981	Ex Selkent, 1995	
7250	EYE250V	Leyland Titan TNLXB2RRSp	Park Royal	H44/26F	1980	Ex Selkent, 1995	
7251	KYV451X	Leyland Titan TNLXB2RR	Leyland	H44/24F	1982	Ex Selkent, 1995	
7261	KYV361X	Leyland Titan TNLXB2RR	Leyland	H44/24F	1981	Ex Selkent, 1995	
7268	CUL168V	Leyland Titan TNLXB2RRSp	Park Royal	H44/24F	1980	Ex Selkent, 1995	
7269	CUL169V	Leyland Titan TNLXB2RRSp	Park Royal	H44/26F	1980	Ex Selkent, 1995	
7274	KYV474X	Leyland Titan TNLXB2RR	Leyland	H44/24F	1982	Ex Selkent, 1995	
7279	CUL79V	Leyland Titan TNLXB2RRSp	Park Royal	H44/26F	1980	Ex Selkent, 1995	
7280	CUL180V	Leyland Titan TNLXB2RRSp	Park Royal	H44/24F	1980	Ex Selkent, 1995	
7287	KYN487X	Leyland Titan TNLXB2RR	Leyland	H44/24F	1982	Ex Selkent, 1995	
7288	KYN288X	Leyland Titan TNLXB2RR	Leyland	H44/24F	1981	Ex Selkent, 1995	
7290	CUL190V	Leyland Titan TNLXB2RRSp	Park Royal	H44/24F	1980	Ex Selkent, 1995	
7294	NUW594Y	Leyland Titan TNLXB2RR	Leyland	H44/24F	1982	Ex Selkent, 1995	
7296	NUW596Y	Leyland Titan TNLXB2RR	Leyland	H44/24F	1982	Ex Selkent, 1995	
7297	KYV397X	Leyland Titan TNLXB2RR	Leyland	H44/24F	1982	Ex Selkent, 1995	
7298	CUL198V	Leyland Titan TNLXB2RRSp	Park Royal	H44/26F	1980	Ex Selkent, 1995	

7301-7309

	Volvo Citybus B10M-50	Northern Counties	DPH43/33F	1989		

7301	F301MYJ	7303	F303MYJ	7305	F305MYJ	7307	F307MYJ	7309	F309MYJ
7302	F302MYJ	7304	F304MYJ	7306	F306MYJ	7308	F308MYJ		

7322	VTV172S	Bristol VRT/SL3/6LXB	Eastern Coach Works	H43/31F	1978	Ex East Midland, 1993
7347	AAP647T	Bristol VRT/SL3/6LXB	Eastern Coach Works	H43/31F	1978	

7352-7358

	Bristol VRT/SL3/6LXB	Eastern Coach Works	H43/31F*	1980	*7353 is DPH43/31F	

7352	JWV252W	7353	JWV253W	7355	JWV255W	7356	JWV256W	7358	JWV258W

7359	DBV29W	Bristol VRT/SL3/6LXB	Eastern Coach Works	DPH43/31F	1980	Ex Ribble, 1986
7360w	AAP660T	Bristol VRT/SL3/6LXB	Eastern Coach Works	H43/31F	1978	
7362w	AAP662T	Bristol VRT/SL3/6LXB	Eastern Coach Works	H43/31F	1979	
7365	DBV25W	Bristol VRT/SL3/6LXB	Eastern Coach Works	DPH43/31F	1980	Ex Ribble, 1986
7366	JWV266W	Bristol VRT/SL3/680(6LXB)	Eastern Coach Works	H43/31F	1981	
7367	JWV267W	Bristol VRT/SL3/680(6LXB)	Eastern Coach Works	H43/31F	1981	
7368	JWV268W	Bristol VRT/SL3/680(6LXB)	Eastern Coach Works	H43/31F	1981	
7369	JWV269W	Bristol VRT/SL3/680(6LXB)	Eastern Coach Works	H43/31F	1981	
7371	AAP671T	Bristol VRT/SL3/6LXB	Eastern Coach Works	H43/31F	1979	
7373	EAP973V	Bristol VRT/SL3/6LXB	Eastern Coach Works	H43/31F	1979	
7374	JWV274W	Bristol VRT/SL3/680(6LXB)	Eastern Coach Works	H43/31F	1981	
7375	JWV275W	Bristol VRT/SL3/680	Eastern Coach Works	H43/31F	1981	
7376	JWV976W	Bristol VRT/SL3/680(6LXB)	Eastern Coach Works	H43/31F	1981	
7377	EAP977V	Bristol VRT/SL3/6LXB	Eastern Coach Works	H43/31F	1979	
7382w	EAP982V	Bristol VRT/SL3/6LXB	Eastern Coach Works	H43/31F	1979	
7392	VPR491S	Bristol VRT/SL3/6LXB	Eastern Coach Works	H43/31F	1978	
7394	HFG193T	Bristol VRT/SL3/6LXB	Eastern Coach Works	H43/31F	1978	
7395	YEL2T	Bristol VRT/SL3/6LXB	Eastern Coach Works	H43/31F	1978	
7397	YEL4T	Bristol VRT/SL3/6LXB	Eastern Coach Works	H43/31F	1978	
7621	UWV621S	Bristol VRT/SL3/6LXB	Eastern Coach Works	CO43/31F	1978	
7623	UWV623S	Bristol VRT/SL3/6LXB	Eastern Coach Works	CO43/31F	1978	

Opposite: **Stagecoach South have a large double-deck requirement that had been filled by the Bristol VRT in NBC days. To this model East Kent added MCW Metrobuses and latterly Stagecoach South have taken Leyland Titans from Selkent in addition to many new Olympians. Shown here with Metrobus 7762, F762EKM on X70 service at Margate and Titan 7251, KYV451Y working with Sussex Coastline whose Titans are all based at Langstone Point depot.** *Malc McDonald/Philip Lamb*

The 1997 Stagecoach Bus Handbook

Liveried for the Shuttlebus service at Portsmouth is Bristol VR 7267, JWV267W. Once fitted with high-back seating, as can be seen here, the vehicle has been refurbished with bus seats.
Phillip Stephenson

7650-7685

Bristol VRT/SL3/6LXB   Eastern Coach Works   H43/31F   1980-81 Ex East Kent, 1993
7655 was rebodied 1983

7650	XJJ650V	7658	XJJ658V	7665	XJJ665V	7672	BJG672V	7680	SKL680X
7651	XJJ651V	7659	XJJ659V	7666	XJJ666V	7673	BJG673V	7681	SKL681X
7652	XJJ652V	7660	XJJ660V	7667	XJJ667V	7674	BJG674V	7682	SKL682X
7653	XJJ653V	7661	XJJ661V	7668	XJJ668V	7675	BJG675V	7683	SKL683X
7654	XJJ654V	7662	XJJ662V	7669	XJJ669V	7677	CJJ677W	7684	SKL684X
7655	XJJ655V	7663	XJJ663V	7670	XJJ670V	7679	CJJ679W	7685	SKL685X
7657	XJJ657V	7664	XJJ664V	7671	BJG671V				

7746-7755

MCW Metrobus Mk2 DR132/11   MCW   H46/31F   1988   Ex East Kent, 1993

7746	E746SKR	7748	E748SKR	7750	E750SKR	7752	E752SKR	7754	E754UKR
7747	E747SKR	7749	E749SKR	7751	E751SKR	7753	E753SKR	7755	E755UKR

7761-7767

MCW Metrobus Mk2 DR132/15   MCW   DPH43/27F   1989   Ex East Kent, 1993

7761	F761EKM	7763	F763EKM	7765	F765EKM	7766	F766EKM	7767	F767EKM
7762	F762EKM	7764	F764EKM						

7771-7775

MCW Metrobus Mk2 DR132/14   MCW   H46/31F   1989   Ex East Kent, 1993

7771	F771EKM	7772	F772EKM	7773	F773EKM	7774	F774EKM	7775	F775EKM

7781	F781KKP	Scania N113DRB	Alexander RH	H47/33F	1989	Ex East Kent, 1993
7782	F782KKP	Scania N113DRB	Alexander RH	H47/33F	1989	Ex East Kent, 1993

7801-7810

Leyland Olympian ON2R56C16Z4 Northern Counties   H51/34F   1990   Ex East Kent, 1993

7801	H801BKK	7803	H803BKK	7805	H805BKK	7807	H807BKK	7809	H809BKK
7802	H802BKK	7804	H804BKK	7806	H806BKK	7808	H808BKK	7810	H810BKK

7811	J811NKK	Leyland Olympian ON2R50C13Z4	Northern Counties	H47/30F	1992	Ex East Kent, 1993
7812	J812NKK	Leyland Olympian ON2R50C13Z4	Northern Counties	H47/30F	1992	Ex East Kent, 1993
7813	J813NKK	Leyland Olympian ON2R50C13Z4	Northern Counties	H47/30F	1992	Ex East Kent, 1993
7814	J814NKK	Leyland Olympian ON2R50C13Z4	Northern Counties	H47/30F	1992	Ex East Kent, 1993

This picture allows a small comparison of the roof-line of Metrobuses 7755, E755UKR and 7762 in Ramsgate; 7762 shows the style used with the mark I version while 7755 is one of the short-lived mark II variety. Metrobuses in the group are now based at Stagecoach South, Manchester and Transit. *Malc McDonald*

7821-7830

Leyland Olympian ON2R50C13Z4 Northern Counties H47/30F 1993 7821-5 ex East Kent, 1993

| 7821 | K821TKP | 7823 | K823TKP | 7825 | K825TKP | 7827 | L827BKK | 7829 | L829BKK |
| 7822 | K822TKP | 7824 | K824TKP | 7826 | L826BKK | 7828 | L828BKK | 7830 | L830BKK |

7950-7988

Bristol VRT/SL3/6LXB Eastern Coach Works H43/31F 1978-81 Ex Alder Valley, 1992

7950w	TPE156S	7962u	GGM82W	7968	WJM828T	7977	CJH117V	7982	CJH142V
7956	GGM86W	7965	WJM825T	7969	WJM829T	7979	CJH119V	7985	CJH145V
7960	GGM80W	7966	WJM826T	7972	WJM832T	7980	CJH120V	7988	KKK888V
7961	GGM81W								

| 8211 | D211VEV | Scania K112CRB | Berkhof Esprite 350 | C40DT | 1987 | Ex East Kent, 1993 |
| 8243 | SIB8243 | Volvo B10M-60 | Plaxton Paramount 3500 III | C49FT | 1991 | Ex East Kent, 1993 |

8404-8410

Volvo B10M-62 Plaxton Première 350 C53F* 1995 *8410 is C49FT

| 8404 | M404BFG | 8406 | M406BFG | 8408 | M408BFG | 8409 | M409BFG | 8410 | M410BFG |
| 8405 | M405BFG | 8407 | M407BFG | | | | | | |

8503	IIL3503	Volvo B10M-61	Van Hool Alizée	C49FT	1988	Ex Bluebird Buses, 1995
8505	IIL3505	Volvo B10M-61	Van Hool Alizée	C49FT	1988	Ex Bluebird Buses, 1995
8618	WVT618	Volvo B10M-61	Plaxton Paramount 3500 III	C50F	1987	Ex Bluebird Buses, 1995
8856	J856NKK	Scania K93CRB	Plaxton Paramount 3500 III	C49FT	1992	Ex East Kent, 1993
8909	J909NKP	Volvo B10M-60	Plaxton Expressliner	C49FT	1992	Ex East Kent, 1993
8910	K910TKP	Volvo B10M-60	Plaxton Expressliner 2	C49FT	1993	Ex East Kent, 1993

8911-8918

Volvo B10M-62 Plaxton Expressliner 2 C49FT 1994-95

| 8911 | M911WJK | 8913 | M913WJK | 8915 | M915WJK | 8917 | M917WJK | 8918 | M918WJK |
| 8912 | M912WJK | 8914 | M914WJK | 8916 | M916WJK | | | | |

| 8996 | PFN873 | Bova FHD12.280 | Bova Futura | C49FT | 1986 | Ex East Kent, 1993 |

Special event vehicles: (traditional liveries)

0135	CD7045	Leyland G7	Short	O27/24R	1922	
0409	409DCD	Leyland Titan PD3/4	Northern Counties	FCO39/30F	1964	
0424	424DCD	Leyland Titan PD3/4	Northern Counties	FCO39/30F	1964	
0770	HKE690L	Bristol VRT/SL2/6LXB	Eastern Coach Works	O43/34F	1973	Ex Hastings & District, 1989
0813	UF4813	Leyland Titan TD1	Brush	O27/24R	1929	
0946	MFN946F	AEC Regent V 3D3RA	Park Royal	H40/32F	1967	Ex Hastings & District, 1989

Livery: 5001-4 South West Trains

Previous Registrations:

400DCD	M490BFG		CSU992	OMA506V, TCS157
401DCD	M401BFG		HUF451X	RUF434X, XLD244
402DCD	M402BFG		HUF579X	RUF430X, 400DCD
403DCD	M403BFG		HUF592X	RUF437X, 407DCD
404DCD	L604VCD		HUF593X	RUF436X, 406DCD
405DCD	L605VCD		HUF603X	RUF429X, 415DCD
406DCD	L606TDY		HUF604X	RUF435X, 405DCD
407DCD	L607TDY		HUF625X	RUF431X, 411DCD
408DCD	L608TDY		HUF626X	RUF438X, 410DCD
409DCD	from new		HUF639X	RUF433X, 420DCD
410DCD	M610APN		IIL3503	E625UNE, TXI2426, E936XSB
411DCD	M611APN		IIL3505	E623UNE, XIA257, E942XSB
412DCD	M612APN		JNJ194V	HFG924V, DSV943
413DCD	M613APN		NFX667	K716PCN
414DCD	M614APN		OUF262W	JWV125W, LYJ145
415DCD	L345KCK		PFN873	C996FKM
416DCD	L346KCK		SIB8243	H826AHS
417DCD	L347KCK		SYC852	JWV126W
418DCD	L348KCK		USV672	FKL172Y
419DCD	L619TDY		VSV564	FKL171Y
420DCD	L620TDY		WVT618	D202LWX
421DCD	L621TDY		XIA586	RYG773R
422DCD	L622TDY		XIA857	PKP548R, XIA256
423DCD	L623TDY		XSU612	PWT278W
424DCD	424DCD, AOR158B		XSU682	OKG158M
472YMF	J713CYG		XYK976	K719PCN
CSU978	HWY718N, CSU934		YLJ332	J715CYG

Operating Companies:

East Kent
3, 97, 195/7, 225-7/54-7/64/4/7, 354/5/60-5/8-78/81/9/90, 632-4/9/40/59-61/90, 844/5, 894-99, 901-4/22-77, 1105/6/8/15/81, 1344, 1401-8, 1546, 1890/8, 7355/71, 7652/3/5/7/8-66/8-75/7/9-85, 7746-55/61--7/71-5/81/2, 7801-14/21-3/6-9, 7977, 8211/43, 8404-10, 8503/5, 8856, 8909-18, 8996

Hampshire Bus
100-3/13/5-7/52/4/64/74/80/2/6/90-2/6, 201-5/6/8/10-14/23/4/39/46-50, 366/7/91-4, 400-3/22/35/8/44/6-50/6-62, 524-40/2-50/6-62/73/81/2, 606-8/15-7/25/7/31/41-3/51/2/5/8/62-5/7-70 749/87, 841-3/6-8/50/3, 915/6, 1072, 1176, 1247/56, 7322/47/52/3/6/8/66/9/73/4/7/92/4/5/7, 7651, 7956/61/5/6/88.

Hants & Surrey
162/89, 207/36, 351-3/79/80, 522/3, 570-2/5-8/84-8, 618/24/35/56/78/85/6/8, 759/80/2, 854-80, 905-14, 1064/94, 1188, 1201/15/8/23/8/36-8/59/61/71, 7650/4/67, 7960/8/9/72/9/80/2/5.

South Coast Buses
107/10/2/4/36/40/2-9/55/9/60/9/73/6/7/9, 241/2, 356-9/21-8, 601-5/9/12-4/9/20/36-8/44/5/50/71-3, 451-5, 501-21/83, 881-90, 7203/5/15/23/33/7/40/44/50/68/74/9/80/7/8/90, 7301-9.

Sussex Bus
2136, 2402, 2586, 2612/46/51/82, 2705, 2857, 2992.

Sussex Coastline
111/8-26/8-35/7-9/63, 209/15-22/8-34/40/3-5, 341-50/95-9, 541/51-69/74/9/80, 610/1/21-3/6/8-30 684/7/91/2, 849/91-3, 917-21, 1180, 1203/72, 7201/11/20/5/9/42/5/8/51/61/9/94/6-8, 7365/7/8/75/6, 7830

TRANSIT

Cleveland Transit Ltd, Church Road, Stockton-on-Tees, Cleveland, TS18 2HW
Hartlepool Transport Ltd, 8 Market Place, Hartlepool, TS24 7SB
Kingston-upon-Hull City Transport Ltd, Foster Street, Kingston-upon-Hull, HU8 8BT

Depots : Faverdale Industrial Estate, Darlington (Stagecoach Darlington); Brenda Road, Hartlepool (Stagecoach Hartlepool); Foster Street, Stoneferry, Kingston-upon-Hull (Stagecoach Kingston-upon-Hull); Church Road, Stockton (Stagecoach Transit). The fleet listed below anticipates the impending renumbering as we believe that it is better to have the book right for the bulk of the year.

32	BTU33W	Leyland Leopard PSU3E/4R	Plaxton Supreme IV Express	C49F	1981	Ex Vale of Llangollen, 1986
33	FSL61W	Leyland Leopard PSU3G/4R	Plaxton Supreme IV Express	C49F	1982	Ex Tayside, 1987
34	FSL62W	Leyland Leopard PSU3G/4R	Plaxton Supreme IV Express	C49F	1982	Ex Tayside, 1987
35	HDZ8683	Volvo B10M-61	Plaxton Paramount 3500	C49F	1984	Ex Allander, Milngavie, 1989
36	837XHW	Volvo B10M-61	Van Hool Alizée	C53F	1987	Ex Streamline, Bath, 1994
42	BUT24Y	Dennis Dorchester SDA801	Plaxton Paramount 3200	C49F	1983	Ex Leicester, 1987
43	BPY403T	Leyland Leopard PSU3E/4R	Plaxton Supreme IV Express	DP53F	1979	
44	HPY423V	Leyland Leopard PSU3F/4R	Plaxton Supreme IV Express	C53F	1980	
50	IIL1319	Volvo B10M-61	Plaxton Paramount 3200 II	C50FT	1986	
51	IIL1321	Volvo B10M-61	Plaxton Paramount 3200 III	C50FT	1987	
52	E52WAG	Volvo B10M-61	Plaxton Paramount 3200 III	C50FT	1988	
53	F53EAT	Dennis Javelin SDA1907	Plaxton Paramount 3200 III	C48FT	1989	
55	F55EAT	Dennis Javelin SDA1907	Plaxton Paramount 3200 III	C49FT	1989	
56	G56SAG	Volvo B10M-61	Plaxton Paramount 3500 III	C48FT	1990	
60	B60WKH	Leyland National 2 NL116HLXCT/1R		B24DL	1985	
61	YAY21Y	Dennis Lancet SD506	Duple Dominant	B25DL	1982	Ex Leicester, 1987
64	J204JKH	Volvo B10M-60	Plaxton Paramount 3500 III	C51FT	1992	Ex York Pullman, 1993
65	J205JKH	Volvo B10M-60	Plaxton Paramount 3500 III	C51FT	1992	Ex York Pullman, 1993
68	F108NRT	Volvo B10M-61	Plaxton Paramount 3500 III	C49FT	1988	Ex Cambus (Premier), 1996
72	K572DFS	Volvo B10M-60	Plaxton Premiére Interurban	C53F	1993	Ex East Midland, 1995
73	K573DFS	Volvo B10M-60	Plaxton Premiére Interurban	C53F	1993	Ex East Midland, 1995
75	K571DFS	Volvo B10M-60	Plaxton Premiére Interurban	C53F	1993	Ex East Midland, 1995
76	K576DFS	Volvo B10M-60	Plaxton Premiére Interurban	C53F	1993	Ex East Midland, 1995
77	K577DFS	Volvo B10M-60	Plaxton Premiére Interurban	C53F	1993	Ex East Midland, 1995
78	P178DRH	Volvo B10M-62	Plaxton Premiére Interurban	DP51F	1996	
79	P179DRH	Volvo B10M-62	Plaxton Premiére Interurban	DP51F	1996	
80	P180DRH	Volvo B10M-62	Plaxton Premiére Interurban	DP51F	1996	
81	P181DRH	Volvo B10M-62	Plaxton Premiére Interurban	DP51F	1996	

102-119

MCW Metrobus DR102 — MCW — H43/30F — 1981

102	LAT512V	105	LAT505V	114	SAG524W	116	SAG526W	118	SAG528W
104	LAT514V	106	LAT506V	115	SAG525W	117	SAG527W	119	SAG529W

121-157

Leyland Fleetline FE30AGR — Northern Counties — H43/31F — 1979-83

121	YVN521T	134	GAJ134V	140	JAJ140W	146	JAJ146W	152	VEF152Y
129	GAJ129V	135	GAJ135V	141	JAJ141W	147	PEF147X	153	VEF153Y
130	GAJ130V	136	GAJ136V	142	JAJ142W	148	PEF148X	154	YAJ154Y
131	GAJ131V	137	JAJ137W	143	JAJ143W	149	PEF149X	155	YAJ155Y
132	GAJ132V	138	JAJ138W	144	JAJ144W	150	VEF150Y	156	YAJ156Y
133	GAJ133V	139	JAJ139W	145	JAJ145W	151	VEF151Y	157	YAJ157Y

189	PRX189B	Leyland Titan PD3/4	Northern Counties	FCO39/30F	1964	Ex Southdown, 1988

206-210

Dennis Dominator DDA904 — Alexander RL — H43/32F — 1984

206	B106UAT	207	B107UAT	208	B108UAT	209	B109UAT	210	B110UAT

211	C111CAT	Dennis Dominator DDA1007	East Lancashire	H43/28F	1986
212	C112CAT	Dennis Dominator DDA1007	East Lancashire	H43/28F	1986
213	C113CAT	Dennis Dominator DDA1007	East Lancashire	DPH43/28F	1986

214-222

		Dennis Dominator DD906*		Northern Counties		H43/31F	1985-86 *219-22 are DDA1009		
214	B214OAJ	216	B216OAJ	218	B218OAJ	220	C220WAJ	222	C222WAJ
215	B215OAJ	217	B217OAJ	219	C219WAJ	221	C221WAJ		

223-231

		Dennis Dominator DDA1006		East Lancashire		H45/30F	1985-86		
223	C123CAT	225	C125CAT	228	C128CAT	229	C129CAT	231	C131CAT
224	C124CAT	226	C122CAT						

232	E132SAT	Dennis Dominator DDA1014		East Lancashire (1992)		H45/21D	1987

233-241

		Dennis Dominator DDA1014		East Lancashire		H45/32F	1987		
233	E133SAT	235	E135SAT	237	E137SAT	239	E139SAT	241	E141SAT
234	E134SAT	236	E136SAT	238	E138SAT	240	E140SAT		

242-251

		Dennis Dominator DDA1016		East Lancashire		H45/31F	1988		
242	E142BKH	244	E144BKH	246	E146BKH	248	E148BKH	250	E150BKH
243	E143BKH	245	E145BKH	247	E147BKH	249	E149BKH	251	E151BKH

252-257

		Dennis Dominator DDA1027		East Lancashire		H47/33F	1989		
252	F152HAT	254	F154HAT	255	F155HAT	256	F156HAT	257	F157HAT
253	F153HAT								

301-316

		Mercedes-Benz 811D		Wright NimBus		B26F	1989	Ex Selkent, 1995	
301	HDZ2601	305	HDZ2605	309	HDZ2609	312	HDZ2612	315	HDZ2615
303	HDZ2603	306	HDZ2606	310	HDZ2610	313	HDZ2613	316	HDZ2616
304	HDZ2604	307	HDZ2607	311	HDZ2611				

321	F621XMS	Mercedes-Benz 811D	Alexander Sprint	B28F	1988	Ex Selkent, 1996
324	F624XMS	Mercedes-Benz 811D	Alexander Sprint	B28F	1988	Ex Selkent, 1996
325	F625XMS	Mercedes-Benz 811D	Alexander Sprint	B28F	1988	Ex Selkent, 1996
329	F629XMS	Mercedes-Benz 811D	Alexander Sprint	B28F	1988	Ex Selkent, 1996

341-354

		Mercedes-Benz 709D		Alexander Sprint		B23F	1996		
341	N341KKH	344	N344KKH	347	N347KKH	350	P350NKH	353	P353NKH
342	N342KKH	345	N345KKH	348	N348KKH	351	P351NKH	354	P354NKH
343	N343KKH	346	N346KKH	349	P349NKH	352	P352NKH		

363	H401DMJ	Renault S75	Reeve Burgess Beaver	B29F	1990	Ex Busways, 1995

364-378

		Renault S75		Plaxton Beaver		B28F	1991	Ex Busways, 1995	
364	J553NGS	367	J227JJR	370	J230JJR	373	J233JJR	376	K343PJR
365	J225JJR	368	J228JJR	371	J231JJR	374	K341PJR	377	K344PJR
366	J226JJR	369	J229JJR	372	J232JJR	375	K342PJR	378	K345PJR

401-408

		Volvo B6-9.9M		Plaxton Pointer		B41F	1993-94		
401	L101GHN	403	L103GHN	405	M105PVN	407	M107PVN	408	M108PVN
402	L102GHN	404	M104PVN	406	M106PVN				

Opposite: **Transit are currently undertaking a renumbering of the fleet, and this is reflected in the fleet list. Shown here are two buses from the main Transit operation. Opposite, top: In addition to Alexander bodying Volvo B10Ms, Northern Counties have also won orders from Stagecoach to body the type with their Paladin model. Shown here is one of the 1995 delivery now 649, M549SPY. Opposite, bottom: Pictured in Stockton is Leyland Fleetline 145, JAJ145W. This too carries a Northern Counties body typical of the early 1980s model.** *Les Peters/Gerald Mead*

438-454

Volvo B6-9.9M — Alexander Dash — DP40F — 1993 — Ex Ribble, 1995

438	L238CCW	443	L243CCK	445	L245CCK	447	L247CCK	450	L250CCK
442	L242CCK	444	L244CCK	446	L246CCK	449	L249CCK	454	L254CCK

455-461

Dennis Dart SFD412 — Alexander Dash — B40F — 1996

455	P455EEF	457	P457EEF	459	P459EEF	460	P460EEF	461	P461EEF
456	P456EEF	458	P458EEF						

501-510

Volvo B10M-55 — Northern Counties Paladin — B48F — 1995

501	M401SPY	503	M403SPY	505	M405SPY	507	M407SPY	509	M409SPY
502	M402SPY	504	M404SPY	506	M406SPY	508	M408SPY	510	M410SPY

514-519

Leyland National 2 NL116L11/2R — B50F* — 1980 — *515/6 are DP48F, 517/8 are B45D

514	KAJ214W	516	KAJ216W	517	KAJ217W	518	KAJ218W	519	KAJ219W
515	KAJ215W								

521-526

Dennis Falcon HC SDA409 — Wadham Stringer — B46D — 1983

521	YDC21Y	523	YDC23Y	524	YDC24Y	525	YDC25Y	526	YDC26Y

527-532

Dennis Falcon HC SDA409 — Northern Counties — B47D — 1985

527	B27PAJ	529	B29PAJ	530	B30PAJ	531	B31PAJ	532	B32PAJ
528	B28PAJ								

533	SHN401R	Leyland National 11351A/2R		B50F	1977	
536	UFG52S	Leyland National 11351A/2R		B50F	1977	Ex Brighton & Hove, 1990
537	SHN407R	Leyland National 11351A/2R		B50F	1977	
539	UFG49S	Leyland National 11351A/2R		B50F	1977	Ex Brighton & Hove, 1990
540	RUF40R	Leyland National 11351A/2R		B44D	1977	Ex Brighton & Hove, 1990
541	F251JRM	Leyland Lynx LX112L10ZR1	Leyland	B51F	1989	Ex Cumberland, 1996
542	F252JRM	Leyland Lynx LX112L10ZR1	Leyland	B51F	1989	Ex Cumberland, 1996
543	F253KAO	Leyland Lynx LX112L10ZR1	Leyland	B51F	1989	Ex Cumberland, 1996
544	C544RAO	Leyland Lynx LX1126LXCTFR1 (Cummins)	Leyland	B51F	1986	Ex Cumberland, 1996
545	E709MFV	Leyland Lynx LX112L10ZR1	Leyland	B51F	1988	Ex Cumberland, 1996
551	N551VDC	Volvo B10M-55	Alexander PS	DP48F	1995	
552	N552VDC	Volvo B10M-55	Alexander PS	DP48F	1995	
553	N553VDC	Volvo B10M-55	Alexander PS	DP48F	1995	

554-558

Volvo B10M-55 — Northern Counties Paladin — B48F — 1997

554	P554FEF	555	P555FEF	556	P556FEF	557	P557FEF	558	P558FEF

601-610

Leyland Lynx LX2R11C15Z4R — Leyland Lynx — B49F — 1989

601	F601UVN	603	F603UVN	605	F605UVN	607	F607UVN	609	F609UVN
602	F602UVN	604	F604UVN	606	F606UVN	608	F608UVN	610	F610UVN

611-620

Leyland Lynx LX2R11C15Z4R — Leyland Lynx — B49F — 1989

611	G611CEF	613	G613CEF	615	G615CEF	617	G617CEF	619	G619CEF
612	G612CEF	614	G614CEF	616	G616CEF	618	G618CEF	620	G620CEF

621	J901UKV	Leyland Lynx LX2R11V18Z4S	Leyland Lynx 2	B49F	1991	Ex Volvo demonstrator, 1992

622-630

Leyland Lynx LX2R11V18Z4R — Leyland Lynx 2 — B49F — 1992

622	K622YVN	624	K624YVN	626	K626YVN	628	K628YVN	630	K630YVN
623	K623YVN	625	K625YVN	627	K627YVN	629	K629YVN		

Opposite: **The Kingston-upon-Hull fleet is now at one within Transit and repainting of the fleet into corporate livery has commenced. Shown here are refurbished Scania 704, F704BAT and Northern Counties-bodied Volvo B10M 711, M711KRH.** *Tony Wilson*

631-642 — Volvo B10B — Plaxton Verde — B52F — 1994

631	L31HHN	634	L34HHN	637	L37HHN	639	M39PVN	641	M41PVN
632	L32HHN	635	L35HHN	638	M38PVN	640	M40PVN	642	M42PVN
633	L33HHN	636	L36HHN						

643-655 — Volvo B10M-55 — Northern Counties Paladin — B48F — 1995-97

643	M543SPY	646	M546SPY	649	M549SPY	652	M552SPY	654	P654FEF
644	M544SPY	647	M547SPY	650	M550SPY	653	P653FEF	655	P655FEF
645	M545SPY	648	M548SPY	651	M551SPY				

701-706 — Scania N112CRB — East Lancashire — B50F* — 1988 — *705 is DP49F

701	F701BAT	703	F703BAT	704	F704BAT	705	F705BAT	706	F706CAG
702	F702BAT								

707-718 — Volvo B10M-55 — Northern Counties Paladin — B48F — 1995

707	M707KRH	710	M710KRH	713	M713KRH	715	M715KRH	717	M717KRH
708	M708KRH	711	M711KRH	714	M714KRH	716	M716KRH	718	M718KRH
709	M709KRH	712	M712KRH						

719-726 — Volvo B10M-55 — Northern Counties Paladin — B48F — 1995

719	P719SKH	721	P721SKH	723	P723SKH	725	P725SKH	726	P726SKH
720	P720SKH	722	P722SKH	724	P724SKH				

800	C100HSJ	Scania N112DRB	East Lancashire	H47/33F	1986	Ex A1 Service, 1995

801-816 — Scania N113DRB — East Lancashire — H51/37F — 1989-90 *809-16 are H47/37F

801	G801JRH	805	G805JRH	808	G808LAG	811	H811WKH	814	H814WKH
802	G802JRH	806	G806JRH	809	H809WKH	812	H812WKH	815	H815WKH
803	G803JRH	807	G807LAG	810	H810WKH	813	H813WKH	816	H816WKH
804	G804JRH								

817	M817KRH	Volvo Olympian YN2RV18Z4	Northern Counties Palatine	H47/29F	1995
818	M818KRH	Volvo Olympian YN2RV18Z4	Northern Counties Palatine	H47/29F	1995
819	M819KRH	Volvo Olympian YN2RV18Z4	Northern Counties Palatine	H47/29F	1995

823-827 — Volvo Olympian YN2RC16V3 — Northern Counties Palatine — H47/30F — 1995

823	M223SVN	824	M224SVN	825	M225SVN	826	M226SVN	827	M227SVN

828	P828FEF	Volvo Olympian	Northern Counties Palatine	H47/30F	1997
829	P829FEF	Volvo Olympian	Northern Counties Palatine	H47/30F	1997
830	P830FEF	Volvo Olympian	Northern Counties Palatine	H47/30F	1997
831	P831FEF	Volvo Olympian	Alexander RL	H51/36F	1997
832	P832FEF	Volvo Olympian	Alexander RL	H51/36F	1997
833	P833FEF	Volvo Olympian	Alexander RL	H51/36F	1997
834	P834FEF	Volvo Olympian	Alexander RL	H51/36F	1997

Previous Registrations:

837XHW	D556MVR	HDZ8683	A845UGB, 2367AT, A491WYS
BTU33W	WLG380W, 93FYB	IIL1319	C50FRH
E709MFV	E709MFV, BMN88G	IIL1321	D51ORH
FSL61W	GSL307W, 666TPJ	PRX189B	417DCD
FSL62W	GSL306W, 6689DP		

UNITED COUNTIES

United Counties Omnibus Co Ltd, Rothersthorpe Avenue,
Northampton, NN4 9UT

Depots : St Johns, Bedford; Station Road, Corby; Stukeley Road, Huntingdon; Northampton Road, Kettering and Rothersthorpe Avenue, Northampton. **Outstations** : Biggleswade; Bishops Stortford; Chown's Mill; Daventry; Desborough; Husbands Bosworth; Little Paxton; Mildenhall; Milton Keynes; Somersham; Thrapston; Uppingham; Wellingborough; Wymington and Yardley Hastings.

The Huntingdon operation is to be divested during the first half of 1997.

81	WLT682	Leyland Tiger TRCTL11/3RZ	Plaxton Paramount 3500 II	C46FT	1986	
82	WLT908	Leyland Tiger TRCTL11/3RZ	Plaxton Paramount 3500 II	C46FT	1986	
83	83CBD	Leyland Tiger TRCTL11/3RZ	Plaxton Paramount 3500	C51F	1983	Ex Stagecoach Malawi, 1994
85	647DYE	Leyland Tiger TRCTL11/3RZ	Plaxton Paramount 3500 II	C46FT	1986	
86	TSU639	Leyland Tiger TRCTL11/3R	Plaxton Paramount 3200 E	C53F	1983	Ex Stagecoach South, 1995
87	TSU640	Leyland Tiger TRCTL11/3R	Plaxton Paramount 3200 E	C53F	1983	Ex Stagecoach South, 1995
88	TSU641	Leyland Tiger TRCTL11/3R	Plaxton Paramount 3200 E	C53F	1983	Ex Stagecoach South, 1995
89	TSU642	Leyland Tiger TRCTL11/3R	Plaxton Paramount 3200 E	C53F	1983	Ex Stagecoach South, 1995

92-96   Volvo B10M-60   Plaxton Premiére 350   C49FT   1992   Ex Park's, 1993 / 94/5 ex Rainworth Travel, 1993

92	J430HDS	93	J439HDS	94	J445HDS	95	J446HDS	96	J450HDS

102	NBD102Y	Leyland Tiger TRCTL11/3R	Plaxton Paramount 3200 E	C53F	1983	
103	NBD103Y	Leyland Tiger TRCTL11/3R	Plaxton Paramount 3200 E	C53F	1983	
104	NBD104Y	Leyland Tiger TRCTL11/3R	Plaxton Paramount 3200 E	C53F	1983	
105	RBD397Y	Leyland Tiger TRCTL11/3R	Plaxton Paramount 3200 E	C53F	1983	
107	F107NRT	Volvo B10M-61	Plaxton Paramount 3500 III	C49FT	1988	Ex Cambus (Premier), 1996

108-114   Leyland Tiger TRCTL11/3RH   Plaxton Paramount 3200 E   C50FT   1983

108	A108TRP	111	A111TRP	112	A112TRP	113	A113TRP	114	A114TRP
110	A110TRP								

115	MSU465	Leyland Tiger TRCTL11/3RH	Duple 340	C53F	1987	Ex Fife Scottish, 1992
116	VLT255	Leyland Tiger TRCTL11/3RZ	Duple Laser 2	C44FT	1985	Ex Stagecoach Malawi, 1993
120	C120PNV	Leyland Tiger TRCTL11/3RZ	Plaxton Paramount 3200 IIE	C53F	1986	
121	C121PNV	Leyland Tiger TRCTL11/3RZ	Plaxton Paramount 3200 IIE	C53F	1986	
122	C122PNV	Leyland Tiger TRCTL11/3RZ	Plaxton Paramount 3200 IIE	C53F	1986	
125	A729ANH	Volvo B10M-61	Plaxton Paramount 3200 E	C48FT	1983	Ex Stagecoach, 1988
126	A728ANH	Volvo B10M-61	Plaxton Paramount 3200 E	C48FT	1983	Ex Stagecoach, 1988

United Counties' express services have used the Coachlinks name as shown here on Plaxton Première Interurban 153, K153DNV, leaving Peterborough for Luton on service X1. In 1995 a new X5 service began between Cambridge and Oxford under the Stagecoach Express branding. *Malc McDonald*

130-135

Volvo B10M-61 — Plaxton Paramount 3200 III — C53F — 1988

130 E130ORP	132 E132ORP	133 E133ORP	134 E134ORP	135 F135URP
131 E131ORP				

144-149

Volvo B10M-60 — Plaxton Premiére 350 — C50F — 1992 — Ex Wallace Arnold, 1995

144 J752CWT	146 K758FYG	147 K759FYG	148 K760FYG	149 K761FYG
145 J753CWT				

150-162

Volvo B10M-60 — Plaxton Premiére Interurban — DP53F* — 1993 — *155-162 are DP51F

150 K150DNV	153 K153DNV	156 L156JNH	159 L159JNH	161 L161JNH
151 K151DNV	154 K154DNV	157 L157JNH	160 L160JNH	162 L162JNH
152 K152DNV	155 L155JNH	158 L158JNH		

168-173

Volvo B10M-62 — Plaxton Premiére Interurban — DP51F — 1996

168 P168KBD	170 P170KBD	171 P171KBD	172 P172KBD	173 P173KBD
169 P169KBD				

301-326

Mercedes-Benz 709D — Alexander Sprint — B23F — 1996

301 N301XRP	307 N307XRP	312 N312XRP	317 N317XRP	322 N322XRP
302 N302XRP	308 N308XRP	313 N313XRP	318 N318XRP	323 N323XRP
303 N303XRP	309 N309XRP	314 N314XRP	319 N319XRP	324 N324XRP
304 N304XRP	310 N310XRP	315 N315XRP	320 N320XRP	325 N325XRP
305 N305XRP	311 N311XRP	316 N316XRP	321 N321XRP	326 N326XRP
306 N306XRP				

332-349

Mercedes-Benz 709D — Alexander Sprint — B25F — 1994

332 M332DRP	337 M337DRP	341 M341DRP	344 M344DRP	347 M347DRP
334 M334DRP	338 M338DRP	342 M342DRP	345 M345DRP	348 M348DRP
335 M335DRP	339 M339DRP	343 M343DRP	346 M346DRP	349 M349DRP
336 M336DRP	340 M340DRP			

350-383

Mercedes-Benz 709D — Alexander Sprint — B25F* — 1992-93 — *351-66 are B21F

350 K350ANV	357 K357ANV	364 L364JBD	371 L371JBD	378 L378JBD
351 K351ANV	358 K358ANV	365 L365JBD	372 L372JBD	379 L379JBD
352 K352ANV	359 K359ANV	366 L366JBD	373 L373JBD	380 L380JBD
353 K353ANV	360 L360JBD	367 L367JBD	374 L374JBD	381 L381NBD
354 K354ANV	361 L361JBD	368 L368JBD	375 L375JBD	382 L382NBD
355 K355ANV	362 L362JBD	369 L369JBD	376 L376JBD	383 L383NBD
356 K356ANV	363 L363JBD	370 L370JBD	377 L377JBD	

401-422

Volvo B6-9.9M — Alexander Dash — B40F — 1993

401 L401JBD	406 L406JBD	411 L411JBD	415 L415JBD	419 L419JBD
402 L402JBD	407 L407JBD	412 L412JBD	416 L416JBD	420 L420JBD
403 L403JBD	408 L408JBD	413 L413JBD	417 L417JBD	421 L421JBD
404 L404JBD	409 L409JBD	414 L414JBD	418 L418JBD	422 L422MVV
405 L405JBD	410 L410JBD			

423-430

Volvo B6-9.9M — Alexander Dash — DP40F — 1994

423 L423XVV	425 L425XVV	427 L427XVV	429 M429BNV	430 M430BNV
424 L424XVV	426 L426XVV	428 L428XVV		

450	P450KRP	Dennis Dart	Alexander Dash	B40F	1996
451	P451KRP	Dennis Dart	Alexander Dash	B40F	1996
452	P452KRP	Dennis Dart	Alexander Dash	B40F	1996
500	LFR862X	Leyland National 2 NL106AL11/1R		B44F	1981	Ex Cumberland, 1993
501	LFR864X	Leyland National 2 NL106AL11/1R		B41F	1982	Ex Cumberland, 1993

Opposite, top: **In 1996, further Interurban vehicles were placed in service on the commuter routes into central London. Photographed at Wellingborough when new was 168, P168KBD.** *Andrew Fulcher*
Opposite, bottom: **Northampton is the location for this picture of a United Counties Olympian, illustrating the peaked dome used on the Northern Counties Palatine in 1993.** *Paul Wigan*

In 1994, six Leyland Olympians were transferred from Fife to United Counties. One of these, 712, K712ASC, is seen entering Cambridge on service 74. *M H A Flynn*

600	F110NES	Leyland Olympian ON6LXCT/5RZ	Alexander RL		H66/44F	1989	Ex East Midland, 1992

601-611			Leyland Olympian ONLXB/1R	Eastern Coach Works	H45/32F*	1981	*601 is DPH45/27F
							*602/5/6 are DPH41/27F

601	ARP601X	604	ARP604X	606	ARP606X	608	ARP608X	610	ARP610X
602	ARP602X	605	ARP605X	607	ARP607X	609	ARP609X	611	ARP611X

612	WLT528	Leyland Olympian ONLXB/1RV	Alexander RL	H43/34F	1987	Ex Bluebird, 1991
613	D383XRS	Leyland Olympian ONLXB/1RV	Alexander RL	H43/34F	1987	Ex Bluebird, 1991
614	WLT512	Leyland Olympian ONLXB/1RV	Alexander RL	H47/34F	1987	Ex Bluebird, 1991
615	685DYE	Leyland Olympian ONLXB/1RV	Alexander RL	H47/34F	1987	Ex Bluebird, 1991
616	GSO6V	Leyland Olympian ONLXB/1RV	Alexander RL	H47/34F	1987	Ex Bluebird, 1991
617	GSO7V	Leyland Olympian ONLXB/1RV	Alexander RL	H47/34F	1987	Ex Bluebird, 1991
618	GSO2V	Leyland Olympian ONLXB/1RV	Alexander RL	H47/34F	1986	Ex Bluebird, 1994

620-649			Leyland Olympian ONLXB/2RZ	Alexander RL	H51/36F*	1988-89	*635-644 are H51/34F
							*645-9 are DPH51/31F

620	F620MSL	626	F626MSL	632	F632MSL	638	F638YRP	644	G644EVV
621	F621MSL	627	F627MSL	633	F633MSL	639	G639EVV	645	G645EVV
622	F622MSL	628	F628MSL	634	F634MSP	640	G640EVV	646	G646EVV
623	F623MSL	629	F629MSL	635	F635YRP	641	G641EVV	647	G647EVV
624	F624MSL	630	F630MSL	636	F636YRP	642	G642EVV	648	G648EVV
625	F625MSL	631	F631MSL	637	F637YRP	643	G643EVV	649	G649EVV

650-654			Leyland Olympian ON2R56G13Z4	Alexander RL	H51/34F	1990	

650	H650VVV	651	H651VVV	652	H652VVV	653	H653VVV	654	H654VVV

655-670			Leyland Olympian ON2R50G13Z4	Northern Counties Palatine	H47/29F	1992	

655	K655UNH	658	K658UNH	661	K661UNH	664	K664UNH	668	K668UNH
656	K656UNH	659	K659UNH	662	K662UNH	665	K665UNH	669	K669UNH
657	K657UNH	660	K660UNH	663	K663UNH	667	K667UNH	670	K670UNH

The 1997 Stagecoach Bus Handbook

The Bristol VR remains in regular use with United Counties as several of the later models have been acquired from within the company. Shown in Northampton is 973, KRU847W, an example that arrived from Hampshire Bus, now part of Stagecoach South, in 1988. *Philip Lamb*

671-685

Volvo Olympian YN2RV18Z4   Northern Counties Palatine   H47/29F   1993

671	L671HNV	674	L674HNV	677	L677HNV	680	L680HNV	683	L683HNV
672	L672HNV	675	L675HNV	678	L678HNV	681	L681HNV	684	L684HNV
673	L673HNV	676	L676HNV	679	L679HNV	682	L682HNV	685	L685JBD

686-692

Volvo Olympian YN2RV18Z4   Alexander RL   H51/36F   1996

686	P686JBD	688	P688JBD	690	P690JBD	691	P691JBD	692	P692JBD
687	P687JBD	689	P689JBD						

708-713

Leyland Olympian ON2R56C13Z4   Alexander RL   H47/32F   1992   Ex Fife Scottish, 1994

708	J808WFS	710	K710ASC	711	K711ASC	712	K712ASC	713	K713ASC
709	K709ASC								

714	J620GCR	Leyland Olympian ON2R56G13Z4	Alexander RL	H51/34F	1991	Ex Bluebird, 1994
715	J621GCR	Leyland Olympian ON2R56G13Z4	Alexander RL	H51/34F	1991	Ex Bluebird, 1994
716	J622GCR	Leyland Olympian ON2R56G13Z4	Alexander RL	H51/34F	1991	Ex Bluebird, 1994

721-740

Bristol VRT/SL3/6LXB   Eastern Coach Works   H43/31F   1980-81 Ex Devon General, 1988-89

721	LFJ862W	725	LFJ854W	732	FDV838V	735	LFJ864W	738	FDV835V
722	LFJ863W	726	LFJ855W	733	LFJ868W	736	LFJ865W	739	LFJ869W
723	LFJ853W	727	LFJ879W	734	FDV812V	737	FDV811V	740	FDV832V
724	LFJ852W	731	FDV809V						

744	LFJ878W	Bristol VRT/SL3/6LXC	Eastern Coach Works	H43/31F	1981	Ex Devon General, 1989
750	FAO417V	Bristol VRT/SL3/6LXB	Eastern Coach Works	H43/31F	1980	Ex Cumberland, 1992
751	FAO418V	Bristol VRT/SL3/6LXB	Eastern Coach Works	H43/31F	1980	Ex Cumberland, 1992
752	FAO419V	Bristol VRT/SL3/6LXB	Eastern Coach Works	H43/31F	1980	Ex Cumberland, 1992
839	LBD839P	Bristol VRT/SL3/6LX	Eastern Coach Works	H43/31F	1975	
840	LEU261P	Bristol VRT/SL3/6LX	Eastern Coach Works	H43/27D	1976	Ex Circle-Line, 1995

849-891

Bristol VRT/SL3/6LXB   Eastern Coach Works   H43/31F   1976-78

849	OVV849R	870	TNH870R	876	WBD876S	885	XNV885S	889	XNV889S
856	OVV856R	871	TNH871R	878	XNV878S	886	XNV886S	890	XNV890S
862	RRP862R	872	TNH872R	879	XNV879S	887	XNV887S	891	XNV891S
863	RRP863R	873	TNH873R	880	XNV880S	888	XNV888S		

| 900 | BAU178T | Bristol VRT/SL3/6LXB | Eastern Coach Works | H43/31F | 1978 | Ex East Midland, 1993 |
| 901 | BAU179T | Bristol VRT/SL3/6LXB | Eastern Coach Works | H43/31F | 1978 | Ex East Midland, 1993 |

902-967

Bristol VRT/SL3/6LXB   Eastern Coach Works   H43/31F   1978-81 919/61 are DPH41/27F

902	CBD902T	915	HBD915T	930	SNV930W	944	URP944W	954	VVV954W
903	CBD903T	916	HBD916T	931	SNV931W	945	URP945W	961	VVV961W
908	FRP908T	917	HBD917T	935	SNV935W	948	VVV948W	962	VVV962W
909	FRP909T	919	HBD919T	936	SNV936W	949	VVV949W	963	VVV963W
910	FRP910T	920	LBD920V	937	SNV937W	950	VVV950W	965	VVV965W
911	FRP911T	921	LBD921V	939	URP939W	952	VVV952W	966	VVV966W
912	FRP912T	923	LBD923V	940	URP940W	953	VVV953W	967	VVV967W
914	HBD914T	926	ONH926V	941	URP941W				

970-974

Bristol VRT/SL3/6LXB   Eastern Coach Works   H43/31F   1980   Ex Hampshire Bus, 1988

| 970 | KRU843W | 971 | KRU845W | 972 | KRU846W | 973 | KRU847W | 974 | KRU852W |

980w	GAJ125V	Leyland Fleetline FE30AGR	Northern Counties	H43/31F	1980	Ex Cleveland, 1995
981	GAJ126V	Leyland Fleetline FE30AGR	Northern Counties	H43/31F	1980	Ex Cleveland, 1995
982w	GAJ127V	Leyland Fleetline FE30AGR	Northern Counties	H43/31F	1980	Ex Cleveland, 1995
983w	GAJ128V	Leyland Fleetline FE30AGR	Northern Counties	H43/31F	1980	Ex Cleveland, 1995
984w	YVN520T	Leyland Fleetline FE30AGR	Northern Counties	H43/31F	1979	Ex Cleveland, 1995
985w	YVN522T	Leyland Fleetline FE30AGR	Northern Counties	H43/31F	1979	Ex Cleveland, 1995
986w	YVN524T	Leyland Fleetline FE30AGR	Northern Counties	H43/31F	1979	Ex Cleveland, 1995
988	OCU802R	Leyland Fleetline FE30AGR	Alexander AL	H44/29F	1977	Ex Busways, 1995
989w	OCU804R	Leyland Fleetline FE30AGR	Alexander AL	H44/29F	1977	Ex Busways, 1995
990w	OCU808R	Leyland Fleetline FE30AGR	Alexander AL	H44/29F	1977	Ex Busways, 1995
991	SDA651S	Leyland Fleetline FE30AGR	Park Royal	H43/32F	1978	Ex G&G Travel, 1995
992w	SDA715S	Leyland Fleetline FE30AGR	MCW	H43/33F	1978	Ex G&G Travel, 1995

Special event vehicles

| 703 | HVS937 | AEC Routemaster R2RH | Park Royal | H36/28R | 1961 | Ex London Buses, 1988 |
| 708 | CUV192C | AEC Routemaster R2RH | Park Royal | H36/28R | 1965 | Ex London Buses, 1988 |

Previous Registrations:

647DYE	C85PRP	RBD397Y	NBD105Y, 83CBD
685DYE	D379XRS	TSU639	FKK839Y
83CBD	A294ANH	TSU640	FKK840Y
A728ANH	A800TGG, 4009SC, A332SNH, WLT908	TSU641	FKK841Y
A729ANH	A798TGG, 7878SC, A320SNH, 647DYE	TSU642	FKK842Y
GSO2V	C472SSOVLT255	B357KNH, Malawi ?,	
GSO6V	D376XRS	WLT512	D384XRS
GSO7V	D377XRS	WLT528	D382XRS
HVS937	WLT682	WLT682	C81PRP
MSU465	D525ESG	WLT908	C82PRP

Livery variations: National Express: 92-6, 115; green and cream (Buckinghamshire Road Car); white & yellow (City Bus).

WESTERN

Western Buses Ltd, A1 Service Ltd,
Sandgate, Ayr, KA7 1DD

Depots :Harbour Road, Ardrossan; Waggon Road, Ayr; Ayr Road, Cumnock; Eastfield Road, Dumfries; Argyll Road, Dunoon; Vicarton Street, Girvan; Mackinlay Place, Kilmarnock; Kirkcudbright; Brodick; Isle of Arran; Pointhouse, Rothesay; Lewis Street, Stranraer; Whithorn.

001-035   Mercedes-Benz 709D   Alexander Sprint   B25F   1995-96

001	N601VSS	007	N607VSS	021	N621VSS	026	N626VSS	031	N631VSS
002	N602VSS	008	N608VSS	022	N622VSS	027	N627VSS	032	N632VSS
003	N603VSS	009	N609VSS	023	N623VSS	028	N628VSS	033	N633VSS
004	N604VSS	010	N610VSS	024	N624VSS	029	N629VSS	034	N634VSS
005	N605VSS	011	N611VSS	025	N625VSS	030	N630VSS	035	N635VSS
006	N606VSS	012	N612VSS						

101	XSJ656T	Leyland Fleetline FE30AGR	Northern Counties	O44/31F	1978	
102	HDS566H	Daimler Fleetline CRG6LX	Alexander D	O44/31F	1970	Ex Clydeside Scottish, 1989
103	GHV948N	Daimler Fleetline CRG6	Park Royal	O44/27F	1974	Ex Selkent, 1995
104	GHV102N	Daimler Fleetline CRG6	Park Royal	O44/27F	1975	Ex Selkent, 1995
105	UWV607S	Bristol VRT/SL3/6LXB	Eastern Coach Works	CO43/31F	1977	Ex Bluebird Buses, 1996
106u	OSJ636R	Leyland Leopard PSU3C/3R	Alexander AY	B53F	1977	Ex Bluebird, 1996
108	J8WSB	Plaxton 425	Lorraine	C51FT	1992	
111	803DYE	Dennis Javelin 12SDA2105	Plaxton Paramount 3200 III	C50F	1990	
113	J13WSB	Dennis Javelin 12SDA1929	Plaxton Paramount 3200 III	C53F	1992	
114	J14WSB	Dennis Javelin 12SDA1919	Plaxton Paramount 3200 III	C53F	1992	
115	J15WSB	Dennis Javelin 12SDA2102	Plaxton Première 320	C53F	1992	

Since Stagecoach took over Western Scottish in 1995 there have been many changes to the operations and the fleet. The Burns Heritage Tour is a new service based on Ayr and using a former Selkent Daimler Fleetline open-top. The vehicle, 104, GHV102N, is pictured here heading for the pick-up point. *Tony Wilson*

116-121

Dennis Dorchester SDA811 — Alexander TC — C53F* — 1987 — 118-20 are C51F

116	WLT526	118	WLT415	119	VLT73	120	WLT447	121	WLT501
117	FSU737								

122-128

Volvo B10M-62 — Plaxton Premiére Interurban DP51F — 1994 — Ex Stagecoach South, 1996

122	M160CCD	124	M162CCD	126	M164CCD	127	M165CCD	128	M166CCD
123	M161CCD	125	M163CCD						

129	WLT416	Volvo B10M-60	Plaxton Paramount 3500 III	C51F	1989	Ex Cambus, 1996
130	YSV730	Volvo B10M-60	Plaxton Paramount 3500 III	C53F	1990	Ex Cambus, 1996
131	YSV735	Volvo B10M-60	Plaxton Paramount 3500 III	C53F	1991	Ex Cambus, 1996
135	VLT104	Volvo B10M-60	Plaxton Expressliner	C53F	1990	Ex Bluebird Buses, 1995
136	WLT794	Volvo B10M-60	Plaxton Expressliner	C53F	1990	Ex Bluebird Buses, 1995
137	WLT809	Volvo B10M-60	Plaxton Expressliner	C53F	1990	Ex Dorset Travel, 1995
138	WLT720	Volvo B10M-60	Plaxton Expressliner	C53F	1990	Ex Dorset Travel, 1995
139	WLT727	Volvo B10M-60	Plaxton Expressliner	C53F	1990	Ex Ribble, 1995
140	WLT830	Volvo B10M-60	Plaxton Expressliner	C53F	1990	Ex Ribble, 1995
141	IIL3507	Volvo B10M-60	Plaxton Paramount 3500 III	C51F	1989	Ex Ribble, 1995

142-160

Volvo B10M-62 — Plaxton Premiére Interurban DP51F — 1996

142	N142XSA	146	N146XSA	150	P150ASA	154	P154ASA	158	P158ASA
143	N143XSA	147	N247XSA	151	P151ASA	155	P255ASA	159	P159ASA
144	N144XSA	148	P148ASA	152	P152ASA	156	P156ASA	160	P160ASA
145	N145XSA	149	P149ASA	153	P153ASA	157	P157ASA		

163	NIB5232	Leyland Tiger TRCTL11/3RH	Plaxton Paramount 3200 II	C51F	1985	Ex Bluebird Buses, 1996
164	NIB5233	Leyland Tiger TRCTL11/3RH	Plaxton Paramount 3200 II	C51F	1985	Ex Bluebird Buses, 1996
165	BYJ919Y	Leyland Tiger TRCTL11/3R	Plaxton Paramount 3200	C50F	1983	Ex Stagecoach South, 1996
166	UWP105	Leyland Tiger TRCTL11/3R	Plaxton Paramount 3200	C50F	1983	Ex Stagecoach South, 1996
168	MSU466	Leyland Tiger TRCTL11/3RH	Duple 340	C46FT	1987	Ex Stagecoach South, 1996
169	XDU599	Leyland Tiger TRCTL11/3RZ	Plaxton Paramount 3500 II	C51FT	1986	Ex Stagecoach South, 1996
170	VLT54	DAF SB2305DHTD585	Plaxton Paramount 3200 III	C57F	1989	Ex Arran Coaches, 1994
171	TSU638	Leyland Tiger TRCTL11/3R	Plaxton Paramount 3200 E	C53F	1983	Ex East Midland, 1995
172	13CLT	Leyland Tiger TRCTL11/3RH	Duple 340	C51FT	1987	Ex Kelvin Central, 1990
173	WLT546	Leyland Tiger TRCTL11/3RH	Duple 340	C51FT	1987	Ex Kelvin Central, 1990
175w	PSO178W	Leyland Tiger TRCTL11/3R	Duple Dominant IV	C51F	1981	Ex Bluebird Buses, 1995
176w	RRS225X	Leyland Tiger TRCTL11/3R	Duple Goldliner IV	C53F	1982	Ex Bluebird Buses, 1995
177w	CSO390Y	Leyland Tiger TRCTL11/2R	Duple Dominant II Express	C49F	1983	Ex Bluebird Buses, 1995
178	CSO386Y	Leyland Tiger TRCTL11/3R	Duple Dominant II Express	C47F	1983	Ex Bluebird Buses, 1995
179	UM7681	Leyland Tiger TRCTL11/3R	Plaxton Paramount 3200	C51F	1984	Ex East Midland, 1995
180	439UG	Leyland Tiger TRCTL11/3R	Plaxton Paramount 3200	C53F	1985	Ex East Midland, 1995
181	5796MX	Leyland Tiger TRCTL11/3RH	Plaxton Paramount 3500	C51F	1985	Ex East Midland, 1995
182	295UB	Leyland Tiger TRCTL11/3RH	Plaxton Paramount 3500	C53F	1985	Ex East Midland, 1995
183	283URB	Volvo B10M-60	Plaxton Paramount 3500 III	C53F	1987	Ex East Midland, 1995
184	K574DFS	Volvo B10M-60	Plaxton Premiére 320	C51F	1993	Ex Fife Scottish, 1995
186	896HOD	Volvo B10M-61	Plaxton Paramount 3500 II	C51F	1985	Ex Stagecoach South, 1995
187	495FFJ	Volvo B10M-61	Plaxton Paramount 3500 II	C52F	1985	Ex Stagecoach South, 1995
188	L582JSA	Volvo B10M-60	Plaxton Premiére Interurban	DP51F	1993	
189	L583JSA	Volvo B10M-60	Plaxton Premiére Interurban	DP51F	1993	
190	L584JSA	Volvo B10M-60	Plaxton Premiére Interurban	DP51F	1993	

191-197

Volvo B10M-61 — Plaxton Paramount 3500 — C49FT* — 1985 — *196/7 are C51FT

191	VCS391	194	VLT37	195	WLT978	196	WLT465	197	WLT697

198	P198OSE	Volvo B10M-61	Plaxton Premiére Interurban	AC71F	1996	
199	P199OSE	Volvo B10M-61	Plaxton Premiére Interurban	AC71F	1996	
200	D230UHC	Mercedes-Benz L608D	Alexander AM	B20F	1986	Ex Stagecoach South, 1995
201	C101KDS	Mercedes-Benz L608D	Alexander AM	B21F	1986	Ex Kelvin Scottish, 1987
203	D41UAO	Mercedes-Benz L608D	Reeve Burgess	B20F	1987	Ex Cumberland, 1995

204-218

Mercedes-Benz L608D — Alexander AM — B21F — 1986 — Ex Kelvin Scottish, 1987

204u	C104KDS	207	D107NUS	210	D110NUS	214	D114NUS	217	D117NUS
205	C105KDS	208	D108NUS	211	D111NUS	215	D115NUS	218u	D118NUS
206	C106KDS	209	D109NUS	213	D113NUS	216	D116NUS		

During 1995, Western Buses acquired several MetroRiders from Fife and East London and these were used to displace Renault minibuses. Shown in Largs carrying A1 Service names is 243, **F121YVP.** *Tony Wilson*

The autumn of 1996 saw the arrival of nineteen Plaxton Interurban-bodied Volvo B10Ms to develop Stagecoach Express services mostly from Ayrshire into Glasgow. Photographed in Renfrew Street, Glasgow shortly after setting off for Irvine is 148, **P148ASA.** *Murdoch Currie*

During 1996 the head office of Western Buses moved from Kilmarnock to Ayr where 336, M736BSJ a Volvo B6 with Alexander Dash bodywork, was photographed in June. *M E Lyons*

219	L882LFS	Mercedes-Benz 709D	Alexander Sprint	B25F	1994	
220	L883LFS	Mercedes-Benz 709D	Alexander Sprint	B25F	1994	
221	G574FSD	Mercedes-Benz 709D	Reeve Burgess Beaver	B25F	1990	Ex Arran Coaches, 1994
222	D122NUS	Mercedes-Benz L608D	Alexander AM	B21F	1986	Ex Kelvin Scottish, 1987
223	D123NUS	Mercedes-Benz L608D	Alexander AM	B21F	1986	Ex Kelvin Scottish, 1987
224u	D124NUS	Mercedes-Benz L608D	Alexander AM	B21F	1986	Ex Kelvin Scottish, 1987
225	L262VSU	Mercedes-Benz 709D	Dormobile Routemaker	B29F	1994	Ex William Hamilton, Maybole, 1995
226u	D136NUS	Mercedes-Benz L608D	Alexander AM	B21F	1986	Ex Kelvin Scottish, 1987
227	G461SGB	Mercedes-Benz 609D	North West CS	C24F	1990	Ex Clyde Coast, 1995
228u	D128NUS	Mercedes-Benz L608D	Alexander AM	B21F	1986	Ex Kelvin Scottish, 1987
229	D129NUS	Mercedes-Benz L608D	Alexander AM	B21F	1986	Ex Kelvin Scottish, 1987
230	D130NUS	Mercedes-Benz L608D	Alexander AM	B21F	1986	Ex Kelvin Scottish, 1987
231	D121NUS	Mercedes-Benz L608D	Alexander AM	B21F	1986	Ex Kelvin Scottish, 1987
232	E638YUS	Mercedes-Benz 609D	Reeve Burgess	C19F	1988	Ex Arran Coaches, 1994
233	C594SHC	Mercedes-Benz L608D	PMT Hanbridge	B20F	1986	Ex Cheltenham & Gloucester, 1995
234	C591SHC	Mercedes-Benz L608D	PMT Hanbridge	B20F	1986	Ex Cheltenham & Gloucester, 1995
237	E645KYW	MCW MetroRider MF158/1	MCW	B30F	1988	Ex East London, 1995

239-244		MCW MetroRider MF158/16	MCW	B28F	1988	Ex East London, 1995

239	F114YVP	240	F118YVP	241	F119YVP	243	F121YVP	244	F128YVP

245	G251TSL	Mercedes-Benz 709D	Alexander Sprint	B25F	1990	Ex Bluebird Buses, 1996
246	G252TSL	Mercedes-Benz 709D	Alexander Sprint	B25F	1990	Ex Bluebird Buses, 1996
247	G253TSL	Mercedes-Benz 709D	Alexander Sprint	B25F	1990	Ex Bluebird Buses, 1996

248-265		Mercedes-Benz 709D	Alexander Sprint	B25F	1995

248	M648FYS	252	M652FYS	256	M656FYS	260	M660FYS	263	M663FYS
249	M649FYS	253	M653FYS	257	M657FYS	261	M661FYS	264	M664FYS
250	M650FYS	254	M654FYS	258	M658FYS	262	M662FYS	265	M665FYS
251	M651FYS	255	M655FYS	259	M659FYS				

266	L916UGA	Mercedes-Benz 709D	Dormobile Routemaker	B29F	1993	Ex Clyde Coast, 1995
267	M667FYS	Mercedes-Benz 709D	Alexander Sprint	B25F	1995	
268	M668FYS	Mercedes-Benz 709D	Alexander Sprint	B25F	1995	
269	K208OHS	Mercedes-Benz 709D	Dormobile Routemaker	B29F	1993	Ex Clyde Coast, 1995
272	K209OHS	Mercedes-Benz 709D	Dormobile Routemaker	B29F	1993	Ex Clyde Coast, 1995
273	D94EKV	Peugeot-Talbot Freeway	Talbot	DP12FL	1987	Ex Sochulbus, Ashford, 1992
274	F334JHS	Peugeot-Talbot Freeway	Talbot	DP12FL	1989	
275	F335JHS	Peugeot-Talbot Freeway	Talbot	DP12FL	1989	
276	G825VGA	Peugeot-Talbot Freeway	Talbot	DP12FL	1990	
279	L577NSB	Mercedes-Benz 709D	Dormobile Routemaker	B21FL	1993	Ex Arran Coaches, 1994
280	L578NSB	Mercedes-Benz 709D	Dormobile Routemaker	B21FL	1993	Ex Arran Coaches, 1994
281	G254TSL	Mercedes-Benz 709D	Alexander Sprint	B25F	1990	Ex Bluebird Buses, 1996
282	G255TSL	Mercedes-Benz 709D	Alexander Sprint	B25F	1990	Ex Bluebird Buses, 1996
283	F53RFS	MCW MetroRider MF150/98	MCW	B25F	1988	Ex Bluebird, 1996
284	F51RFS	MCW MetroRider MF150/98	MCW	B25F	1988	Ex Bluebird, 1995
285	F52RFS	MCW MetroRider MF150/98	MCW	B25F	1988	Ex Bluebird, 1995
286	F63RFS	MCW MetroRider MF150/100	MCW	B25F	1988	Ex Bluebird, 1995
287	F64RFS	MCW MetroRider MF150/99	MCW	B25F	1988	Ex Bluebird, 1995
288	F65RFS	MCW MetroRider MF150/101	MCW	B25F	1988	Ex Bluebird, 1995
289	F54RFS	MCW MetroRider MF150/98	MCW	B25F	1988	Ex Bluebird, 1996
294	E643DCK	Renault-Dodge S46	Dormobile	B25F	1987	Ex Fife Scottish, 1994
296	E646DCK	Renault-Dodge S46	Dormobile	B25F	1987	Ex Fife Scottish, 1994
297	F197ASD	Mercedes-Benz 609D	Reeve Burgess Beaver	B23F	1988	Ex Clyde Coast, Ardrossan, 1996

301-310

	Dennis Dart 9.8SDL3017		Alexander Dash		B40F		1992	
301	J301BRM	303	J303BRM	305	J305BRM	307	J307BRM	309	J309BRM
302	J302BRM	304	J304BRM	306	J306BRM	308	J308BRM	310	J310BRM

312-341

	Volvo B6-9.9M		Alexander Dash		DP40F		1994	
312	M772BCS	321	M721BCS	326	M726BCS	334	M734BSJ	338	M738BSJ
313	M773BCS	322	M722BCS	327	M727BCS	335	M735BSJ	339	M739BSJ
318	M718BCS	323	M723BCS	332	M732BSJ	336	M736BSJ	340	M740BSJ
319	M719BCS	324	M724BCS	333	M733BSJ	337	M737BSJ	341	M741BSJ
320	M720BCS	325	M725BCS						

351-358

	Volvo B6-9.9M		Alexander Dash		B40F		1994	
351	M674SSX	353	M676SSX	355	M678SSX	357	M680SSX	358	M681SSX
352	M675SSX	354	M677SSX	356	M679SSX				

390-398

	Dennis Dart SFD412		Alexander Dash		B40F		1996-97	
390	P390LPS	392	P392LPS	394	P394LPS	396	P396BRS	398	P398BRS
391	P391LPS	393	P393LPS	395	P395BRS	397	P397BRS		

399	L208PSB	Dennis Dart 9SDL3031	Marshall C36	B39F	1994	Ex Arran Coaches, 1994

405-410

	Dennis Dorchester SDA801		Plaxton Paramount 3200E		C49F		1983	404/5/7-10 ex Clydeside, 1989
405w	HSB889Y	407w	HSB887Y	408w	HSB883Y	409w	CSO526Y	410w	HSB884Y
406w	HSB841Y								

427	ESU435	Volvo B10M-61	East Lancashire (1994)	DP51F	1982	
431	VLT154	Volvo B10M-61	East Lancashire (1994)	DP51F	1981	
501	M151FGB	Volvo B10B	Wright Endurance	B51F	1994	Ex A1 Service, 1994

505-512

	Volvo B10M-56		Alexander PS		DP48F		1995	
505	M488ASW	507	M871ASW	509	M469ASW	511	M483ASW	512	M468ASW
506	M869ASW	508	M485ASW	510	M481ASW				

565-594

	Volvo B10M-55		Alexander PS		DP48F		1995	
565	M480ASW	571	M471ASW	577	M477ASW	583	M466ASW	589	M789PRS
566	M486ASW	572	M472ASW	578	M478ASW	584	M784PRS	590	M790PRS
567	M487ASW	573	M473ASW	579	M479ASW	585	M785PRS	591	M791PRS
568	M489ASW	574	M474ASW	580	M870ASW	586	M786PRS	592	M792PRS
569	M482ASW	575	M475ASW	581	M484ASW	587	M787PRS	593	M793PRS
570	M470ASW	576	M476ASW	582	M872ASW	588	M788PRS	594	M467ASW

Most of the former A1 fleet that passed to Western are now painted into corporate livery. Shown passing through Stevenston is 599, WLT439, one of only two Plaxton Derwent-bodied vehiocles currently operating in the Stagecoach group. *Malc McDonald*

597	WLT774	Volvo B10M-56	Duple 300	B53F	1988	Ex A1 Service, 1995
598	WLT538	Volvo B10M-56	Duple 300	B53F	1988	Ex A1 Service, 1995
599	WLT439	Volvo B10M-55	Plaxton Derwent	B55F	1990	Ex A1 Service, 1995
616	N616USS	Volvo B10M-62	Plaxton Expressliner 2	C44FT	1995	
617	N617USS	Volvo B10M-62	Plaxton Expressliner 2	C44FT	1995	
620	TMS404X	Leyland Leopard PSU3G/4R	Alexander AYS	B53F	1982	Ex Fife, 1996
621	TMS405X	Leyland Leopard PSU3G/4R	Alexander AYS	DP49F	1982	Ex Fife, 1996
622	TMS407X	Leyland Leopard PSU3G/4R	Alexander AYS	DP49F	1982	Ex Fife, 1996
623	XMS423Y	Leyland Leopard PSU3G/4R	Alexander AYS	B53F	1982	Ex Fife, 1996
624	WFS136W	Leyland Leopard PSU3F/4R	Alexander AYS	B53F	1980	Ex Bluebird Buses, 1995
625	YSF98S	Leyland Leopard PSU3D/4R	Alexander AYS	B53F	1977	Ex Bluebird Buses, 1995
626	YSF100S	Leyland Leopard PSU3E/4R	Alexander AYS	B53F	1977	Ex Bluebird Buses, 1995
627	NPA229W	Leyland Leopard PSU3E/4R	Plaxton Supreme IV Express	C53F	1981	Ex Bluebird Buses, 1995
629	GMS285S	Leyland Leopard PSU3E/4R	Alexander AYS	B53F	1978	Ex Kelvin Scottish, 1987
630	GMS292S	Leyland Leopard PSU3E/4R	Alexander AYS	B55F	1978	Ex Kelvin Scottish, 1987

633-680		Leyland Leopard PSU3E/4R*	Alexander AY	B53F*	1977-80	*637 is DP49F

*667/70/1/6/8-80 are PSU3D/4R; 633 ex Clydeside Scottish, 1989

633	GCS33V	647	GCS47V	657	GCS57V	665	GCS65V	676	TSJ76S
637	GCS37V	648	GCS48V	658	GCS58V	667	TSJ67S	678	TSJ78S
638	GCS38V	649	GCS49V	660	GCS60V	669	GCS69V	679	TSJ79S
641	GCS41V	651	GCS51V	661	GCS61V	670	TSJ70S	680	TSJ80S
645	GCS45V	653	GCS53V	662	GCS62V	671	TSJ71S		

Opposite, top: Pictured at the Moffat terminus of service 382 is Western 255, M655FYS, one of a batch of eighteen Mercedes-Benz 709Ds delivered in 1995. *Murdoch Currie*
Opposite, bottom: The former A1 Service operation now carries names in Stagecoach lettering. Shown here is 927, N861VHH, a Volvo Olympian with Alexander RH bodywork. From this batch of twenty one, the seventeen which operate the main Kilmarnock to Ardrossan service are being repainted into the former A1 service livery. *Tony Wilson*

681	TMS406X	Leyland Leopard PSU3G/4R	Alexander AYS	B49F	1982	Ex Fife Scottish, 1996
682	GSO82V	Leyland Leopard PSU3E/4R	Alexander AYS	B53F	1980	Ex Fife Scottish, 1996
683	GSO83V	Leyland Leopard PSU3E/4R	Alexander AYS	B49F	1980	Ex Fife Scottish, 1996
684	GSO84V	Leyland Leopard PSU3E/4R	Alexander AYS	B49F	1980	Ex Fife Scottish, 1996
685	TSJ85S	Leyland Leopard PSU3D/4R	Alexander AY	B53F	1978	
686	XMS422Y	Leyland Leopard PSU3G/4R	Alexander AYS	B53F	1982	Ex Fife Scottish, 1996
687	WFS138W	Leyland Leopard PSU3F/4R	Alexander AYS	B53F	1980	Ex Fife Scottish, 1996
688	WFS142W	Leyland Leopard PSU3F/4R	Alexander AYS	B53F	1980	Ex Fife Scottish, 1996
689	GSO77V	Leyland Leopard PSU3E/4R	Alexander AYS	B55F	1980	Ex Highland Country, 1996

691-699

Leyland Leopard PSU3E/4R*   Alexander AY   B53F   1977-80 695-7 ex Clydeside Scottish, 1989
*691-3 are PSU3D/4R; 692/6 are B55F

691	TSJ31S	693	TSJ33S	696	BSJ896T	698	BSJ930T	699	BSJ931T
692	TSJ32S	695	BSJ895T	697	BSJ917T				

701	UIB3541	Leyland National 11351A/1R		B48F	1979	Ex Kelvin Central, 1989

702-706

Leyland National 11351A/3R   B48F   1978-79 Ex British Airways, Heathrow, 1993

702	UIB3542	703	UIB3543	704	OIW7024	705	OIW7025	706	UIB3076

710	KMA399T	Leyland National 11351A/1R(Gardner)		B51F	1979	Ex A1 Service, 1994
721	703DYE	Bedford YMT	Duple Dominant II Express	C49F	1981	Ex Arran Coaches, 1994
727	D799USB	Bedford YMT	Duple Dominant	B55F	1987	Ex Arran Coaches, 1994
728	D918GRU	Bedford YMT	Plaxton Derwent	B53F	1987	Ex Arran Coaches, 1994
729	FSU739	Bedford YNV	Plaxton Paramount 3200 III	C57F	1987	Ex Arran Coaches, 1994

771-791

Leyland National 2 NL116L11/1R   B52F*   1980-81 Ex Kelvin Scottish, 1988
*774/5/85/9-91 are B48F

771	WAS771V	775	MDS865V	780	YFS308W	785	NLS985W	790	YFS310W
773	RFS583V	778	MDS858V	781	MSO18W	786	SNS826W	791	YFS309W
774	YFS304W	779	RFS579V	783	NLS983W	789	NLS989W		

792	KRS540V	Leyland National 2 NL106L11/1R		B41F	1980	Ex Bluebird, 1993
793	KRS542V	Leyland National 2 NL106L11/1R		B41F	1980	Ex Bluebird, 1993
795	MSO10W	Leyland National 2 NL106L11/1R		B41F	1980	Ex Bluebird, 1993
796	NLP388V	Leyland National 2 NL116L11/3R		B48F	1980	Ex British Airways, Heathrow, 1993
797	JTF971W	Leyland National 2 NL116AL11/1R		B48F	1981	Ex Mitchell, Plean, 1994
801	UNA863S	Leyland Atlantean AN68A/1R	Park Royal	H43/32F	1978	Ex GM Buses, 1991
802	WVM884S	Leyland Atlantean AN68A/1R	Park Royal	H43/32F	1978	Ex GM Buses, 1991
804	ANA211T	Leyland Atlantean AN68A/1R	Northern Counties	H43/32F	1978	Ex GM Buses, 1991
805	BNC936T	Leyland Atlantean AN68A/1R	Park Royal	H43/32F	1979	Ex GM Buses, 1991
806	RJA702R	Leyland Atlantean AN68A/1R	Northern Counties	H43/32F	1977	Ex GM Buses, 1991
807	UNA772S	Leyland Atlantean AN68A/1R	Northern Counties	H43/32F	1977	Ex GM Buses, 1991
809	VBA161S	Leyland Atlantean AN68A/1R	Northern Counties	H43/32F	1978	Ex GM Buses, 1992
810	UNA824S	Leyland Atlantean AN68A/1R	Park Royal	H43/32F	1977	Ex GM Buses, 1992
811	UNA840S	Leyland Atlantean AN68A/1R	Park Royal	H43/32F	1977	Ex GM Buses, 1992
812	WVM888S	Leyland Atlantean AN68A/1R	Park Royal	H43/32F	1978	Ex GM Buses, 1992
817	HGD213T	Leyland Atlantean AN68A/1R	Alexander AL	H45/33F	1979	Ex A1 Service, 1995
819	KSD62W	Leyland Atlantean AN68B/1R	Alexander AL	H45/33F	1980	Ex A1 Service, 1995
840	ULS660T	Leyland Fleetline FE30AGR	Eastern Coach Works	H43/32F	1979	Ex Kelvin Central, 1989
843	ASA23T	Leyland Fleetline FE30AGR	Eastern Coach Works	H43/32F	1978	Ex Northern Scottish, 1987
847	ASA27T	Leyland Fleetline FE30AGR	Eastern Coach Works	H43/32F	1978	Ex Northern Scottish, 1987

Western 894, E864RCS, is one of six Volvo B10M double-deck buses in the Western fleet four being new to Western Scottish, while the other pair came from A1 Service providers. Photographed as it sets out to start an afternoon schools duty in Ayr is 864, E864RCS. *M E Lyons*

851-889

							Leyland Fleetline FE30AGR		Northern Counties		H44/31F	1978-79

859-6/9/80/5/9 ex Clydeside Scottish, 1988-89

851	XSJ651T	858	XSJ658T	865	XSJ665T	870	BCS870T	880	ECS880V
853w	XSJ653T	859	XSJ659T	866	XSJ666T	871w	BCS871T	882	ECS882V
854	XSJ654T	860w	XSJ660T	867	XSJ667T	877	ECS877V	888	BCS868T
855	XSJ655T	861	XSJ661T	868	XSJ668T	878	ECS878V	889	BCS869T
857w	XSJ657T	862	XSJ662T	869	XSJ669T	879	ECS879V		

892	A308RSU	Volvo Citybus B10M-50	East Lancashire	H47/36F	1983	Ex A1 Service, 1995
893	B24CGA	Volvo Citybus B10M-50	Alexander RV	H47/37F	1985	Ex A1 Service, 1995
894	E864RCS	Volvo Citybus B10M-50	Alexander RV	DPH41/29F	1987	
895	E865RCS	Volvo Citybus B10M-50	Alexander RV	DPH45/33F	1987	
896	E866RCS	Volvo Citybus B10M-50	Alexander RV	DPH45/33F	1987	
897	E867RCS	Volvo Citybus B10M-50	Alexander RV	DPH43/33F	1987	

901-906

							Leyland Olympian ONLXB/1R		Roe	H47/29F	1982-83	Ex A1 Service, 1995

901	HSB698Y	903	CUB73Y	904	EWY74Y	905	EWY75Y	906	EWY76Y
902	CUB72Y								

907	C800HCS	Leyland Olympian ONLXB/1R	Eastern Coach Works	H45/32F	1986	Ex A1 Service, 1995
908	F41XCS	Leyland Olympian ONCL10/1RZ	Leyland	H47/31F	1989	Ex A1 Service, 1995
909	F524WSJ	Leyland Olympian ONCL10/1RZ	Leyland	H47/31F	1989	Ex A1 Service, 1995
910	F149XCS	Leyland Olympian ONCL10/1RZ	Leyland	H47/31F	1989	Ex A1 Service, 1995
911	PJI4983	Leyland Olympian ONTL11/2RSp	Eastern Coach Works	CH45/24F	1985	Ex Cleveland Transit, 1995

912-932

		Volvo Olympian YN2RV18Z4		Alexander RH		H47/32F		1995	

912	M490ASW	917	N851VHH	921	N855VHH	925	N859VHH	929	N863VHH
913	M491ASW	918	N852VHH	922	N856VHH	926	N860VHH	930	N864VHH
914	M492ASW	919	N853VHH	923	N857VHH	927	N861VHH	931	N865VHH
915	N849VHH	920	N854VHH	924	N858VHH	928	N862VHH	932	N866VHH
916	N850VHH								

933-942

		Leyland Titan TNLXB2RRSp		Park Royal		H44/26D		1978-80 Ex East London, 1995	

933	EYE236V	935	CUL179V	937	WYV5T	939	WYV29T	941	EYE246V
934	CUL189V	936	CUL209V	938	WYV27T	940	CUL197V	942	EYE248V

943-949

		Leyland Titan TNLXB2RRSp		Leyland		H44/26D*		1981-83 Ex East London, 1995	
								*Lower deck seating varies	

943	GYE252W	945	GYE273W	947	OHV684Y	948	A833SUL	949	A876SUL
944	GYE254W	946	GYE281W						

950-960

		Leyland Titan TNLXB2RRSp		Leyland		H44/26D*		1983 Ex Selkent, 1996	
								*Lower deck seating varies	

950	A824SUL	953	OHV714Y	955	OHV762Y	957	OHV800Y	959	NUW618Y
951	OHV700Y	954	OHV728Y	956	OHV780Y	958	OHV809Y	960	NUW614Y
952	OHV710Y								

964	WYV49T	Leyland Titan TNLXB2RRSp	Park Royal	H44/22D	1979	Ex Selkent, 1995
965	WYV56T	Leyland Titan TNLXB2RRSp	Park Royal	H44/22D	1979	Ex Selkent, 1995
966	CUL208V	Leyland Titan TNLXB2RRSp	Park Royal	H44/26D	1980	Ex Selkent, 1995
967	KYV410X	Leyland Titan TNLXB2RRSp	Leyland	H44/24D	1982	Ex Selkent, 1995

Special event vehicles - traditional liveries

1081	YSD350L	Leyland Leopard PSU3/3R	Alexander AY	B41F	1972	
1074	YYS174	Bedford C5Z1	Duple Vista	C21FM	1960	Ex David MacBrayne, 1970
1082	RCS382	Leyland Titan PD3A/3	Alexander	L35/32RD	1961	
1059	UCS659	Albion Lowlander LR3	Alexander	H40/31F	1963	

Previous Registrations:

13CLT	D317SGB	UIB3542	EGT451T
283URB	E551UHS	UIB3543	WGY589S
295UB	B421CMC	UM7681	A317ONE
439UG	B422CMC	VCS376	TSD158Y, WLT652
495FFJ	B193CGA	VCS391	B191CGA
5796MX	B106REL	VLT37	B194CGA
703DYE	TSD153Y	VLT54	G262EHD
803DYE	H661UWR	VLT73	D219NCS
896HOD	B192CGA	VLT104	TSD154Y
CSO386Y	ASA10Y, TSV780	VLT154	NCS121W, WLT415, WGB646W
CSO390Y	ASA9Y, TSV779	WLT415	D218NCS
ESU435	GGE127X, FSU737, TOS530X	WLT439	G569ESD
F149XCS	F523WSJ	WLT444	TSD159Y
FSU737	D217NCS	WLT447	D220NCS
FSU739	GGE128X	WLT465	B196CGA
HDS566H	SMS402H, 703DYE	WLT501	D221NCS
HSB698Y	CUB50Y	WLT526	D216NCS
IIL3507	F410DUG	WLT538	E159XHS
KRS540V	GSO6V	WLT546	D318SGB
KRS542V	GSO8V	WLT697	B197CGA
M151FGB	M1ABO	WLT720	B198CGA
OIW7024	GLP433T	WLT727	TSD155Y
OIW7025	GLP427T	WLT774	E158XHS
PJI4983	B577LPE	WLT794	TSD156Y
PSO177W	BSG549W, 630DYE, WGB175W, CSU920	WLT809	TSD150Y
PSO178W	BSG547W, WLT741, WGB176W, CSU921	WLT830	TSD157Y
RRS225X	MSC556X, CSU923	WLT874	TSD152Y
TSU638	FKK838Y	WLT978	B195CGA
UIB3076	EGT458T, WGY598S		
UIB3541	EGB89T		

1997
Stagecoach
BUS HANDBOOK
OVERSEAS OPERATIONS

January 1997

KENYA BUS

Kenya Bus Services Ltd, General Waruingi Street, Eastleigh,
P O Box 41001, Nairobi, Kenya.

Depots : Mombasa and Nairobi.

201-220

		Dennis Dragon 1820		AVA		H115F*	1995-96		

*206-11 seat 99, 212-17 seat 103.

201	KAG544H	205	KAG933E	209	KAG060M	213	KAG470T	217	KAG025X
202	KAG931E	206	KAG542J	210	KAG601M	214	KAG471T	218	KAG405W
203	KAG292E	207	KAG543J	211	KAG602M	215	KAG472T	219	KAG522X
204	KAG932E	208	KAG544J	212	KAG264R	216	KAG770V	220	KAH560B

301-320

		ERF Trailblazer 6LXB		Suleman		B47D	1983-85		

301	KUW565	304	KUY289	310	KWE764	319	KWQ732	320	KWT363
303	KUY279	305	KUY829						

321-331

		ERF Trailblazer 6LXB		Labh Singh		B49D*	1986-88	*330 is B43D, 331 is B46D	

334-8 are B47D, 325 is B51F

321	KXQ484	324	KXR388	326	KYD117	328	KYV458	330	KYY078
322	KXR065	325	KYD116	327	KYW205	329	KYV457	331	KYW206
323	KXR282								

334	KYH176	ERF Trailblazer 6LXB	Suleman	B47D	1987
336	KYM857	ERF Trailblazer 6LXB	Suleman	B47D	1987
337	KYN019	ERF Trailblazer 6LXB	Suleman	B47D	1987
338	KYS305	ERF Trailblazer 6LXB	Suleman	B47D	1988

341-396

		ERF Trailblazer 6LXB MkII		Labh Singh		B45D*	1993-94	*347 is B46D, 378 is B48D	

341	KAC649X	352	KAD528A	363	KAD447C	374	KAD407E	385	KAD199J
342	KAC929X	353	KAD526A	364	KAD553C	375	KAD860F	386	KAD386J
343	KAC023Y	354	KAD619A	365	KAD743D	376	KAD147G	387	KAD378J
344	KAC022Y	355	KAD841A	366	KAD737D	377	KAD117G	388	KAD659K
345	KAC021Y	356	KAD902A	367	KAD779D	378	KAD194G	389	KAD822K
346	KAC287Y	357	KAD535D	368	KAD826D	379	KAD233G	390	KAD899Y
347	KAC290Y	358	KAD126C	369	KAD899D	380	KAD589H	391	KAD902Y
348	KAC289Y	359	KAD127C	370	KAD994D	381	KAD641H	392	KAD937Y
349	KAC288Y	360	KAD158C	371	KAD021E	382	KAD846H	393	KAD938Y
350	KAD527A	361	KAD225C	372	KAD261E	383	KAD947H	396	KAD688A
351	KAD521A	362	KAD368C	373	KAD360E	384	KAD075J		

The dual-door layout arrangement of a standard Labh Singh body style is shown here on ERF Trailblazer 387, KAD378J. The Nairobi operation is split into three teams indicated by the letters following the fleet numbers, in this case team C.
Andrew Jarosz

400-450   ERF Trailblazer 6LXB MkII   Labh Singh*   B52D   1994-95

*424/9/35/41/3-7/9/50 are bodied by Choda

400	KAE660C	410	KAE061G	420	KAE164L	430	KAE098Q	442	KAE959R
401	KAE026D	411	KAE991E	421	KAE981M	431	KAE375Y	443	KAE112W
402	KAE975C	412	KAE793H	422	KAE985M	432	KAE285S	444	KAE838X
403	KAE977C	413	KAE792H	423	KAE018P	433	KAE286S	445	KAG241C
404	KAE137D	414	KAE697K	424	KAE109P	435	KAE716T	446	KAG920B
405	KAE138D	415	KAE696K	425	KAE183P	436	KAE793T	447	KAG818D
406	KAE609E	416	KAE698K	426	KAE287P	437	KAE052S	448	KAG819D
407	KAE011G	417	KAE699K	427	KAE351P	438	KAE053S	449	KAG751D
408	KAE992E	418	KAE856K	428	KAE394P	439	KAE749T	450	KAG927D
409	KAE012G	419	KAE857K	429	KAE023Q	441	KAE821V		

451	KAG641G	ERF Trailblazer 6LXB MkII	Choda	B51D	1995

452-459   ERF Trailblazer 6LXB MkII   Labh Singh   B52D   1995

452	KAG772J	454	KAG287K	456	KAG661L	458	KAG684L	459	KAG716L
453	KAG052K	455	KAG288K	457	KAG683L				

460	KAG756L	ERF Trailblazer 6LXB MkII	Choda	B52D	1996

461-484   ERF Trailblazer 6LXB MkII   Labh Singh   B52D*   1996   *Seating varies

461	KAG842N	468	KAG654S	473	KAG173V	477	KAG174V	481	KAG864X
462	KAG094P	469	KAG672S	474	KAG008Y	478	KAG962W	482	KAG053Y
465	KAG179P	470	KAG394T	475	KAG244V	479	KAG789X	483	KAG092Y
466	KAG334P	471	KAG582U	476	KAG291V	480	KAG848X	484	KAG094Y
467	KAG181R	472	KAG859U						

485-494   ERF Trailblazer 6LXB MkII   Choda   B49D*   1996   *Seating varies

485	KAG095Y	487	KAG333Y	489	KAG749Z	491	KAH097A	493	KAH368H
486	KAG287Y	488	KAG341Y	490	KAH096A	492	KAH367A	494	KAH616B

495	KAH781B	ERF Trailblazer 6LXB MkII	Labh Singh	B49D	1996
496	KAH881B	ERF Trailblazer 6LXB MkII	Choda	B49D	1996
497	KAH962B	ERF Trailblazer 6LXB MkII	Labh Singh	B49D	1996

498-502   ERF Trailblazer 6LXB MkII   Choda   B49D   1996

498	KAH717C	499	KAH747C	500	KAH768C	501	KAH769C	502	KAH930C

503-518   ERF Trailblazer 6LXB MkII   Labh Singh   B49D*   1996   *Seating varies

503	KAH049D	507	KAH184G	510	KAH291G	513	KAH764H	516	KAH207J
504	KAH389D	508	KAH185G	511	KAH293G	514	KAH951H	517	KAH238J
505	KAH392D	509	KAH270G	512	KAH763H	515	KAH129J	518	KAH645K
506	KAH049G								

601	KAA128N	DAF TB2100DHT	Labh Singh	B47D	1990
602	KAA351N	DAF TB2100DHT	Labh Singh	B47D	1990
603	KAA330N	DAF TB2100DHT	Labh Singh	B47D	1990
604	KAA313Q	DAF TB2100DHT	Labh Singh	B47D	1990

605-616   DAF TB2100DHT   Labh Singh   B43D   1992

605	KAC145H	608	KAC253H	611	KAC592J	613	KAC865J	615	KAC519L
606	KAC146H	609	KAC447H	612	KAC672J	614	KAC887J	616	KAC243K
607	KAC252H	610	KAC485J						

620-628   ERF Trailblazer 6LXB MkII   Labh Singh   B45D*   1994-96 *626-8 are B52F

620	KAD105Z	622	KAE689A	624	KAE919A	626	KAE750T	628	KAE689A
621	KAD135Z	623	KAE918A	625	KAE649T	627	KAG095P		

701-720

Leyland Victory J MkII — Labh Singh — B49D* — 1979-80 *710 is B47D, 713 is B48D

701	KVR629	706	KVR952	709	KVS307	713	KVT703	717	KVU018
702	KVR652	707	KVR995	710	KVS284	714	KVT857	719	KVU211
703	KVR787	708	KVS025	712	KVT664	715	KVT909	720	KVU156

721-736

Leyland Victory J MkII — Labh Singh — B49D* — 1980-82 *722 is B44D, *730 is B42D, 731 is B41D,

721	KVU237	725	KVW013	728	KVY046	731	KVY237	735	KSJ158
723	KVV809	726	KVX651	729	KVY074	733	KVZ703	736	KSJ265
724	KVV957	727	KVX664	730	KVY316	734	KVZ919		

748-779

Leyland Victory J MkII — Labh Singh — B49D* — 1980-82 *747 are B48D, *755 is B59D, 778 is B46D

748	KSP337	756	KTF527	763	KTK846	770	KTQ249	776	KTR678
749	KSW894	757	KTF834	764	KTM915	773	KTR405	777	KTT617
752	KSW875	758	KTF809	765	KTM946	774	KTR553	778	KTT881
754	KSW879	762	KTJ235	768	KTQ004	775	KTR630	779	KTV814
755	KTF528								

797-824

Leyland Victory J MkII — Labh Singh — B49D* — 1980-82 *Seating varies

797	KTW268	803	KUG560	809	KUG938	815	KUJ874	820	KUJ890
798	KTW190	804	KUH104	810	KUG978	816	KUJ638	821	KUM688
799	KTY110	805	KUG585	811	KUH141	817	KUJ998	822	KUM870
800	KUF144	806	KUJ641	812	KUH254	818	KUJ889	823	KUM534
801	KUG599	807	KUG850	813	KUH275	819	KUK083	824	KUK271
802	KUG474	808	KUG860	814	KUJ561				

831-850

Leyland Victory J MkII — Labh Singh — B49D* — 1983-84 *Seating varies

831	KUY105	835	KWA577	839	KWB295	843	KWK134	847	KWM059
832	KWA562	836	KWA574	840	KWC826	844	KWK144	848	KWM145
833	KWA575	837	KWB994	841	KWE920	845	KWL823	849	KWM189
834	KWA576	838	KWB286	842	KWE971	846	KWL923	850	KWN536

851-874

Leyland Victory J MkII — Labh Singh — B49D* — 1984-85 *870 is B45D

851	KWP262	856	KWR077	861	KWS725	866	KWT169	871	KWX948
852	KWQ584	857	KWR105	862	KWS971	867	KWT337	872	KWY155
853	KWQ808	858	KWR140	863	KWS985	868	KWV976	873	KWY371
854	KWQ914	859	KWS524	864	KWT030	869	KWX587	874	KXA037
855	KWQ946	860	KWS690	865	KWT146	870	KWX892		

876-900

Leyland Victory J MkII — Labh Singh — B49D* — 1985-86 *Seating varies

876	KXD797	881	KXG262	886	KXH624	891	KXJ173	896	KXM065
877	KXK017	882	KXG278	887	KXH875	892	KXJ369	897	KXN855
878	KXK503	883	KXH320	888	KXH896	893	KXJ474	898	KXN982
879	KXD761	884	KXH321	889	KXH993	894	KXK610	899	KXP038
880	KXD781	885	KXH623	890	KXJ010	895	KXK708	900	KXP187

901-930

ERF Trailblazer 6LXB MkII — Labh Singh — DP66F* — 1995-96 *901 is DP67F

901	KAE837V	907	KAE640Z	913	KAG816G	919	KAH804B	925	KAH010G
902	KAE109W	908	KAG291A	914	KAG173H	920	KAH891B	926	KAH021G
903	KAE385W	909	KAG056C	915	KAG373H	921	KAH876C	927	KAH294G
904	KAE002Y	910	KAG817D	916	KAG869Z	922	KAH177D	928	KAH013J
905	KAE230Y	911	KAG820D	917	KAH215A	923	KAH835E	929	KAH005J
906	KAG260A	912	KAG092E	918	KAH617B	924	KAH882E	930	KAH130J

946-951

Leyland Victory J — Labh Singh — B49D — 1979

946	KVK649	948	KVK751	949	KVK823	950	KVK941	951	KVK993
947	KVK708								

961	KUF067	Leyland Victory J	Labh Singh	B49D	1982	Rebuild
962	KUG695	Leyland Victory J	Labh Singh	B45D	1982	Rebuild
963	KUT967	Leyland Victory J	Labh Singh	B49D	1983	Rebuild
964	KNY401	Leyland Victory J	Labh Singh	B47D	1985	Rebuild
966	KZF894	Leyland Victory J MkIII	Labh Singh	B49D	1988	
968	KQD250	Leyland Victory J	Labh Singh	B48D	1975	Rebuild
969	KPW753	Leyland Victory J	Labh Singh	B48D	1974	Rebuild
970	KPW294	Leyland Victory J	Labh Singh	B45D	1974	Rebuild

991-997

		Leyland Victory J MkIII	Labh Singh	B49D*	1979	*991 is B43D

991	KZC129	993	KZA013	995	KYZ546	996	KZD894	997	KZB481
992	KZC481	994	KZF416						

Operational units:
City 301-96, 400-518, 601-16, 701-900/49-97.
Country 201-20, 620-8, 901-30.

The numbers of Leyland Victory models is declining as new ERF Trailblazers are delivered. Pictured while operating service 8 is 968, KQD250, a Leyland Victory J which was re-built in 1975.
Stagecoach International

Twenty Dennis Dragons with Duple-Metsec bodies assembled by AVE are now in service with Kenya Bus. One of these is pictured operating service 9.
Stagecoach International

MALAWI

Stagecoach Malawi, P O Box 176, Blantyre, Malawi.

Depots: Chichiri, Lilongwe, Makata and Mzuzu.

1	BH9601	Volvo B10M-61	Plaxton Paramount 3500 III	C46FT	1988	Ex Travellers, London, 1991
2w	BH9602	Volvo B10M-61	Plaxton Paramount 3500 III	C46FT	1988	Ex Travellers, London, 1991
3	BH9603	Volvo B10M-61	Plaxton Paramount 3500 III	C46FT	1988	Ex Travellers, London, 1991
4	BH9604	Volvo B10M-61	Plaxton Paramount 3500 III	C46FT	1988	Ex Travellers, London, 1991
5	BJ4981	Volvo B10M-61	Plaxton Paramount 3500 III	C46FT	1990	Ex Wallace Arnold, 1993
6	BJ8256	Volvo B10M-61	Plaxton Paramount 3500 II	C46FT	1986	Ex Wallace Arnold, 1994
7	BJ8257	Volvo B10M-61	Plaxton Paramount 3500 II	C46FT	1986	Ex Wallace Arnold, 1994

101-134
Leyland Victory J MkII   PEW(1996)   B53D   1982

101	BK2902	108	BK2904	115	BK2918	122	BK2932	129	BK2925
102	BK2903	109	BK2908	1##16	BK2912	1##23	BK2931	130	BK2928
103	BK2915	110	BK2906	117	BK2917	124	BK2934	1##31	BK2926
104	BK2907	111	BK2927	118	BK2913	125	BK2909	132	BK3893
105	BK2911	112	BK2921	1##19	BK2819	126	BK2930	1##33	BK2900
106	BK2901	113	BK2929	1##20	BK2816	127	BK2920	134	BK2935
107	BK2914	114	BK2905	121	BK2933	128	BK2910		

200w   BJ5851   Mercedes-Benz 812D   ?   B F   1993

204-232
ERF Trailblazer 6LXB   PEW   B61F   1993

204	BJ6020	210	BJ6112	216	BJ6255	222	BJ6414	228	BJ6512
205	BJ6021	211	BJ6137	217	BJ6258	223	BJ6419	229	BJ6521
206	BJ6066	212	BJ6147	218	BJ6313	224	BJ6439	230	BJ6525
207	BJ6070	213	BJ6157	219	BJ6341	225	BJ6450	231	BJ6542
208	BJ6080	214	BJ6205	220	BJ6353	226	BJ6460	232	BJ6594
209	BJ6079	215	BJ6245	221	BJ6405	227	BJ6471		

346	BF363	Leyland Victory J MkII	AUT	B53D	1980
347	BF364	Leyland Victory J MkII	AUT	B55D	1981
348	BF365	Leyland Victory J MkII	AUT(1986)	B53D	1981

350-371
Leyland Victory J MkII   AUT   B57D   1985-87

350	BG150	355	BG1255	360	BG1260	364	BG7364	368	BG7368
351	BG151	356	BG1256	361	BG149	365	BG7365	369	BG7369
352	BG152	357	BG1257	362	BG7362	366	BG7366	370	BG7370
353	BG153	358	BG1258	363	BG7363	367	BG7367	371	BG7371
354	BG154	359	BG1259						

422	BG2422	Leyland Victory J MkII	AUT(1989)	B59F	1985
423	BG2423	Leyland Victory J MkII	AUT(1988)	B59F	1985
425	BG2425	Leyland Victory J MkII	AUT(1989)	B49D	1985
429	BH1889	AVM Dahmer DH825	AUT	B59F	1989
431	BH1891	AVM Dahmer DH825	AUT	B59F	1989
432	BH1892	AVM Dahmer DH825	AUT	B59F	1989
434	BH1894	AVM Dahmer DH825	AUT	B59F	1989

438-443
DAF TB2105   AUT   B59F   1989

438	BH1808	440	BH1910	441	BH1911	442	BH1912	443	BH1913
439	BH1909								

Opposite: **First of the 1996 delivery of ERF SuperTrailblazers for Malawi was 501, seen here liveried for Expressline work when new. The vehicles introduce a higher level of comfort on the Expressline service. As can be seen, luggage is carried on a roof-rack accessible from the rear by ladder.** *Stagecoach Malawi*

A further view of SuperTrailblazer 501 showing the rear near side. Further examples of this model are due for delivery during 1997.
Stagecoach Malawi

In addition to the twenty Dennis Dragons in Kenya, ten with Duple-Metsec bodywork are also operated by Malawi. These are numbered from 2001, and 2002, BJ4153 is seen in an overall advertisement scheme while heading for Blantyre.
Stagecoach Malawi

447-465 — ERF Trailblazer — PEW — B59F — 1990-92

447	BH5747	**453**	BH2318	**456**	BH2577	**458**	BH2451	**464**	BJ2713
451	BH5751	**454**	BH2381	**457**	BH2450	**459**	BJ2711	**465**	BJ3094
452	BH9333	**455**	BH2576						

470-489 — Volvo B10M-55 — Alexander PS — B53F — 1993

470	BJ5558	**475**	BJ5643	**479**	BJ5779	**482**	BJ5967	**486**	BJ6195
471	BJ5551	**476**	BJ5604	**480**	BJ5960	**483**	BJ6075	**487**	BJ6249
473	BJ5553	**477**	BJ5752	**481**	BJ5966	**485**	BJ6411	**489**	BJ6764
474	BJ5554	**478**	BJ5753						

500	BJ7150	ERF SuperTrailblazer	PEW	B??F	1994

501-510 — ERF SuperTrailblazer — PEW — B??F — 1996

501	BK2971	**503**	BK3046	**505**	BK2924	**507**	BK3251	**509**	BK3273
502	BK2976	**504**	BK3047	**506**	BK2923	**508**	BK3259	**510**	BK3274

720-798 — Leyland Victory J MkII — AUT — B57F — 1981-85 — *720/1 are B59F, 773 is B56F

720	BG2420	783	BF8810	787	BF8814	791	BF8978	793	BF8980
721	BG2421	784	BF8811	790	BF8977	792	BF8979	798	BF8985
773	BF2232	785	BF8812						

800-819 — Leyland Victory J MkII — AUT — B53F — 1985

800	BF8987	803	BG133	806	BG136	809	BG139	815	BG145
801	BG131	804	BG134	807	BG137	812	BG142	819	BG691
802	BG132	805	BG135	808	BG138	814	BG144		

826-861 — Leyland Victory J MkII — AUT — B53F — 1986-87

826	BG3826	837	BG3837	845	BG3845	850	BG3850	856	BG3856
827	BG3827	838w	BG3838	846	BG3846	851	BG3851	857	BG3857
828	BG3828	839	BG3839	847	BG3847	852	BG3852	858	BG3858
829	BG3829	841	BG3841	848	BG3848	854	BG3854	859	BG3859
830	BG3830	842	BG3842	849	BG3849	855	BG3855	861	BG3861
836	BG3836	844	BG3844						

862-897 — ERF Trailblazer — PEW — B61F — 1991-92

862	BH5862	870	BH5870	877	BH5877	884	BH9599	891	BJ1191
863	BH5863	871	BH5871	878	BH8178	885	BJ445	892	BJ1192
864	BH5864	872	BH5872	879	BH8179	886	BJ446	893	BJ1283
865	BH5865	873	BH5873	880	BH5752	887	BJ447	894	BJ1284
866	BH5866	874	BH5874	881	BH9596	888	BJ448	895	BJ1285
867	BH5867	875	BH5875	882	BH9597	889	BJ1193	896	BJ1286
868	BH5868	876	BH5876	883	BH9598	890	BJ1194	897	BJ1287
869	BH5869								

898-949 — ERF Trailblazer — PEW — B61F — 1992

898	BJ1604	909	BJ2063	920	BJ3247	930	BJ3600	940	BJ4044
899	BJ1605	910	BJ2064	921	BJ3246	931	BJ3604	941	BJ4064
900	BJ1606	911	BJ2065	922	BJ3354	932	BJ3673	942	BJ4051
901	BJ1754	912	BJ2331	923	BJ3373	933	BJ3674	943	BJ4161
902	BJ1755	913	BJ2332	924	BJ3387	934	BJ3675	944	BJ4212
903	BJ1756	914	BJ2333	925	BJ3402	935	BJ3857	945	BJ4213
904	BJ1974	915	BJ3095	926	BJ3403	936	BJ3858	946	BJ4301
905	BJ1975	916	BJ3136	927	BJ3461	937	BJ3872	947	BJ4258
906	BJ1976	917	BJ3203	928	BJ3519	938	BJ3971	948	BJ4394
907	BJ2061	918	BJ3244	929	BJ3521	939	BJ3997	949	BJ4438
908	BJ2062	919	BJ3245						

950	BJ5517	ERF Trailblazer	PEW	B47F	1993	

951-960 — ERF Trailblazer — PEW — B59F — 1990-92

951	BH5748	953	BF5750	955	BJ2715	957	BJ3094	959	BH5745
952	BH5749	954	BJ2712	956	BJ2710	958	BH5744	960	BH5746

961-969 — ERF Trailblazer — PEW — B59F — 1996

961	BK3381	963	BK3383	965	BK3492	967	BK3494	969	BK3705
962	BK3382	964	BK3491	966	BK3493	968	BK3702		

970-980 — ERF Trailblazer — PEW — B59F — 1994-95

970	BJ9093	973	BJ9592	975	BJ9516	977	BJ9517	979	BJ9130
971	BJ9138	974	BJ9558	976	BJ9123	978	BJ9122	980	BJ6595
972	BJ9140								

2001-2010 — Dennis Dragon DDA1814 — Duple-Metsec — H67/41F — 1992

2001	BJ3701	2003	BJ4302	2005	BJ4397	2007	BJ4575	2009	BJ4618
2002	BJ4153	2004	BJ4370	2006	BJ4505	2008	BJ4590	2010	BJ4915

Previous Registrations:

BH9601	E584UHS		BH9604	E579UHS		BJ8256	C102DWR
BH9602	E585UHS		BJ4981	G502LWU		BJ8257	C104DWR
BH9603	E587UHS						

STAGECOACH PORTUGAL

Stagecoach Portugal, Av do Brasil, 45-1 - 1700 Lisboa, Portugal

Depots : Queluz de Baixo and Cascais

101-150 Scania L113CLB Marcopolo B37D 1996

101	52-47-GM	111	64-86-GV	121	62-41-HA	131	20-02-HF	141	20-14-HF
102	80-96-GP	112	64-87-GV	122	90-78-HA	132	20-05-HF	142	20-15-HF
103	80-99-GP	113	64-88-GV	123	90-79-HA	133	20-06-HF	143	20-16-HF
104	80-98-GP	114	64-89-GV	124	90-80-HA	134	20-07-HF	144	
105	80-97-GP	115	64-90-GV	125	90-81-HA	135	20-08-HF	145	49-66-HG
106	80-93-GP	116	62-36-HA	126	90-82-HA	136	20-09-HF	146	49-67-HG
107	80-94-GP	117	62-37-HA	127	90-83-HA	137	20-10-HF	147	49-68-HG
108	80-95-GP	118	62-38-HA	128	90-84-HA	138	20-11-HF	148	49-69-HG
109	64-84-GV	119	62-39-HA	129	20-03-HF	139	20-12-HF	149	49-70-HG
110	64-85-GV	120	62-40-HA	130	20-04-HF	140	20-13-HF	150	49-71-HG

166	CG-74-44	UTIC-AEC Reliance U2045	Caetano(1987)	B42D	1972	Ex Rodoviária del Lisboa, 1996
183	EL-44-91	UTIC-AEC Reliance U2055	Caetano(1987)	B42D	1972	Ex Rodoviária del Lisboa, 1996
188	DE-62-72	UTIC-AEC Reliance U2055	UTIC(1990)	B42D	1972	Ex Rodoviária del Lisboa, 1996
191	CG-62-04	UTIC-AEC Reliance U2055	Caetano(1988)	B42D	1972	Ex Rodoviária del Lisboa, 1996
219	IM-97-87	UTIC-AEC Reliance U2055	UTIC(1990)	B42D	1974	Ex Rodoviária del Lisboa, 1996
301	EU-37-57	Volvo B10R-55	Camo	DP34D	1980	Ex Rodoviária del Lisboa, 1996
302	FS-09-78	Volvo B10R-55	Camo	DP34D	1980	Ex Rodoviária del Lisboa, 1996
473	GT-83-73	Volvo B58-60P	Caetano	DP49D	1979	Ex Rodoviária del Lisboa, 1996
482	GT-83-64	Volvo B58-60P	Caetano	DP49D	1979	Ex Rodoviária del Lisboa, 1996
490	GT-83-70	Volvo B58-60P	Caetano	DP49D	1979	Ex Rodoviária del Lisboa, 1996
491	IS-72-66	Volvo B58-60P	Caetano	DP49D	1979	Ex Rodoviária del Lisboa, 1996

534-551 Volvo B10R-55 Camo DP48D* 1979 Ex Rodoviária del Lisboa, 1996
*551 is B49D

534	IS-98-38	535	NP-75-76	536	HS-59-99	537	HS-70-33	551	ES-83-85

555-575 Volvo B10R-55 Camo B34D 1979-80 Ex Rodoviária del Lisboa, 1996

555	EU-37-45	572	FU-30-97	573	FU-31-00	574	CT-68-99	575	CT-69-01
571	FU-30-95								

584-628 Volvo B10R-55 Camo B40D 1981 Ex Rodoviária del Lisboa, 1996

584	FS-09-56	593	FS-09-77	595	FS-09-60	597	FS-09-58	625	FS-09-73
591	FS-09-80	594	FS-09-55	596	FS-09-54	622	IV-72-52	628	FS-09-57
592	FS-09-79								

665	RP-69-35	Volvo B10M-55A	Camo U90	AB49T	1987	Ex Rodoviária del Lisboa, 1996
783	AL-47-83	UTIC-AEC Reliance U2035	UTIC(1987)	B42D	1969	Ex Rodoviária del Lisboa, 1996
785	IL-88-36	UTIC-AEC Reliance U2035	UTIC(1985)	B42D	1969	Ex Rodoviária del Lisboa, 1996
790	FB-76-06	UTIC-AEC Reliance U2035	UTIC(1986)	B42D	1970	Ex Rodoviária del Lisboa, 1996
791	BH-42-09	UTIC-AEC Reliance U2035	Camo(1987)	B42D	1970	Ex Rodoviária del Lisboa, 1996
792	BH-42-08	UTIC-AEC Reliance U2035	Eurobus(1987)	B42D	1970	Ex Rodoviária del Lisboa, 1996
794	FA-55-45	UTIC-AEC Reliance U2045	UTIC(1986)	B42D	1971	Ex Rodoviária del Lisboa, 1996
797	EB-67-53	UTIC-AEC Reliance U2045	Caetano(1987)	B42D	1971	Ex Rodoviária del Lisboa, 1996
798	GC-70-23	UTIC-AEC Reliance U2055	UTIC	B39D	1972	Ex Rodoviária del Lisboa, 1996
799	GC-76-76	UTIC-AEC Reliance U2055	UTIC	B39D	1972	Ex Rodoviária del Lisboa, 1996
800	CG-32-08	UTIC-AEC Reliance U2055	UTIC	B36D	1972	Ex Rodoviária del Lisboa, 1996

Opposite: **The Stagecoach corporate livery is starting to appear in Portugal with the delivery of new buses and the repainting of old examples.   The upper picture shows 103, 80-99-GP, one of the new Scania L113 buses with Marcopolo bodywork, the Brazilian bus builder that has an assembly plant in Portugal. The lower picture illustrates the corporate colours on newly repainted 830, EH-83-23, a UTIC-AEC Reliance with UTIC bodywork.** *Stagecoach Portugal*

801	CG-32-09	UTIC-AEC Reliance U2055	UTIC	B36D	1972	Ex Rodoviária del Lisboa, 1996
802	GC-70-20	UTIC-AEC Reliance U2055	UTIC	B52D	1972	Ex Rodoviária del Lisboa, 1996
806	GO-54-92	UTIC-AEC Reliance U2055	UTIC	B39D	1975	Ex Rodoviária del Lisboa, 1996
807	GO-54-93	UTIC-AEC Reliance U2055	UTIC	B39D	1975	Ex Rodoviária del Lisboa, 1996
808	AT-91-50	UTIC-AEC Reliance U2055	UTIC	B39D	1975	Ex Rodoviária del Lisboa, 1996
809	AT-91-52	UTIC-AEC Reliance U2055	UTIC	B39D	1975	Ex Rodoviária del Lisboa, 1996
820	GG-70-11	UTIC-AEC Reliance U2055	UTIC	B47D	1972	Ex Rodoviária del Lisboa, 1996
821	GG-32-07	UTIC-AEC Reliance U2055	UTIC	B38D	1972	Ex Rodoviária del Lisboa, 1996
824	EH-63-39	UTIC-AEC Reliance U2055	UTIC	B48D	1973	Ex Rodoviária del Lisboa, 1996
826	DN-45-88	UTIC-AEC Reliance U2055	UTIC	B47D	1973	Ex Rodoviária del Lisboa, 1996
830	EH-83-23	UTIC-AEC Reliance U2041	UTIC	C39D	1973	Ex Rodoviária del Lisboa, 1996
833	ER-60-86	UTIC-AEC Reliance U2055	UTIC	B39D	1974	Ex Rodoviária del Lisboa, 1996
834	ER-60-87	UTIC-AEC Reliance U2055	UTIC	B39D	1974	Ex Rodoviária del Lisboa, 1996
836	DO-89-76	UTIC-AEC Reliance U2055	UTIC	B39D	1975	Ex Rodoviária del Lisboa, 1996
839	DO-89-74	UTIC-AEC Reliance U2055	UTIC	B39D	1975	Ex Rodoviária del Lisboa, 1996
840	GO-33-61	UTIC-AEC Reliance U2055	UTIC	B39D	1975	Ex Rodoviária del Lisboa, 1996
845	BP-45-14	UTIC-AEC Reliance U2075	UTIC	B39D	1976	Ex Rodoviária del Lisboa, 1996
847	BP-45-15	UTIC-AEC Reliance U2075	UTIC	B39D	1976	Ex Rodoviária del Lisboa, 1996
848	EN-67-93	UTIC-AEC Reliance U2075	UTIC	B39D	1976	Ex Rodoviária del Lisboa, 1996
849	IM-97-84	UTIC-AEC Reliance U2055	UTIC(1990)	B42D	1974	Ex Rodoviária del Lisboa, 1996
850	CO-48-73	UTIC-AEC Reliance U2055	UTIC(1990)	B42D	1974	Ex Rodoviária del Lisboa, 1996
856	FV-68-50	UTIC-AEC Reliance U2075	UTIC	B39D	1976	Ex Rodoviária del Lisboa, 1996
859	IU-81-04	UTIC-AEC Reliance U2075	UTIC	C55D	1976	Ex Rodoviária del Lisboa, 1996
860	HV-82-98	UTIC-AEC Reliance U2075	UTIC	C55D	1976	Ex Rodoviária del Lisboa, 1996
863	GP-32-77	UTIC-AEC Reliance U2077	UTIC	C55D	1977	Ex Rodoviária del Lisboa, 1996
866	BZ-73-12	UTIC-AEC Reliance U2077	UTIC	DP49D	1979	Ex Rodoviária del Lisboa, 1996
867	BZ-73-13	UTIC-AEC Reliance U2077	UTIC	DP48D	1979	Ex Rodoviária del Lisboa, 1996
868	BZ-73-24	UTIC-AEC Reliance U2077	UTIC	DP48D	1979	Ex Rodoviária del Lisboa, 1996
869	BZ-73-22	UTIC-AEC Reliance U2077	UTIC	DP49D	1979	Ex Rodoviária del Lisboa, 1996
870	BZ-73-10	UTIC-AEC Reliance U2077	UTIC	DP49D	1979	Ex Rodoviária del Lisboa, 1996
871	BZ-73-11	UTIC-AEC Reliance U2077	UTIC	DP48D	1979	Ex Rodoviária del Lisboa, 1996
872	BZ-73-23	UTIC-AEC Reliance U2077	UTIC	DP48D	1979	Ex Rodoviária del Lisboa, 1996

885-898 UTIC-Leyland MTL11R UTIC Europa C53D* 1982 Ex Rodoviária del Lisboa, 1996
*885/7/9 are DP57D

885	CF-08-63	888	CU-20-01	890	CF-08-66	892	DG-05-43	894	HC-09-88
886	EA-08-86	889	FF-09-76	891	DG-05-44	893	EF-06-24	898	CL-08-58
887	EA-08-87								

Caetano-bodied Volvo B58 CV-70-82 is number 915 in the Stagecoach Portugal fleet and dates from 1979. This example is seen in the former Rodoviária del Lisboa livery of white and orange.
Stagecoach Portugal

900-918   Volvo B58-60P   Caetano   DP49D*   1979   Ex Rodoviária del Lisboa, 1996
*908-917 are DP48D

900	IS-12-02	906	IS-49-12	910	CV-70-93	913	CV-70-88	916	GT-83-74
901	CV-70-94	907	GT-83-72	911	CV-70-89	914	GT-83-65	917	IS-72-65
904	CV-70-91	908	GT-83-68	912	CV-70-85	915	CV-70-82	918	IS-72-67
905	IS-12-01	909	GT-83-71						

920	SS-47-77	Magirus-Deutz 230E113	S Caetano	C53D	1980	Ex Rodoviária del Lisboa, 1996
922	TM-98-25	Magirus-Deutz 230E113	S Caetano	C53D	1981	Ex Rodoviária del Lisboa, 1996

930-937   Volvo B10R-59   Camo   DP48D*   1980   Ex Rodoviária del Lisboa, 1996
*932-7 are DP48D

930	HS-59-93	932	ES-83-88	934	ES-83-79	936	ES-83-84	937	EU-51-03
931	HS-59-97	933	HS-59-94	935	ES-83-82				

938-967   Volvo B10R-55   Camo   DP34D   1979-81 Ex Rodoviária del Lisboa, 1996
*948 is DP48D; 965 is B40D; 967 is B39D

938	EU-37-35	943	EU-37-37	949	EU-37-55	955	IV-72-53	963	FS-09-67
939	EU-37-36	944	EU-37-40	950	EU-37-56	959	FS-09-62	964	FS-09-68
940	EU-37-38	945	EU-37-43	951	IV-72-51	960	DV-03-13	965	GO-08-85
941	EU-37-39	946	EU-37-54	954	BS-64-71	962	FS-09-74	967	FS-09-57
942	EU-37-44	948	IS-98-43						

970	TX-14-72	Scania K113CLB	S Caetano Algarve	C49F	1991	Ex Rodoviária del Lisboa, 1996
971	VX-75-26	Scania K113CLB	S Caetano Algarve	C49F	1991	Ex Rodoviária del Lisboa, 1996

980-984   Volvo B10M-55A   Camo U90   AB49T   1987   Ex Rodoviária del Lisboa, 1996

980	RP-95-43	981	RP-95-44	982	RM-54-78	983	QM-54-94	984	QM-89-83

986	OQ-79-80	Volvo B10MA	Caetano	AB52T	1991	Ex Rodoviária del Lisboa, 1996

991-999   DAF FA45150L10   Camo Olympus   B19D   1994   Ex Rodoviária del Lisboa, 1996

991	87-40-EI	994	87-33-EI	997	87-41-EI	998	87-36-EI	999	87-42-EI
992	87-34-EI	996	87-38-EI						

Livery: White and orange or white and green (minibuses)

A further view of the new Scania single-deck buses for the Portugal operation. The dual-door layout is demonstrated on 109, 64-84-GV. Interestingly, the UK is one of the few EU countries still to introduce the EU symbol on the registration plates.
Stagecoach Portugal

STAGECOACH NEW ZEALAND

Stagecoach Wellington, 45 Onepu Road, Kilbirnie, Wellington, New Zealand
Cityline Hutt Valley, Waterloo Interchange, Oxford Terrace, Lower Hutt
Cityline Auckland; Stagecoach Auckland, Railway Street West, Papakura
Runciman Motors, 4 Masefield Street, Upper Hutt

1	TB6042	Ford R1114	New Zealand Motor Bodies	DP48F	1976
2	NA4281	Isuzu MR113	Coachwork International	B28F	1987
3	FL4281	Ford R1014	New Zealand Motor Bodies	DP40F	1973
4	NA4279	Isuzu MR113	Coachwork International	DP28F	1987
5	NA3943	Isuzu MR113	Coachwork International	DP28F	1987
6	SK700	Isuzu ECR570	Demac	C45F	1986
7	FL4279	Ford R192	New Zealand Motor Bodies	DP41F	1972
8	NY58	Isuzu ECR570	Coachwork International	DP45F	1988
9	MQ8716	Isuzu ECR570	Coachwork International	DP49F	1986
10	JR48	Ford R1114	New Zealand Motor Bodies	DP48F	1980
11	ON223	Isuzu ECR570	Austral	B45F	1989
12	PT2685	Hino RG197	Coachwork International	B37D	1991
13	JR47	Ford R1114	New Zealand Motor Bodies	DP48F	1980
14	IN2551	Ford R1114	New Zealand Motor Bodies	DP48F	1977
15	JZ7041	Ford R1114	New Zealand Motor Bodies	DP48F	1981
16	OB1552	Isuzu ECR570	Coachwork International	DP49F	1988
17	JR2616	Mercedes-Benz 0303	New Zealand Motor Bodies	B41D	1980
18	JW8024	Mercedes-Benz 0303	New Zealand Motor Bodies	B41D	1980
19	LE4641	Hino BX341	New Zealand Motor Bodies	DP48F	1983
21	MC609	Isuzu ECR570	Coachwork International	DP49F	1985

22-26   Volvo B10M-56   Alexander PS   DP50F   1994   Ex Stagecoach Hong Kong, 1996

22	UO8044	23	UO7966	24	UO7989	25	UO8020	26	UO8000

27-35   MAN 10-100   Coachwork International   DP28F   1990

27	OU3699	29	OZ8661	31	OZ8664	33	OZ8666	35	OZ8668
28	OZ8699	30	OZ8660	32	OZ8665	34	OZ8667		

37-57   Mercedes-Benz 709D   Alexander Sprint   B25F   1996

37	UN5515	42	UN5521	46	UO3110	50	UP7144	54	UP8933
38	UN5517	43	UN5522	47	UO3112	51	UP7145	55	UP8934
39	UN5518	44	UO3084	48	UP4829	52	UP8928	56	UP8944
40	UN5519	45	UO3085	49	UP4840	53	UP8929	57	UP8945
41	UN5520								

141-170   MAN SL202   Coachwork International   B40D   1986-89

141	NF2109	147	NH2755	153	NL9414	159	NL9540	165	NZ8003
142	NF2117	148	NI5642	154	NL9420	160	NL9566	166	NZ8266
143	NH2634	149	NI5704	155	NL9466	161	OB1550	167	OG8397
144	NH2652	150	NI5718	156	NL9460	162	NT9387	168	OG8398
145	NH2754	151	NL9377	157	NL9461	163	PA6879	169	OG8399
146	NH2756	152	NL9393	158	NL9531	164	NZ8004	170	OG8551

171-180   MAN 16.200 UOCL   Coachwork International   B39D   1989-91

171	ON525	173	PL5272	175	PL5274	177	PL5823	179	PP5206
172	PL5003	174	PL5273	176	PL5822	178	PL5824	180	PP5205

181	PP5219	MAN 16.240 UOCL	Coachwork International	B41D	1991

Two interesting additions to the Hutt Valley operations are illustrated here. Above is 4, NA4279, a Isuzu MR113 with Coachwork International bodywork photographed as it heads for Eastbourne and one of pair of the type fitted with dual-purpose seating. Below is 29, OZ8661, one of ten MAN-10 midibuses used on the Hutt Valley services of Cityline. *Stagecoach Wellington*

201-234

Volvo B58 Trolleybus — Hawke Coachwork — B40D — 1981-83

201	KA9102	207	JY5832	213	KA9184	220	KA7235	226	KD7487
202w	KA9108	208	JY5831	214	KA9185	221	KD7490	227	KH4274
203w	PE8106	209	KA9103	216	KA9192	222	KD7488	229	KH4358
204	JM7127	210	KA9109	217	NA87	223	KD7485	232	KJ8245
205w	JM7125	211	KA9110	218	KA7233	224	KD7486	233	KJ8244
206	JY6549	212	KA9111	219	KA7234	225	KH4273	234	LQ2643

235-254

Volvo B58 Trolleybus — International Coachwork — B40D — 1984-85

235	LW6465	239	MB7635	243	ME9235	247	MJ2016	251	MJ2168
236	MA8821	240	MB7638	244	ME9236	248	MJ2015	252	MJ2169
237	MA5210	241	MB7636	245	ME2504	249	MJ2014	253	MJ2171
238	MA5209	242	MB7637	246	MJ2012	250	MJ2013	254	MJ2172

255-268

Volvo B58 Trolleybus — International Coachwork — B40D — 1986

255	MO1322	258	SC2911	261	MS1706	264	MS1703	266	MS1813
256	MO1321	259	MO1397	262	MS1705	265	MS1814	268	MS1815
257	MO1391	260	MS1707	263	MS1704				

270	MC6399	Hino AC140	Micanta	C23F	1985
290	PD1036	Renault S75	Coachwork International	B23F	1990
291	PD1037	Renault S75	Coachwork International	B23F	1990
292	PD1038	Renault S75	Coachwork International	B23F	1990
293	PE5096	Renault S75	Coachwork International	B23F	1990
294	RM4511	Toyota Hiace	Toyota	M15	1992	Ex Wellington, 1993

401-415

Leyland Leopard PSU3C/2R — Hawke Coachwork — B40D — 1976-77

401	HZ2712	406	HE2656	409	HQ3907	412	IL4519	415	IL4461
403	GA6806	408	HQ3899	410	PW8450	413	IL4518		

417-478

Leyland Leopard PSU3E/2R — Hawke Coachwork — B40D — 1978-79 479/80 ex Goldstar, Frankton, 1992

417	IU9434	428	IX3782	442	JA1198	455	JF1910	468	LH1322
418	IU9433	429	IX3807	443	JC2506	456	JF1911	469	JA1184
419	IU9432	433	IX7765	444	JC2568	457	JF1913	470	JA1197
420	IU9431	434	IX7763	445	JC2569	458	JF1914	472	JC2505
421	IX7733	435	IU9931	446	JC2570	459	IX3806	474	JD181
423	IX3304	436	IU9932	447	JD184	461	IX3815	475	JC2520
424	IX3302	438	JC2431	448	JD183	462	IX7767	476	JD199
425	IX3781	439	JC2430	449	JD182	463	IX7766	477	JF1902
426	IX3660	440w	JA1187	451	JD197	464	TD5442	478	JF1912
427	IX3783	441	JA1185	452	JF1903	466	KP7998		

479	IX3303	Leyland Leopard PSU3E/2R	Hawke Coachwork	B45D	1979	Ex Goldstar, Frankton, 1992
480	IX7734	Leyland Leopard PSU3E/2R	Hawke Coachwork	B45D	1979	Ex Goldstar, Frankton, 1992
481	LA5234	Leyland Leopard PSU3E/2R	Hawke Coachwork	B44D	1983	Ex Invercargill, 1992
482	JT684	Leyland Leopard PSU3E/2R	Hawke Coachwork	B40D	1982	Ex Cesta Travel, 1993

501-520

MAN 11.190 HOCL — Designline — B39D — 1994-95

501	SS5537	505	TB6105	509	SY1641	513	TA2667	517	TB6042
502	SS5538	506	SW4400	510	SY1631	514	TA2691	518	TB6050
503	ST7109	507	SW4435	511	SZ5917	515	TA2714	519	TB6056
504	SX7724	508	SW4436	512	SZ5918	516	TB6023	520	TB6057

Opposite: **Wellington is the location of both of these pictures. The upper picture shows MAN midibus 504, SX7724, posing for the camera with the harbour in the background. The lower picture is of trolleybus 224, KD7486 having emerged from the Hataitai Bus Tunnel which was built as a tram tunnel and operated exclusively as such until the last tram operated in 1964. It now carries buses and trolleybuses only and is controlled by traffic lights.** *Stagecoach Wellington*

Delivery of MAN products for Wellington continues with low-floor models being numbered from 601. Shown heading for Happy Valley is 539, TG5876. *Stagecoach Wellington*

521-554

MAN 11.190 HOCL   Designline   B39D   1995

521	TB6106	528	TE2325	535	TG5856	542	TG5895	549	TJ2515
522	TB6107	529	TE2326	536	TG5857	543	TG5896	550	TJ2516
523	TD2564	530	TE2327	537	TG5871	544	TG5897	551	TR1643
524	TD2593	531	TF6235	538	TG5872	545	TG5898	552	TR1644
525	TD2594	532	TF6236	539	TG5876	546	TG5899	553	TR1645
526	TD2630	533	TF6237	540	TG5877	547	TH5837	554	TR1646
527	TD2631	534	TG5855	541	TG5878	548	TH5838		

601-626

MAN 11.190 HOCL   Designline   B39D   1995-96

601	TJ2541	607	UB490	612	UB496	617	UB483	622	UF5846
602	TJ2542	608	UB491	613	UB500	618	UB482	623	UF5847
603	UB487	609	UB492	614	UB499	619	UB484	624	UF5850
604	UB488	610	UB497	615	UB498	620	UB485	625	UF5851
605	TU1498	611	UB495	616	UF5845	621	UF5849	626	UF5852
606	UB489								

627-656

MAN 11.190 HOCL   Designline   B39D   1996

627	UF5853	633	UH7204	639	UH7216	645	UH7213	651	UL5052
628	UF5854	634	UH7205	640	UH7217	646	UH7214	652	UL5053
629	UF5855	635	UH7206	641	UH7218	647	UL5044	653	UL5060
630	UF5856	636	UH7207	642	UH7212	648	UL5045	654	UL5042
631	UF5857	637	UH7208	643	UH7219	649	UL5046	655	UO9429
632	UF5858	638	UH7215	644	UH7220	650	UL5051	656	UO9427

5907	1055IC	Hino BG300	Emslie	C41F	1980
6009	JZ6948	Bedford NFM/6BD1	NZ Motor Bodies	B37D	1981
6890	MI8415	Hino RK176	Coachwork International	B45D	1987

7193-7253 — Hino RK176 — Coachwork International — B47D* — 1987-88 *6890/7193/7-7200 are B45D

7193	NA6078	7201	NK8507	7237	NA7358	7245	NL7826	7250 NL7831
7197	NA6060	7231	NA7353	7238	NA7359	7246	NL7827	7251 NA7832
7198	NA6947	7232	NA7350	7239	NA7361	7247	NL7828	7252 NA7833
7199	NA6946	7233	NA7351	7242	NL7824	7248	NL7829	7253 NL7834
7200	NA6945	7236	NA7357	7244	NL7825	7249	NL7830	

7255-7556 — Hino RK177 — Coachwork International — B47D — 1988-89

7255	NL7823	7266	NL8272	7278	NX9487	7538	OB4207	7547 OE7912
7256	NL7790	7267	NL7793	7279	NX9488	7539	OB4208	7548 OE7917
7258	NL7796	7268	NL8264	7532	NX9510	7540	OB4215	7549 OG5328
7259	NL7797	7269	NL8265	7533	NX9509	7542	OB4213	7551 OG5327
7260	NL7799	7270	NL8266	7534	NX9507	7543	OB4212	7553 OG5341
7261	NL7794	7271	NL8273	7535	NX9508	7544	OB4214	7554 OG5342
7263	NL7791	7273	NL8267	7536	NX9516	7545	OE7913	7555 OG5343
7264	NL7792	7274	NL8268	7537	NX9517	7546	OE7916	7556 OG5344
7265	NL7798	7276	NX9485					

7605-7618 — Mercedes-Benz L608D — Alexander — B19F — 1986 — Ex Stagecoach South, 1994

7605	SX6698	7607	SZ205	7610	TE3787	7616	TD8481	7618 TJ4753
7606	SX6699	7608	TA7124	7614	TA7468	7617	TD8460	

Kelburn Cable Car

1		Habegger	Habegger	S28D	1979
2		Habegger	Habegger	S28D	1979

Previous Registrations:

MQ9796	SK700	TA7124	C814SDY	TD8481	C799SDY
SX6698	C816SDY	TA7468	D951UDY	TE3787	C815SDY
SX6699	D231UHC	TD8460	C801SDY	TJ4753	C803SDY
SZ205	D225UHC				

Operations:

Cityline Auckland: 5, 37-53, 150/8/61/5/9, 413/25/62/4, 501-22, 6890, 7193, 7231-3/42/56/9/63/4/7/71/8/9, 7532-5/40/2-6/8/9/51/5/6.

Cityline Hutt Valley: 4/6/8/12/6-8, 22/5/6/8-30/2-5, 54-7, 290-4, 410/2/7/9/24/8/9, 546-54, 7197-201, 7236-9/44-53/5/8/60/1/5/6/8-70/3/4/6, 7536-9/47/53/4, 7605-8/14/8.

Stagecoach Auckland: 523-9, 619/20

Runcimans: 1-3/7/9-11/3-5/19, 21/3, 401/3/6/21/3/7/33/5/6/8/41/8/51/2/7/69/76, 5907, 6009

Stagecoach Wellington: Remainder

The success of former Stagecoach South minibuses is highlighted by the arrival of twenty-one new Alexander Sprint models built in the UK. Illustrating the type operating with Cityline is 57, UP8945.
Stagecoach Wellington

SWEBUS

Swebus AB, Kungsgatan 29, 111 56 Stockholm

Swebus operate around 3300 vehicles in Sweden, 322 in Finland, 247 in Norway and 127 in Denmark. Vehicles are allocated to the 24 districts. The list produced below is the latest information available and was believed correct to Autumn 1996. Unfortunately, seating configurations are not yet available, though most are thought to have high-back seating. The publishers would welcome any additional details, including seating configurations and liveries or photographs.

1	LDA195	Scania B83	Arvika	1953
2	LYS263	Volvo LV101	Volvo	1939
3	AGM191	Volvo B63506	Volvo	1963
4	BZE573	Scania BF76-59	Hägglund	1966
5	GCS253	Volvo B71518	SKV	1964
7	EGP181	Scania BF76-63	Lier	1967
8	CHM068	Volvo B58-60T	Van Hool Vistadome	1971
9	ENF031	Volvo B58-60T	Säffle	1969
10	MXF427	Volvo B513	Säffle	1948
11	MLC010	Scania B63	Hägglund	1954
12	CGL690	Scania V8113		1932
17	MXC222	Volvo B10M-60	Van Hool Alizée	1986
19	EZS682	Volvo B10M-60	Van Hool Alizée	1987
24	LOX225	Volvo B10R-59	Säffle	1983
25	LXJ717	Volvo B10M-65	Säffle	1984
34	OAT766	Volvo B10M-60	Säffle	1989
162	AKX822	Volvo B58-65	GDG	1980
183	KWA308	Volvo B10M-60	Van Hool Alizée	1981
187	ESR862	Volvo B10M-65	Alpus 260S	1982
192	KWW890	Volvo B10M-60	Van Hool	1982
193	KXO980	Volvo B10M-60	Van Hool	1982
194	KPF670	Volvo B10M-60	Van Hool	1982

195-202

Volvo B10M-65 — Alpus 260S — 1982-83

195	JKX164	196	LMM435	197	LMB065	200	LKO186	202	LKU446

205	KXK870	Volvo B10M-60	Van Hool Alizée	1982
209	KZS880	Volvo B10M-60	Van Hool Alizée	1982
213	LLA798	Volvo B10M-65	Alpus 260S	1983
215	LKY888	Volvo B10M-65	Alpus 260S	1983
216	LLN568	Volvo B10M-65	Alpus 260S	1983
218	LDT919	Volvo B10M-65	Alpus 260S	1983
219	LCE617	Volvo B10M-70B	Van Hool Alizée	1983
220	LCL977	Volvo B10M-70B	Van Hool Alizée	1983
221	LCG567	Volvo B10M-70B	Van Hool Alizée	1983
222	LKK878	Volvo B10M-60	Van Hool	1983
223	LKJ638	Volvo B10M-60	Van Hool	1983
224	LKS778	Volvo B10M-60	Van Hool	1983

225-247

Volvo B10M-65 — Alpus 260S — 1983-84

225	LDR519	233	LHB990	240	LOR064	244	CTL685	246	CGK905
229	LGZ770	238	LOO424	241	LPB484	245	CJL885	247	CDJ995
230	LHJ890	239	LON274	242	LPM194				

250	LRK131	Mercedes-Benz 0303/9	Mercedes-Benz	1983
253	LRP491	Mercedes-Benz 0303/9	Mercedes-Benz	1983
254	LRZ391	Mercedes-Benz 0303/9	Mercedes-Benz	1983

256-266

Volvo B10M-60* — Van Hool Alizée — 1983 — *256 is a B10M-65

256	LCU577	260	LCB827	264	LCD607	265	LBY697	266	LBY837

268-283   Volvo B10M-65   Alpus 260S   1983-84

268	LOX717	271	KFR401	277	LOL587	280	LPO727	282	LPB647
269	LPA877	275	GRL111	278	LOO757	281	LPP737	283	LOM667
270	KHN341	276	LPD667	279	LOY587						

284-289   Volvo B10M-70B   Van Hool Alizée   1984

284	GMF091	286	GZX311	287	HFP341	288	GNL001	289	GYU331
285	HXB391								

290-301   Volvo B10M-65   Alpus 260S*   1984   *299/300 are Alpus 260SR

290	DBZ804	293	DFM714	296	FRL794	298	GBA564	300	FPN426
291	DMA814	294	EFO584	297	DPA514	299	EXA844	301	GHZ266
292	EFO654								

304-312   Volvo B10M-60   Van Hool Alizée   1984

304	BBY230	306	ATX260	308	BBS360	310	AZW210	312	BSH340

314	GPS481	Volvo B10M-70B	Van Hool Alizée	1984
317	FYA346	Volvo B10M-70B	Van Hool Alizée	1985

321-348   Volvo B10M-65   Alpus 260SR*   1984-85   *333-6 are 260S

321	GOW406	327	GOU196	334	GFU436	339	HOL923	344	HCG773
322	GHR136	328	HJC450	335	GPZ196	340	LBC873	345	JGX763
323	GEK166	330	EYF200	336	GLC136	341	LET823	346	JYP613
324	GMB196	331	GAC190	337	AFM903	342	LBB863	347	LAW613
325	GGX036	332	FSO096	338	GYB543	343	JNG703	348	LFJ983
326	GLK266	333	GGH266						

349	AWG978	Volvo B10M-70B	Van Hool Alizée	1985
350	AXD918	Volvo B10M-70B	Van Hool Alizée	1985
351	AEG908	Volvo B10M-70B	Van Hool Alizée	1985

352-363   Volvo B10M-65   Alpus 260S*   1984-85

352	FDB030	355	CLT921	358	DFB761	360	BHA863	362	BEC703
353	CZM601	356	CZM841	359	BCM983	361	ABP883	363	AAG603
354	CTB961	357	CME731						

364	MPD326	Volvo B10M-70B	Van Hool Alizée	1985
365	MPE026	Volvo B10M-70B	Van Hool Alizée	1985
366	MOP116	Volvo B10M-65	Alpus 260SR	1985
367	MOU156	Volvo B10M-65	Alpus 260SR	1985
368	EMG263	Mercedes-Benz 0303/9	Mercedes-Benz	1985
369	EFU173	Mercedes-Benz 0303/9	Mercedes-Benz	1985
370	FBB053	Mercedes-Benz 0303/9	Mercedes-Benz	1985
371	FWE373	Mercedes-Benz 0303/9	Mercedes-Benz	1985

372-389   Volvo B10M-60   Van Hool Alizée   1985

372	GOF598	375	GZG618	384	EKH509	388	FWO150	389	FXM340
373	GPC918	382	CXE911						

394	MXA086	Scania K112CLS	Alpus 260SR	1986

395-411   Volvo B10M-65   Alpus 260SR   1985-86

395	MON266	399	MMY066	403	MPL076	406	MOT146	409	MPF106
396	MNU016	400	MLR356	404	MPR026	407	MOY246	410	MOM326
397	MNU186	401	MLU386	405	MPW126	408	MOX306	411	MON026
398	MMP176	402	MLP276						

412-429   Volvo B10M-70B   Van Hool Alizée   1986-87   419-25 are B10M-60

412	MPF400	415	MMZ243	418	MJJ585	423	MNF023	426	MME283
413	MPN220	416	MJE545	419	MNL373	424	MND243	427	MHZ845
414	MNJ433	417	MJK655	420	MNK293	425	MNN153	429	MDJ775

436-444 — Volvo B10M-65 — Alpus 260S — 1987

436	KAF010	**438**	JUM210	**440**	JJC390	**442**	JPU440	**444**	JMN160
437	KAW010	**439**	JNL110	**441**	JUT410	**443**	JXD290		

445	NWG985	Volvo B9M-46	Alpus	1987
446	NWB935	Volvo B9M-46	Alpus	1987
449	DZL361	Volvo B10M-50B	Van Hool Alizée	1987
451	HEU823	Volvo B10M-70B	Van Hool Alizée	1987

452-460 — Volvo B10M-70B — Van Hool Alizée — 1987

452	JJF563	**454**	KME603	**456**	JPU993	**459**	HFU963	**460**	JBY993
453	JOC663	**455**	JGH923	**458**	HGP993				

467-475 — Volvo B10M-65R — Alpus 260S — 1988

467	NEE179	**469**	NKR320	**471**	NMM312	**473**	NMJ082	**475**	NLW482
468	NKN390	**470**	NLW242	**472**	NMN322	**474**	NML162		

476	NOM959	Volvo B10M-70B	Van Hool Alizée	1988
477	NOC739	Volvo B10M-70B	Van Hool Alizée 310	1988
478	NOA959	Volvo B10M-70B	Van Hool Alizée	1988
479	NNS629	Volvo B10M-70B	Van Hool Alizée	1987
480	NDK389	Volvo B10M-65	Alpus 260SR	1988
481	ASR794	Scania K113CLB	Van Hool Alizée	1988
482	AOC764	Scania K113CLB	Van Hool Alizée	1988

483-488 — Volvo B10M-60 — Van Hool Alizée — 1988

483	NDR093	**484**	NEE063	**485**	NEB273	**487**	NEO043	**488**	NDL043

489	NEA333	Volvo B10M-58B	Van Hool Alizée 310	1988
490	NEF383	Volvo B10M-58B	Van Hool Alizée 310	1988
491	NED433	Volvo B10M-70B	Van Hool Alizée	1988
492	NEG223	Volvo B10M-70B	Van Hool Alizée	1988
494	NEN103	Volvo B10M-70B	Van Hool Alizée	1988
495	KSO416	Volvo B10M-65	Van Hool Alizée	1988
496	KON186	Volvo B10M-65	Van Hool Alizée	1988

498-508 — Volvo B10M-65 — Alpus 260SR — 1989

498	OOL259	**500**	OOD299	**502**	ONJ039	**503**	ONT329	**504**	ONT499
499	OOH479	**501**	OOP059						

505	OBT252	Volvo B10M-70B	Alpus 260SR	1989
506	OBK342	Volvo B10M-70B	Alpus 260SR	1989
507	OCB102	Volvo B10M-70B	Alpus 260SR	1989
508	ODE132	Volvo B10M-70B	Alpus 260SR	1989

509-514 — Volvo B10M-70B — Säffle — 1989

509	OSK141	**511**	OSM301	**512**	OSH371	**513**	OSN171	**514**	ORZ191
510	OSE271								

515	OZW174	Volvo B10M-70B	Alpus 260SR	1989
516	OZR454	Volvo B10M-70B	Alpus 260SR	1989
517	OZR074	Volvo B10M-70B	Alpus 260SR	1989
518	OZM344	Volvo B10M-70B	Alpus 260SR	1989
519	OBC955	Volvo B10M-65	Alpus 260SR	1989
520	OBL785	Volvo B10M-65	Alpus 260SR	1990
521	OBH525	Volvo B10M-65	Alpus 260SR	1990

522-529 — Volvo B10M-65 — Van Hool Alizée — 1989

522	ODD143	**524**	ODG483	**526**	ODB363	**528**	OOR314	**529**	ODM353
523	ODO443	**525**	ODJ403	**527**	ODM113				

530	OBU402	Volvo B10M-58B	Van Hool Astral	1989
531	OBH262	Volvo B10M-58B	Van Hool Astral	1989

532-539   Volvo B10M-65*   Van Hool Alizée   1989   *Models varey

532	OZT474	**534**	OZH244	**536**	OBB635	**538**	OZE454	**539**	OZU314
533	OAD454	**535**	OZW004	**537**	OBB565				

540	OZJ014	Volvo B10M-70B	Alpus 260SR	1989
541	OJF918	Volvo B10M-65	Alpus 260SR	1990

542-546   Volvo B10M-70B   Säffle   1990

542	OHS708	**543**	OJG618	**544**	OHZ828	**545**	OHT958	**546**	OJG858

547	OHX738	Volvo B10M-70B	Alpus 260SR	1990
548	OHR558	Volvo B10M-70B	Alpus 260SR	1990
549	OFX749	Volvo B10M-56B	Van Hool Astral	1990
550	OFC929	Volvo B10M-56B	Van Hool Astral	1990

551-556   Volvo B10M-65   Alpus 260SR   1989

551	OFX679	**553**	OFN919	**554**	OGA809	**555**	OFX509	**556**	OFN849
552	OFD939						

557	OFZ699	Volvo B10M-70B	Alpus 260SR	1990
576	BCW148	Volvo B10M-65	Ajokki 5000	1982
577	CZO348	Volvo B10M-65	Ajokki 5000	1982
579	CBL078	Volvo B10M-65	Ajokki 5000	1982
580	CML338	Volvo B10M-65	Ajokki 5000	1982
590	MLH159	Volvo B10R-59	Säffle	1986
591	MLD429	Volvo B10R-59	Säffle	1986
593	BRZ164	Volvo B10M-65	Säffle	1988
594	BJP194	Volvo B10M-65	Säffle	1988

595-599   Scania CN113   Scania   1988-89

595	NLL725	**596**	NON755	**597**	NLH635	**598**	OYT369	**599**	OZK119

600	OMH191	Volvo B10M-55L	Säffle		1989
601	OMB131	Volvo B10M-55L	Säffle		1989
609	HEX494	Volvo B10M-70B	Kutter 9		1986
610	OLU361	Volvo B10M-55L	Säffle		1989
611	OMC141	Volvo B10M-65	Säffle		1989
612	OCO163	Volvo B10M-55L	Säffle		1989
630	KSL265	Scania CR112	Scania		1981
632	DMF497	Volvo B10R-59	Säffle		1981
633	FXH183	Scania CR112	Scania		1982
636	LWA195	Scania CR112	Scania		1983
637	DRB725	Volvo B10M-65	Säffle		1984
638	BRO798	Volvo B10M-60	Van Hool Alizée		1985
639	HGE199	Scania CN112	Scania		1985
640	MKC258	Scania K112	Van Hool Alizée		1986
641	AHH250	Scania CN112	Scania		1987
642	MAM609	Volvo B10M-60	Van Hool Alizée		1987
643	NHE292	Volvo B9M-46	Ajokki Victor		1988
644	CTD185	Scania K113	Ajokki Victor		1991
645	NAT695	Renault Master	Renault	M	1988
648	OAP273	Volvo B10M-60	Delta Star 501		1990
650	OHP896	Scania CN113	Scania		1989
651	OZP602	Mercedes-Benz 0410	?		1989
653	KOP337	Volvo B9M-46	Ajokki Victor		1990
654	CMW575	Scania K113T	Ajokki Regal		1992
655	JKA519	Scania CN113	Scania		1992
656	PFG603	Volvo B10M-65	Carrus Fifty		1992
658	PKN907	Volvo B9M-55	Kiitokori		1992
659	OUN340	Volvo B10M-70B	Ajokki Royal		1989
660	PJW623	Auwaerter Neoplan N116	Auwaerter Cityliner		1992
661	FNT548	Scania BF76-59	SKV		1965
663	LWS989	Mercedes-Benz L608D			1983
664	PFH853	Volkswagen Kombi	Volkswagen	M	1992
665	PET873	Volkswagen Kombi	Volkswagen	M	1992
703	MCJ705	Scania K112T	Ikarus Club		1986
706	CXM462	Scania K112	Kutter 9 Clipper		1984

710	LNB134	Volvo B10M-65	Wiima M303		1983
711	LSM034	Scania K112	Ajokki 6000		1983
712	PGA435	Renault Master	Renault	M	1994
713	PFA655	Renault Master	Renault	M	1991
714	MPA120	Renault Master	Renault	M	1988
715	PJJ106	Renault Trafic	Renault	M	1993
716	PHK127	Renault Trafic	Renault	M	1993
717	ASB084	Renault Trafic	Renault	M	1991
722	EWZ381	Scania K112T	Wiima K202		1987
725	LRJ191	Scania K112	Kutter 9 Clipper		1983
727	LAY491	Scania K112	Kutter 9 Clipper		1983
728	DXG614	Scania K112	Ajokki City		1985
729	ETE789	Scania K112	Ajokki City		1985
730	LRE443	Scania K112	Ajokki		1984
731	LUA413	Scania K112	Ajokki		1984
740	GRA865	Scania BR116S	Ajokki 5000D		1981
741	GLM675	Scania BR116S	Ajokki 5000D		1981
742	PAE988	Ontario II	Ontario II		1989
743	FPG706	Volvo B10M-65	Delta Plan 200	F	1982
744	LHY235	Volvo B10M-65	Säffle		1983
745	LJE185	Volvo B10M-65	Säffle		1983
746	DEW648	Volvo B10M-65	Säffle		1984
747	DPU898	Volvo B10M-65	Säffle		1984
748	LXB658	Scania K112	Delta Plan 200	F	1984
749	LXG538	Scania K112	Delta Plan 200	F	1984
750	BBG571	Volvo B10M-70B	Van Hool Alizée		1985
751	DWR510	Scania K112	Ajokki Express	DP F	1985
752	MNK301	Volvo B9M-46	Säffle		1986
753	MSE798	Volvo B10M-70B	Säffle		1987
754	MSL748	Volvo B10M-70B	Van Hool Alizée		1987
755	NUL865	Volvo B10M-70	Säffle		1988
756	NUN885	Volvo B10M-70	Säffle		1988
757	GYA416	Volvo B10M-65	Säffle		1989
758	GYR146	Volvo B10M-65	Säffle		1989
759	HFY386	Volvo B10M-65	Säffle		1989
760	JFL136	Volvo B10M-65	Säffle		1989
761	OHN249	Volvo B10M-70B	Säffle		1989
762	OLP451	Volvo B10M-65	Säffle		1989
763	OMF131	Volvo B10M-65	Säffle		1989
764	OYK025	Scania CK113	Scania		1989
765	OYN295	Scania CK113	Scania		1989
766	PMG420	Volvo B10M-70B	Säffle 2000		1992
767	FBD010	Scania CR112	Scania		1982
768	LEJ446	Scania CR112	Scania		1982
769	AGF075	Scania CN112	Scania		1985
770	JKA016	Scania CN113	Scania		1988
771	OSY815	Neoplan N4007NF	Neoplan		1990
772	LJM385	Volvo B10M-60	Van Hool Alizée		1983
773	LHS564	Volvo B10M-70B	Van Hool Alizée		1984
774	MDU200	Volvo B10M-60	Van Hool Alizée		1986
775	NUY725	Volvo B10M-60	Van Hool Alizée		1988
776	OFT608	Volvo B10M-60	Van Hool Alizée		1990
777	OGS598	Volvo B10M-58B	Van Hool Alizée		1990
778	BCL426	Kässbohrer Setra S210H	Kässbohrer	C	1985
780	MYH377	Mercedes-Benz O409	Backaryd		1985
781	MLW701	Mercedes-Benz 711D			1989
782	BYP738	Mercedes-Benz 410D			1992
783	KSJ483	Volvo F408		M	1981
784	CJT609	Volvo F407		M	1979
785	MKR695	Scania CN112	Scania		1987
786	DEW195	Scania CN113	Scania		1991
787	DGZ165	Scania CN113	Scania		1991
788	PJW766	Scania CN113	Scania		1992
789	PJW696	Scania CN113	Scania		1992
790	FYZ319	Volvo B10R-59	Säffle		1987
791	GUF339	Volvo B10R-59	Säffle		1987
792	GRO089	Volvo B10R-59	Säffle		1987
793	HNM019	Scania CN112	Scania		1985
794	HEB129	Scania CN112	Scania		1985
795	OHS816	Scania CK113	Scania		1989
796	OJB536	Scania CK113	Scania		1989
798	OFY181	Volvo B10M-60	Vest Ambassador		1989

800-805

		Ontario II		Ontario			1989		
800	PAM894	802	PAM923	803	PAM922	804	PAU002	805	PAU007
801	PAM893								

806	JDS371	Volvo B10M-65	Ajokki Express	DP F	1990
807	EDB023	Volvo B10M-65	Ajokki Express	DP F	1990
812	HPU386	Scania L113	Aabenraa		1991
813	HLS165	Kässbohrer Setra SG219	Kässbohrer	B	1991
817	KPN843	Volvo B10M-65	Wiima		1981

824-828

		Scania K113		Ajokki Express		DP	1992		
824	PKB972	825	PKP992	826	PXF504	827	PWZ584	828	PWS604

829-833

		Volvo B10M-70		Säffle 2000			1992		
829	PLN934	830	PLJ904	831	PLK764	832	PLL844	833	PLN554

834-838

		Volvo B10M-65		Säffle 2000			1992		
834	PLB864	835	PLS664	836	PLD644	837	PLG814	838	PLC944

845	FCU722	Volvo B10M-65	Alpus 260S		1982
846	LAL494	Volvo B10M-65	Alpus 260S		1982
847	LAB274	Volvo B10M-65	Alpus 260S		1982
849	BHR952	Volvo B10M-60	Wiima		1982
853	LBX630	Volvo B9M-60	Skandia Meteor		1983
854	LNO055	Volvo B9M-60	Skandia Meteor		1984
855	LJS155	Scania K82	Ajokki 5000E	DP	1982
856	DPE645	Scania K112	Van Hool Alizée		1983
857	LAL341	Scania CR112	Scania		1983
858	GHE292	Scania CR112	Scania		1983
859	LAO463	Scania CR112	Scania		1983
860	LAN224	Scania CR112	Scania		1983
861	LKY156	Volvo B10M-65	Alpus 260S		1982
862	LCM817	Volvo B10M-70B	Van Hool Alizée		1983
863	LCD777	Volvo B10M-70B	Van Hool Alizée		1983
865	LPL546	Volvo B9M-65	Skandia		1984
866	FSP536	Volvo B10M-65	Skandia Meteor		1983
867	JLT637	Volvo B9M-65	Skandia		1984
869	CHK595	Volvo B10M-65	Alpus 260S		1983
870	MPE196	Volvo B10M-70B	Van Hool Alizée		1986
871	AXD821	Volvo B10L-55L	Säffle	F	1985
872	AJG891	Volvo B10L-55L	Säffle	F	1985
873	HUU053	Scania K112	Helmark		1985
874	FXU974	Volvo B10M-65	Alpus 260S		1984
875	FSG276	Volvo B10M-65	Alpus 260S		1984
876	FTU047	Volkswagen Caravelle	Volkswagen	M	1985
877	MTX143	Scania K112T	Ajokki Express	DP F	1987
878	MTY223	Scania K112T	Ajokki Express	DP F	1987
879	MOM186	Volvo B10M-70B	Van Hool Alizée		1986
880	MTO013	Scania K112T	Ajokki Express	DP F	1987
881	MUB143	Scania K112T	Ajokki Express	DP F	1987
882	MTU373	Scania K112T	Ajokki Express	DP F	1987
883	MTL083	Scania K112T	Ajokki Express	DP F	1987
884	AUE738	Volvo B10M-70B	Van Hool Alizée		1985
885	DWF989	Volvo B10M-70B	Van Hool Alizée		1985
886	DMZ589	Volvo B10M-70B	Van Hool Alizée		1985
887	FWM440	Volvo B10M-65	Alpus 260SR		1984
888	BET673	Volvo B10M-65	Alpus 260SR		1985
889	MHW715	Volvo B10M-65	Wiima		1987
890	MUE173	Scania K112T	Ajokki Express	DP F	1987
891	MHC905	Volvo B10M-65	Wiima		1987
892	MHN825	Volvo B10M-65	Wiima		1987
893	EML421	Volvo B10M-70	Wiima		1987
894	MHO905	Volvo B10M-65	Wiima		1987
895	MHY735	Volvo B10M-65	Wiima		1987
896	MJH656	Volvo B10M-65	Wiima		1987
897	MML066	Volvo B10M-65	Alpus 260SR		1985
898	MNC206	Volvo B10M-65	Alpus 260SR		1985
899	KLL224	Kässbohrer Setra SG221UL	Kässbohrer		1988
900	NDE757	Scania CN112	Scania	DP F	1988

901	NDJ627	Scania CN112	Scania	DP F		1988
902	NCW717	Scania CN112	Scania	DP F		1988
903	NLG393	Scania CN112	Scania	DP F		1988
904	EHP915	Scania K112T	Ajokki Express	DP F		1988
905	HHZ598	Scania K112T	Ajokki Express	DP F		1988

906-911   Volvo B10M-65   Alpus 260SR   1987-88

906	JLP110	907	JLP350	909	NDM239	910	NEE489	911	NDZ479

912	OTG344	Scania K113	Aabenraa		1989
913	OUY091	Scania CK113	Scania		1989
914	OKY093	Volvo B10M-70	Säffle		1989
915	DJA948	Scania CK113	Scania		1990
916	OKE667	Scania CN113A	Scania		1990
917	OKM797	Scania CN113A	Scania		1990
918	OKG757	Scania CN113A	Scania		1990
919	OLR094	Kässbohrer Setra SG219SL	Kässbohrer		1990
920	OLN134	Kässbohrer Setra SG219SL	Kässbohrer		1990
921	OLN374	Kässbohrer Setra SG219SL	Kässbohrer		1990
922	OUG441	Scania CK113	Scania		1989
923	OWF454	Scania CK113	Scania		1989
924	OZB405	Scania CK113	Scania		1989
925	ORL491	Volvo B10M-65	Säffle		1989
926	OPP151	Volvo B10M-65	Säffle		1989
927	OOA040	Scania K113	Ajokki Express		1989
928	OKB261	Scania K113	Ajokki Express		1989
929	OKB021	Scania K113	Ajokki Express		1989
930	OKG071	Scania K113	Ajokki Express		1989
931	OLD173	Volvo B10M-70	Säffle		1989
932	OCA302	Scania K113T	Ajokki Express		1989
933	OBG222	Scania K113T	Ajokki Express		1989
934	OJG013	Scania K113T	Ajokki Express		1989
935	OKP343	Volvo B10M-65	Säffle		1989
936	OUJ221	Scania CK113	Scania		1989
937	OUZ001	Scania CK113	Scania		1989
938	OUJ391	Scania CN113	Scania		1989
939	OUS431	Scania CN113	Scania		1989
940	OUZ171	Scania CN113	Scania		1989
941	OKE361	Scania K113T	Ajokki Express		1989
942	OJZ341	Scania K113T	Ajokki Express		1989
943	OKH151	Scania K113T	Ajokki Express		1989
944	ORL181	Volvo B10M-70	Säffle		1989
945	OYH325	Scania CK113	Scania		1989
946	OJU481	Scania K113T	Ajokki Express		1989
947	OKK231	Scania K113T	Ajokki Express		1989
948	OUY471	Scania CK113	Scania		1989
949	OYJ335	Scania CK113	Scania		1989
950	OYT102	Scania K113T	Aabenraa		1989
951	OLJ272	Ford Transit	Ford	M	1989
952	OKS320	Scania K112T	Ajokki Express		1988
954	JGJ171	Volvo B10M-65	Ajokki Victor		1990
955	HZY201	Volvo B10M-65	Ajokki Victor		1990
956	JGX241	Volvo B10M-65	Ajokki Victor		1990
957	PKP512	Scania K113	Carrus Fifty		1992
960	MKO686	Volvo B9M-46	Helmark		1986
962	DXR222	Volvo B10M-60	Van Hool Alizée		1987
963	GJG216	Scania K112T	Ajokki Royal		1988
964	OJF483	Scania K113T	Ajokki Royal		1989
965	ONZ380	Scania K113	Ajokki Express		1989
966	BKD548	Scania K113	Ajokki Victor		1989
967	OOF470	Scania K113	Ajokki Express		1989
968	OJN443	Scania K113T	Ajokki Royal		1989
973	EMG971	Volvo B10M-65	Delta		1985
974	OEK333	Volvo B10M-70B	Ajokki Express		1989
975	ODU423	Volvo B10M-70B	Ajokki Express		1989
976	OEM283	Volvo B10M-70B	Ajokki Express		1989
977	OED453	Volvo B10M-70B	Ajokki Express		1989
978	GJT097	Volvo B10M-65B	Delta Star 501		1989
979	CDL490	Volvo B10M-70	Aabenraa		1991
980	CFM060	Volvo B10M-70	Aabenraa		1991
981	DHF053	Volvo B10M-70	Aabenraa		1990
982	DGR383	Volvo B10M-70	Aabenraa		1990

983	DGX323	Volvo B10M-65	Aabenraa		1990				
984	DDD293	Volvo B10M-65	Aabenraa		1990				
985	AZT082	Volvo B10M-65	Säffle		1990				
986	AWA012	Volvo B10M-55L	Säffle		1990				
987	AUF222	Volvo B10M-55L	Säffle		1990				
988	ASS422	Volvo B10M-55L	Säffle		1990				
989	AWC272	Volvo B10M-55L	Säffle		1990				
990	BDC462	Volvo B10M-55L	Säffle		1990				
991	DGC363	Volvo B10M-55L	Aabenraa		1990				
992	KCX062	Volvo B10M-65	Aabenraa		1990				
993	MBY392	Volvo B10M-65	Aabenraa		1990				
994	DDM193	Volvo B10M-65	Aabenraa		1990				
995	OLZ124	Kässbohrer Setra S215HDH	Kässbohrer		1989				
996	CMF595	Kässbohrer Setra S215HD	Kässbohrer		1982				
998	CCN218	Scania K113	Ajokki Victor		1991				
999	OSU010	Kässbohrer Setra S216HDS	Kässbohrer		1990				
1000	OLX104	Kässbohrer Setra S216HD	Kässbohrer		1990				
1001	DFL678	Scania K113	Ajokki Victor		1989				
1003	CRL078	Scania K113T	Delta Star 701		1991				
1004	CRN168	Scania K113T	Delta Star 701		1991				
1005	AJP955	Kässbohrer Setra S228DTI	Kässbohrer Imperial		1989				
1006	DYJ092	Scania K112T	Van Hool Astrobel	CH / F	1987				
1007	EKN372	Scania K92	Van Hool Alizée		1987				
1008	MKO877	Auwaerter Neoplan N212	Auwaerter Jetliner		1987				
1010	BDU101	Volvo B10M-65	Skandia Meteor		1984				
1012	MUR927	Scania K92	Skandia Meteor		1987				
1014	AJY751	Volvo B10M-55L	Säffle		1985				
1015	EEY159	Volvo B10M-55L	Säffle		1991				
1020	DGM839	Volvo B10M-60	Säffle		1985				
1021	BKX929	Volvo B10M-60	Säffle		1985				
1022	NTN845	Volvo B10M-60	Säffle		1987				
1023	NLH472	Volvo B10M-60	Säffle		1990				
1024	DRW283	Volvo B10M-60	Säffle		1990				
1025	DPF293	Volvo B10M-60	Säffle		1990				
1026	NLX725	Renault Master FB30	Renault	M	1988				
1027	NGO624	Renault Master FB30	Renault	M	1988				
1028	MWT402	Renault Master FB30	Renault	M	1989				
1029	NSB715	Volvo FL6.14	Helmark Meteor	M	1988				
1030	FXG992	Renault Master FB30	Renault	M	1988				
1031	BNH199	Scania B86	Ajokki 5000D		1980				
1034	BDB180	Volvo F4.08	Skandia		1980				
1035	LBJ870	Volvo F4.08	Skandia		1983				
1036	HJW651	Volvo B10M-45	Skandia Meteor		1985				
1037	DUN002	Volvo B9M-46	Van Hool Alizée		1987				
1038	FLO762	Volvo B9M-46	Van Hool Alizée		1987				
1039	OLT111	Volvo B9M-46	Vest Ambassadör		1989				
1040	NSZ737	Auwaerter Neoplan N214SH	Auwaerter Jetliner		1988				
1042	PHK512	Van Hool A508	Van Hool	B	1992				
1043	GMK478	Mercedes-Benz 0303/15KHP	Mercedes-Benz		1991				

1052-1057 — Volvo B10M-60 — Van Hool Alizée — 1984-89

1052	LSY896	1053	JXW182	1055	MMS785	1056	OBA313	1057	BLZ609

1058	BDX690	Volvo B10M-50B	Van Hool Astral		1988
1059	NNM201	Volvo B10M-60	Van Hool Alizée		1988
1060	NFO442	Volvo B10M-50B	Van Hool Astral		1988
1061	OUL250	Volvo B10M-60	Van Hool Alizée		1988
1062	APF301	Volvo B10M-60	Van Hool Alizée		1990
1064	AOP390	Auwaerter Neoplan N116	Auwaerter Cityliner		1991
1066	PSW685	Auwaerter Neoplan N117/3	Auwaerter Spaceliner		1993
1068	PRD602	Auwaerter Neoplan N117/3	Auwaerter Spaceliner		1993
1070	PRJ652	Auwaerter Neoplan N117/3	Auwaerter Spaceliner		1993
1071	EKZ594	Auwaerter Neoplan N117/3	Auwaerter Spaceliner		1993
1072	ANS100	Auwaerter Neoplan N116	Auwaerter Cityliner		1991
1075	OSB189	Volvo B10M-60	Van Hool Alizée		1989
1079	LRJ547	Scania CR112	Scania		1994
1080	HWW240	Scania K92	Scania		1987
1083	NUT837	Auwaerter Neoplan N213	Auwaerter Jetliner		1988
1084	FCA101	Auwaerter Neoplan N116	Auwaerter Cityliner		1991
1085	ANA238	Auwaerter Neoplan N117/3	Auwaerter Spaceliner		1991
1086	MWL498	Auwaerter Neoplan N116/3	Auwaerter Cityliner		1989
1087	MER157	Auwaerter Neoplan N116/3	Auwaerter Cityliner		1989

1089	MEW257	Auwaerter Neoplan N116/3	Auwaerter Cityliner		1989
1090	NTM402	Auwaerter Neoplan N117/3	Auwaerter Spaceliner		1988
1092	PSB935	Auwaerter Neoplan N117/3	Auwaerter Spaceliner		1993
1095	NGG193	Auwaerter Neoplan N116/3	Auwaerter Cityliner		1988
1098	HXG181	Auwaerter Neoplan N416	Auwaerter		1987
1104	MML012	Toyota Hiace	Toyota	M15	1986
1105	OGU425	Mercedes-Benz 1120/L42	Delta Star 21	B21F	1989
1110	PDY027	Auwaerter Neoplan N117/3	Auwaerter Spaceliner		1994
1111	POU540	Auwaerter Neoplan N116/3	Auwaerter Cityliner		1994
1113	LEC707	Volvo B10R-59	Aabenraa		1983
1114	LDX797	Volvo B10R-59	Aabenraa		1983
1116	LEA787	Volvo B10R-59	Aabenraa		1983
1117	PKN760	Auwaerter Neoplan N116/3	Auwaerter Cityliner		1993
1118	FJJ305	Auwaerter Neoplan N213	Auwaerter Jetliner		1991

1119-1124 — Volvo B10R-59 — Säffle — 1984

1119	FNN341	1121	FEC141	1122	FLJ201	1123	FDA461	1124	FLR331
1120	FJY331								

1125	PKJ970	Auwaerter Neoplan N116/3	Auwaerter Cityliner		1993
1129	GBM757	Volvo B10R-59	Säffle		1985
1130	GGB717	Volvo B10R-59	Säffle		1985
1131	MKZ098	Volvo B10M-50B	Van Hool Astral		1986
1132	AEB535	Volvo B12-61B	Van Hool Alizée		1992
1135	MAP128	Volvo B10R-59	Säffle		1986
1136	MBB488	Volvo B10R-59	Säffle		1986
1139	MBG298	Volvo B10M-60	Säffle		1986

1141-1160 — Volvo B10R-59 — Säffle — 1987-90

1141	MCD533	1147	NTN183	1152	ORG866	1155	ORF546	1158	OCY935
1142	MBB543	1148	NTN013	1153	ORF926	1156	OBW945	1159	OCG765
1143	MAZ714	1149	NTC333	1154	ORH636	1157	OBO995	1160	OCU605
1144	MBD644	1150	NTG373						

1162	NGK250	Mercedes-Benz 0303	Mercedes-Benz		1987
1163	FDD565	Mercedes-Benz 0303/9	Mercedes-Benz		1979
1164	AWU265	Scania CN112A	Scania		1985
1165	MYL286	Scania CN112A	Scania		1986
1166	MYX106	Scania CN112A	Scania		1986
1167	OUK042	Scania K113T	Van Hool Alizée		1991

1175-1188 — Scania CN112 — Scania — 1982

1175	FWW288	1178	CUF166	1181	GCN389	1184	LAJ097	1187	LFS420
1176	EHO314	1179	GBD317	1182	FFA252	1185	LGW258	1188	LHJ261
1177	EFY355	1180	KAK108	1183	EXJ304	1186	LGY359		

1191-1197 — Volvo B10MA-55 — Säffle — AB D — 1986

1191	FEA673	1193	ASD938	1194	MZH228	1195	MYU498	1197	MZU228
1192	BTA670							

1199	LFG395	Volvo B6FA	Delta Mini	F	1982
1200	GMG935	Volvo B10M-60	Van Hool Alizée		1981
1201	OUN011	Scania CN113A	Scania		1989
1222	OUU381	Scania CN113A	Scania		1989

1223-1228 — Volvo B10R-59 — Säffle — 1983

1223	EYJ796	1225	FAF696	1226	EXT566	1227	FAZ956	1228	ESM516
1224	EJA546							

1229	OUX221	Scania CN113A	Scania		1989
1230	OUR041	Scania CN113A	Scania		1989

1231-1236 — Volvo B10R-59 — Säffle — 1987

1231	MUC527	1233	MUA817	1234	MUD607	1235	MUG567	1236	MUG947
1232	MTR957							

1237	OUO331	Scania CN113A	Scania				1989	
1238	OUF361	Scania CN113A	Scania				1989	
1239	OUN181	Scania CN113A	Scania				1989	
1240	OUH211	Scania CN113A	Scania				1989	

1241-1245

Volvo B10R-59 — Säffle — 1991

1241	HXY336	**1242**	HZA076	**1243**	JAM006	**1244**	JCN056	**1245** JEA466

1246	OUO401	Scania CN113A	Scania				1989	
1247	OJA163	Scania CN113A	Scania				1989	
1248	OHH473	Scania CN113A	Scania				1989	
1259	OUT061	Scania CN113A	Scania				1989	

1250-1259

Auwaerter Neoplan N4014NF — Auwaerter — 1992

1250 PXU605	**1252** PXZ565	**1254** PXT905	**1256** PYF895	**1258** PXT525
1251 PXR985	**1253** PYA605	**1255** PXT765	**1257** PXP595	**1259** PXY935

1260	OUL293	Auwaerter Neoplan N4007	Auwaerter	1989
1261	OUW413	Auwaerter Neoplan N4007	Auwaerter	1989
1262	OWE393	Auwaerter Neoplan N4007	Auwaerter	1989

1263-1273

Scania CN112* — Scania — 1987-88 *1266 is CR112 & 1966

1263 MTP739	**1266** KFU170	**1268** NRY995	**1270** NSM975	**1272** NSJ645
1264 MTE749	**1267** NRW665	**1269** NSC995	**1271** NSN675	**1273** NRX815

1274-1282

Scania CR112 — Scania — 1983

1274 ATU233	**1276** LMX511	**1278** LLC813	**1280** ELT695	**1282** LED877
1275 LMX500	**1277** LMX902	**1279** LMT904	**1281** LBM826	

1284-1289

Scania CN113 — Scania — 1990-92

1284 FAY385	**1286** CSO734	**1287** PJD683	**1288** PJF913	**1289** PJD823
1285 CRY974				

1290	MTC332	Scania CN112	Scania	1986
1291	MSO362	Scania CN112	Scania	1986

1292-1324

Scania CR112 — Scania — 1982-84

1292 DLL222	**1299** EHX064	**1306** LWK973	**1313** LOD958	**1319** JJR589
1293 BDL493	**1300** ERE215	**1307** LWL684	**1314** HLP849	**1320** JPZ649
1294 ELS294	**1301** LNT768	**1308** KOX975	**1315** JMT529	**1321** HYY719
1295 EHF355	**1302** LWW789	**1309** LUB616	**1316** HKT979	**1322** JDW569
1296 GAC267	**1303** LUU570	**1310** LOH727	**1317** JJM859	**1323** JYT779
1297 FJE338	**1304** LWL721	**1311** LHO508	**1318** HHK569	**1324** HJT999
1298 EUL250	**1305** BPS196	**1312** LOG748		

1325-1345

Scania CN112 — Scania — 1984

1325 GOH809	**1330** GES919	**1334** BTO243	**1338** LXK443	**1342** LYN203
1326 GFL619	**1331** GCB939	**1335** BND373	**1339** LZP123	**1343** LZW473
1327 GDG959	**1332** GDJ739	**1336** LZE443	**1340** LXO003	**1344** LZJ003
1328 GPX579	**1333** CBW253	**1337** LZC353	**1341** LXP183	**1345** LYE473
1329 GJR509				

1346-1351

Scania CN113A — Scania — 1992-93

1346 PKA916	**1348** PKJ977	**1349** PJX517	**1350** PKF877	**1351** PJO797
1347 PKE627				

1352-1369

Scania CN112 — Scania — 1987

1352 MXE839	**1356** MER678	**1360** MTY939	**1364** KTM090	**1367** MTB579
1353 MEP598	**1357** MFC558	**1361** MTH609	**1365** MTM879	**1368** NSH875
1354 MEZ708	**1358** MUE579	**1362** MTN959	**1366** MTB959	**1369** NRU595
1355 MFE888	**1359** MTY559	**1363** MTG909		

1370	LOF658	Scania CR112		Scania		1984			
1371	CSD504	Scania CN113		Scania		1991			

1372-1382

Scania CN112A — Scania — 1985-87

1372	FXW036	1375	GLC952	1377	GBM822	1379	GRD883	1381	GWB923
1373	GBS126	1376	FNA982	1378	FYY912	1380	GBY583	1382	GWY833
1374	GAR892								

1383	PKY615	Scania CN113A		Scania		1992
1384	PKW835	Scania CN113A		Scania		1992
1385	PKZ935	Scania CN113A		Scania		1992
1386	PKW905	Scania CN113A		Scania		1992
1387	OHJ808	Volvo B10M-55L		Säffle		1990
1388	OHE868	Volvo B10M-55L		Säffle		1990
1389	ORH343	Volvo B10M-55L		Säffle		1991
1390	OPO183	Volvo B10M-55L		Säffle		1991
1391	LPW968	Volvo B10M-55L		Säffle		1984

1392-1397

Volvo B10M-60 — Säffle — 1991

1392	DGE569	1394	BJN815	1395	BKB965	1396	BHN605	1397	BHM765
1393	BGJ845								

1399	ECY456	Volvo B58-60		Säffle		1979
1400	DEY107	Volvo B58-60		Säffle		1979
1404	DMG030	Volvo B58-60		Säffle		1980
1407	GOK112	Volvo B10M-60		Säffle		1984

1408-1418

Volvo B10M-55L — Säffle — 1990

1408	OHE798	1411	OGY918	1413	OGZ548	1415	OHC608	1417	OHD928
1409	OGY778	1412	OHM828	1414	OGX838	1416	OHA518	1418	OHM758
1410	OHN698								

1419-1457

Volvo B10M-55L — Säffle — 1980-84

1419	AUS506	1427	LCL667	1435	LDS527	1443	LGM538	1451	LYM667
1420	KSU272	1428	LCF937	1436	LGH988	1444	LGR578	1452	LYD697
1421	BDU113	1429	LBU817	1437	LGN788	1445	LYK717	1453	LXX747
1422	LDX557	1430	LCK967	1438	LGZ848	1446	LYH947	1454	LXY517
1423	LDX937	1431	LCJ727	1439	LKE598	1447	LXZ907	1455	LYH637
1424	LEA927	1432	LBN617	1440	LGC798	1448	LZL937	1456	LXX987
1425	LEE587	1433	LBM777	1441	LGU988	1449	LZP977	1457	LZT767
1426	LEA547	1434	LBG667	1442	LEE756	1450	LZM947		

1458	BGB703	Volvo B10M-60		Säffle		1985

1459-1473

Volvo B58-60 — Säffle — 1978-79

1459	KLP778	1461	EGM052	1466	KLC147	1469	BNK255	1472	EME362
1460	DZJ082	1465	KLD006	1468	BJH174	1470	DXA096	1473	EGK342

1475	BSJ574	Volvo B10M-60		Säffle		1982
1476	ERJ525	Volvo B10M-60		Säffle		1982

1488-1494

Volvo B10M-55L — Säffle — 1983-84

1488	LPU968	1490	LOO303	1491	LPR463	1493	LOG103	1494	LPN123

1495-1544

Scania CN113 — Scania — 1989

1495	JWT156	1504	EAP698	1514	AEH658	1523	ABY598	1537	CRD508
1496	JOE346	1506	DXT728	1515	AEX598	1525	BAT898	1540	OMY967
1497	JAR256	1507	DCR588	1517	BSK538	1526	BXP648	1541	ONE817
1498	NLZ347	1508	EEP508	1518	BNR518	1528	CCH908	1542	ONG527
1499	BMA023	1511	DTZ988	1519	AAT978	1535	BCL868	1543	ONK587
1500	NMM317	1512	CHY598	1520	CKC958	1536	BBY898	1544	OMX957
1501	EJO578	1513	CTU588						

1545-1552 — Volvo B10MA-55 — Säffle — 1992

1545 PNB963	**1546** PNG843	**1547** PMT633	**1549** PND743	**1552** PMZ743			

1553-1576 — Volvo B10MA-55 — Säffle — 1981-83

1553 KPB537	**1559** KYT180	**1564** KXT394	**1568** APD137	**1572** LKK999
1554 KZR718	**1560** KTO161	**1565** KYZ075	**1569** DGC288	**1574** LBZ539
1556 KXW889	**1561** KTM462	**1566** KNC096	**1570** LKZ609	**1575** LCE549
1558 KYJ870	**1563** KNJ273	**1567** CDK575	**1571** LKJ519	**1576** LCA509

1578-1586 — Volvo B10MA-55 — Säffle — 1986

1578 GND508	**1581** AUP716	**1583** MHB513	**1585** MSA794	**1586** MRU794
1579 HJG538	**1582** MHD913	**1584** MHE853		

1587 JXR459	Volvo B58-65	Säffle	1978

1588-1601 — Volvo B10MA-55 — Säffle — 1986-91

1588 MSK844	**1590** NLS397	**1597** OSU243	**1600** OPR273	**1601** OPR103
1589 MYR917	**1596** OPE413	**1599** OWW403		

1605 BRD949	Volvo B10M-60	Säffle	1982
1606 EGP981	Volvo B10M-60	Säffle	1982
1607 DMZ792	Volvo B10M-60	Säffle	1982

1608-1614 — Volvo B10M-60 — Säffle — 1993

1608 PJO406	**1610** PJD036	**1612** PHU316	**1613** PLD466	**1614** PLH026
1609 PHW246	**1611** PJH076			

1688 KCJ609	Volvo B58-65	Säffle	1979
1689 KCF819	Volvo B58-65	Säffle	1979
1708 GHX584	Volvo B58-65	Säffle	1979
1725 PWP611	Hino RB145	Hino	1992
1727 PNH864	Hino RB145	Hino	1992

1728-1753 — Volvo B58-65 — Säffle — 1980

1728 BJZ028	**1743** CJW139	**1747** CPM409	**1748** CTS159	**1753** CTT309
1736 BGB308				

1765 FOG451	Volvo B58-65	VBK	1980
1793 BUW655	Scania CR112	Scania	1980
1798 BAB094	Scania CR112	Scania	1980
1802 CEY860	Scania CR112	Scania	1980
1811 KUA812	Volvo B10M-55L	Van Hool A	1980
1812 KWB754	Volvo B10M-55L	Van Hool A	1981
1817 CES554	Scania CR112	Scania	1980
1818 BZN825	Scania CR112	Scania	1980
1823 KUO809	Volvo B10M-55L	Van Hool A	1980
1825 KST843	Volvo B10M-55L	Van Hool A	1981
1826 KUT654	Volvo B10M-55L	Van Hool A	1981

1828-1885 — Volvo B10M-65 — Säffle — 1980-81

1828 KNM558	**1842** KNA581	**1857** KWT107	**1871** KPG067	**1877** KOS467
1831 KNL641	**1843** KNJ561	**1858** KXR133	**1872** FPR268	**1878** KYX224
1835 KNF531	**1844** KZM613	**1861** KXM481	**1873** KZZ166	**1879** KZE106
1837 KNJ860	**1849** KRM845	**1863** KYO459	**1874** KYO194	**1880** KPJ227
1839 KPC925	**1851** KNK697	**1864** KYU339	**1875** KZX386	**1884** KZU446
1840 KZD643	**1853** KRR645	**1867** KXS202	**1876** KPB327	**1885** EYA168
1841 KNJ664	**1856** KXC377			

1889-1904 — Volvo B10M-65 — VBK — 1981

1889 KZK642	**1893** KYM990	**1897** KXR959	**1901** KWL099	**1903** KWP349
1881 KWT553	**1896** KYA679	**1900** KUB198	**1902** KWR049	**1904** KWS299

1909 KSS920	Volvo B10M-60	Van Hool Alizée	1981

The number of available pictures of Swebus is limited. Here we see 2001, FJZ231, a Volvo B10M with Säffle bodywork and Uddevalla depot codes. The majority of vehicles in Scandinavia are to the British dual-purpose standard while many buses are also dual-doored. *Malcolm Tranter*

1913-1934   Scania CR112   Scania   1981

1913	KRL479	1922	KOW464	1923	KOU224	1933	EFX687	1934	FYM958

1940-1946   Volvo B10M-55L   Van Hool   1981

1940	CEO820	1942	EBB551	1944	CRF553	1945	BTJ603	1946	DHC937
1941	CBG920	1943	KYZ792						

1954-2001   Volvo B10M-65   Säffle   B   D   1982

1954	EBL545	1964	FOO071	1971	GXE379	1980	BRS408	1994	FZG280
1956	HWJ269	1965	FOP081	1972	JRB369	1982	KSR499	1996	BPR288
1957	FJM220	1966	ARC086	1973	FMW405	1985	AMT426	1997	BSX198
1958	FYP350	1967	AFH417	1974	AJH276	1987	ASD147	1998	FKC460
1959	FXB360	1968	FKD230	1975	AME277	1989	FXG181	1999	FKG031
1961	FNP321	1969	FFU110	1977	FKB070	1990	GCR252	2000	FTP212
1962	FOO451	1970	JYX059	1978	FYN400	1991	CAK398	2001	FJZ231
1963	APT377								

2003-2012   Volvo B10M-65   VBK   1981

2003	EJU708	2007	EFZ658	2010	DNR572	2011	DPN652	2012	DTG922
2005	EKS838	2009	EHK564						

2017-2024   Scania CR112   Scania   1982

2017	DSA388	2018	CFE406	2022	BZZ464	2023	BUK395	2024	BLH255

2025-2033   Volvo B10M-65   Aabenraa   1982

2025	FNN144	2028	EWL204	2031	BEJ301	2032	EMU432	2033	AJR469
2027	EUU189								

The Swebus name and logo are to be retained within the Stagecoach operation with the symbol in red and the text in dark blue. Here we see another of the Volvo B10M-65s, 1967, AFH417, with Säffle bodywork, here in standard fleet livery. *Malcolm Tranter*

2035-2074   Volvo B10M-65   Säffle   1982-83

2035	LFS201	2044	LFY255	2053	LEZ277	2060	LFT082	2069	LEU310
2036	LFN331	2045	LFT465	2054	LFB017	2063	LFJ471	2070	LEH480
2039	LFZ273	2046	LGA235	2055	LMW258	2064	LMG488	2071	LEX331
2041	LEJ180	2047	LFX005	2057	LFX242	2066	LBN166	2073	LFH483
2042	LFK161	2048	LFJ301	2058	LFF142	2067	LFU302	2074	LFH184
2043	LFS215	2051	LFY403	2059	LFJ312	2068	LES390		

2078-2094   Volvo B10M-65   Aabenraa   1982

2078	BDG305	2082	FAZ093	2086	DWC852	2090	CDL186	2093	EMR962
2080	DEC460	2084	ASH318	2087	GZS563	2091	GOR661	2094	FMY692
2081	GHC451	2085	EGO591	2089	DYZ805	2092	FRM981		

2095	LGX121	Scania CR112	Scania	1982
2096	LGU041	Scania CR112	Scania	1982
2097	LJC134	Scania CR112	Scania	1982
2098	LAD047	Scania CR112	Scania	1982

2100-2129   Volvo B10M-55L   Van Hool Alizée   1982

2100	LDU285	2106	LCZ363	2111	LEJ276	2118	LKU444	2124	LHJ241
2101	LEN055	2107	LHJ024	2113	LAF288	2120	LEU026	2125	LHC041
2102	LDY445	2108	LHJ194	2114	LGT399	2121	LJJ452	2127	LHC432
2103	LGR025	2109	ALL505	2115	LFL164	2122	LHG221	2128	LML152
2104	LGE391	2110	LHC215	2117	LKF295	2123	LGX271	2129	LMM162
2105	LGD152								

2140	LKW055	Volvo B10M-60	Van Hool Alizée	1982

2142-2151

Volvo B10M-65   Aabenraa   1982

2142	LHJ252	2144	LHF163	2146	LGG177	2148	LHU389	2150	LHJ492
2143	LHN363	2145	LHZ319	2147	LBG348	2149	LHY044	2151	LHC122

2152	LHA292	Scania CR112	Scania	1983
2153	LDU086	Scania CR112	Scania	1983
2154	LAO277	Scania CR112	Scania	1983
2157	DJC179	Volvo B10M-65	Aabenraa	1981

2158-2201

Scania CR112   Scania   1983

2158	LMJ614	2168	LMN574	2174	LAF641	2180	LZC857	2191	DJO609
2159	LMY565	2169	LBR936	2175	LAJ682	2181	LYS998	2192	DXL950
2160	LAZ546	2170	LFJ587	2176	LLJ873	2183	CXW984	2197	LSS975
2164	LMU590	2171	LMP608	2177	GMN994	2184	DFB955	2198	LSP645
2165	LMS651	2172	LAZ989	2178	DMG555	2189	CXS883	2199	LSX835
2166	LMF592	2173	LAZ680	2179	DMP536	2190	DJL554	2201	LSO945

2207-2242

Volvo B10M-65   Säffle   1983

2207	LCW520	2214	LCO640	2222	LCN940	2229	LWJ202	2237	LWA222
2208	LCP580	2215	LCL850	2223	LWJ372	2230	LUX462	2238	LWB092
2209	LCG510	2216	LCK600	2224	LWF342	2231	LWN162	2239	LWM152
2210	LCE590	2217	LCG990	2225	LWE262	2232	LWL142	2240	LWH292
2211	LCS670	2218	LCX530	2226	LWK062	2233	LUK222	2241	LWC482
2212	LCD650	2219	LCJ910	2227	LWP492	2235	LUG372	2242	LWB232
2213	LCC640	2221	LCR730	2228	LWL452	2236	LUP342		

2243-2262

Volvo B10M-65   Aabenraa   1983

2243	LNF123	2247	LRZ433	2251	LTZ023	2254	LSK413	2260	LWM073
2244	LND343	2248	LOT173	2252	LWP313	2256	LUB313	2261	LSK033
2245	LLO393	2249	LOU323	2253	LWP003	2257	LWD483	2262	LTO283
2246	LOC373	2250	LNM213						

2263-2281

Volvo B10M-55L   Säffle   1983-84

2263	LZA374	2268	LZC224	2272	LYR034	2276	LZF184	2279	LYU374
2264	LYO014	2269	LYZ234	2273	LZG194	2277	LYX454	2280	LYL464
2266	LYY464	2270	LYZ164	2274	LYW444	2278	LYM164	2281	LYO254
2267	LYN244	2271	LYX144	2275	LYN174				

2283-2290

Volvo B10M-55L   Van Hool Alizée   1983

2283	LWT765	2285	AUS975	2287	CAM625	2289	LUM965	2290	LTH655
2284	BED885	2286	BNP615	2288	LXB855				

2291	AWM525	Volvo B10M-65	Van Hool Alizée	1983
2292	BUP705	Volvo B10M-65	Van Hool Alizée	1983
2293	BUD705	Volvo B10M-65	Van Hool Alizée	1983
2294	LUH555	Volvo B10M-65	Van Hool Alizée	1983

2296-2312

Volvo B10M-70B   Van Hool Alizée   1983-84

2296	JMH868	2300	KOK878	2303	LPK908	2306	KGE838	2309	BAA670
2297	KTU918	2301	KZD798	2304	KRL688	2307	LZA950	2311	LYM670
2298	HAD928	2302	JAZ748	2305	LPU758	2308	LZN720	2312	LYF620
2299	LPY538								

2314-2363

Volvo B10M-65   Säffle   1983-85

2314	LYZ839	2326	CMB362	2336	KCO455	2346	AHT295	2356	ACK405
2315	LYU979	2327	JWO025	2338	LOW095	2348	AON415	2357	ABO235
2316	LYU669	2328	JCY395	2339	LOP295	2349	AHZ235	2358	DHC165
2318	LNN640	2329	JKM305	2340	LPT295	2350	AJN075	2359	CXE125
2319	LNG830	2330	KJB155	2341	LFU195	2351	AGX315	2360	DAR195
2320	CSA402	2331	HXH055	2342	LNZ295	2352	AGO425	2361	DGD105
2321	CKS222	2332	JSB475	2343	LMR195	2353	ANE475	2362	LBR095
2322	CLM172	2333	JMO055	2344	LXT395	2354	ACS235	2363	DFE075
2324	CRY492	2334	KYX395	2345	LZP095	2355	ACD215		

2367-2395   Volvo B10M-55L   Säffle   1984-85

2367	FLZ514	2373	GHU554	2379	DKH534	2385	ELU974	2391	LTU376
2368	DCP594	2374	FOP624	2380	DNK934	2386	FHH634	2392	LUE246
2369	GND714	2375	DFX794	2381	DOJ834	2387	DOK764	2393	LUO226
2370	DYS874	2376	ECX534	2382	DDE714	2388	ESS734	2394	LOY246
2371	FGZ834	2377	EGD704	2383	FDU894	2389	LSO046	2395	LRT256
2372	FTX894	2378	EGC864	2384	DXF974	2390	LSZ196		

2402-2416   Volvo B10M-65   Van Hool Alizée   1985

2402	DHU403	2406	FBN591	2409	FGH811	2412	EWL701	2415	FHT941
2404	EMW881	2407	EHR791	2410	GNJ601	2413	FHU881	2416	FTP541
2405	FSR581	2408	GJW771	2411	GEU791	2414	FJX621		

2417-2424   Volvo B10M-60   Van Hool Alizée   1984-85

2417	DBG400	2420	DNM040	2421	DGB690	2422	CYO680	2424	DKL520
2418	CSY400								

2425-2440   Volvo B10M-70B   Van Hool Alizée   1985

2425	FLA602	2429	GGO792	2432	FRW622	2435	DYD409	2438	DPW209
2426	FZL952	2430	GFA632	2433	GMM662	2436	DLL179	2439	EAD269
2427	GCN562	2431	GDB912	2434	GGR572	2437	DSK499	2440	DUD489
2428	FWC732								

2441-2468   Volvo B10M-70B   Säffle   1984-85

2441	GFL538	2448	FLR290	2454	FDX160	2460	BGL521	2465	CDJ591
2442	EXD668	2449	FMB470	2455	FTF430	2461	CFN871	2466	BGH811
2443	EOF688	2450	FJR170	2457	CCS591	2462	CCN791	2467	CHL651
2446	FJS010	2451	FEB160	2458	CGE871	2463	BHD841	2468	BYG871
2447	FDW150	2452	FPU130	2459	CGE701	2464	BCG681		

2469-2479   Volvo B10M-55L   Säffle   1985

2469	CDT483	2472	DPK093	2474	DCR173	2476	FKE463	2478	FPX383
2470	CHL493	2473	ECJ033	2475	DLC123	2477	FMU293	2479	FNN443
2471	DKC153								

2480-2530   Volvo B10M-65   Säffle   1985

2480	ETU502	2491	EXA552	2500	FDU973	2509	EEZ473	2522	FSA923
2481	EDS592	2492	EHB912	2501	GMW863	2510	FLZ493	2523	GNU523
2482	ECK732	2493	ETC853	2502	DWO084	2511	EOU173	2524	FCD723
2483	FBZ972	2494	GBS903	2503	EXB623	2512	DWP513	2525	FLG963
2484	FCA632	2495	FLM183	2504	EMU883	2513	DTY833	2527	GUO593
2486	EFZ892	2496	EDS443	2505	EFC803	2517	EXR893	2528	FXN923
2487	FBY652	2497	FGC353	2506	ESZ793	2518	ESX773	2529	FSD573
2488	EAN922	2498	FGG393	2507	FMN303	2519	GJO963	2530	GRE813
2489	EPO542	2499	EGR383	2508	EXH173				

2531-2562   Scania CN112   Scania   1985

2531	FUR105	2538	GCK479	2545	BOH568	2551	BLO748	2557	AEB095
2532	FMF055	2539	BEO578	2546	BNY688	2552	BPT768	2558	BGL175
2533	FZS415	2540	BGA808	2547	AZO878	2553	BZG668	2559	BSY495
2534	FTS215	2541	AYH858	2548	BAS698	2554	HLB399	2560	BSY325
2535	FTZ335	2542	AYU618	2549	BAB968	2555	GSD039	2561	ARJ425
2536	FMA175	2543	BGB508	2550	BHH848	2556	GJM279	2562	ARC085
2537	GPU145	2544	BCG578						

2563-2577   Scania K112   Aabenraa   1984-86

2563	LRO918	2568	EBN075	2570	BXS165	2572	CLP055	2577	CEC955
2567	CNY295	2569	DRL365	2571	DDE125	2574	GJO844		

2579-2584   Volvo B10M-65   Säffle   1986

2579	DNN615	2581	DMM565	2582	CXD615	2583	DZE895	2584	DKW995
2580	DYU545								

2585	CYU615	Volvo B10M-55L		Säffle			1986		
2586	CPX795	Volvo B10M-55L		Säffle			1986		
2589	CKO615	Volvo B10M-55L		Säffle			1986		

2591-2596   Volvo B10M-70B   Säffle   1985-86

2591	ESA825	**2593**	FPX785	**2594**	FSO905	**2595**	MWK096	**2596**	MWL176
2592	FPP595								

2597	BRY307	Volvo B10M-60	Van Hool Alizée	1982
2599	MFZ173	Volvo B10M-60	Van Hool Alizée	1986
2600	MFX083	Volvo B10M-60	Van Hool Alizée	1986
2601	MGD483	Volvo B10M-60	Van Hool Alizée	1986
2602	MLY513	Volvo B10M-65	Van Hool Alizée	1986
2605	MLS713	Volvo B10M-65	Van Hool Alizée	1986
2606	MLZ903	Volvo B10M-65	Van Hool Alizée	1986

2607-2626   Volvo B10M-70B   Van Hool Alizée   1986

2607	MGH043	**2611**	MGC233	**2615**	MDN493	**2619**	MCR073	**2623**	MCU483
2608	MFP103	**2612**	MGE183	**2616**	MDK083	**2620**	MCM343	**2624**	MCK013
2609	MFN323	**2613**	MGB153	**2617**	MDY163	**2621**	MDE353	**2625**	MCS153
2610	MFS053	**2614**	MFO023	**2618**	MDW213	**2622**	MDB323	**2626**	MDA243

2627-2631   Volvo B10M-55L   Säffle   1986

2627	MJK119	**2628**	MJR489	**2629**	MJN079	**2630**	MJS189	**2631**	MJO159

2632	MDC349	Volvo B10M-60	Säffle	1986
2633	MDB269	Volvo B10M-60	Säffle	1986
2634	MDB199	Volvo B10M-60	Säffle	1986

2635-2670   Volvo B10M-70B   Säffle   1986

2635	MMU059	**2642**	MNG329	**2653**	MXT090	**2659**	MJZ280	**2665**	MJO111
2636	MNK109	**2643**	MXW480	**2654**	MXC430	**2660**	MJP450	**2666**	MJR201
2637	MMW299	**2645**	MXG300	**2655**	MXJ320	**2661**	MKB410	**2667**	MKA481
2638	MMW129	**2646**	MXR210	**2656**	MXW310	**2662**	MJS141	**2668**	MJT151
2639	MNM059	**2648**	MNF249	**2657**	MXT300	**2663**	MKB491	**2669**	MHO103
2640	MNA439	**2649**	MMR269	**2658**	MXU240	**2664**	MJU091	**2670**	MHE053
2641	MND469	**2652**	MNB449						

2672-2702   Volvo B10M-65   Alpus 260SR   1986-87

2672	MLF412	**2681**	MLZ462	**2687**	MCM755	**2693**	MCY815	**2698**	MZT926
2673	MLA462	**2682**	MLR192	**2688**	MCW965	**2694**	MCX735	**2699**	MZS846
2675	MLR402	**2683**	MLL382	**2689**	MCS945	**2695**	MCN905	**2700**	MZS536
2677	MLL212	**2684**	MML042	**2690**	MCO535	**2696**	MCW655	**2701**	MZT546
2679	MLX372	**2685**	MDC745	**2691**	MDA965	**2697**	MCT885	**2702**	MZO506
2680	MLS272	**2686**	MCP785	**2692**	MCX665				

2703-2744   Volvo B10M-70   Säffle   1986

2703	MBN491	**2711**	MBR421	**2722**	MLN202	**2730**	MMB342	**2738**	MHH223
2704	MCB461	**2712**	MBZ241	**2723**	MLZ362	**2731**	MLY112	**2739**	MHG213
2705	MCC231	**2713**	MBX221	**2724**	MLX412	**2732**	MLN442	**2740**	MHM323
2706	MBK151	**2714**	MBT131	**2725**	MLR232	**2733**	MHP353	**2741**	MHB333
2707	MCD481	**2718**	MLT012	**2726**	MLH402	**2734**	MHU153	**2742**	MHR363
2708	MBX151	**2719**	MLX272	**2727**	MMT082	**2735**	MHK093	**2743**	MHO273
2709	MCB081	**2720**	MLO142	**2728**	MMS212	**2736**	MHO343	**2744**	MHT383
2710	MCE181	**2721**	MLT252	**2729**	MMR132	**2737**	MHP423		

2749-2755   Scania K112   Aabenraa   1987

2749	EHT149	**2750**	EEM179	**2751**	EYZ259	**2754**	EHK309	**2755**	EHC109

2758-2770   Volvo B10M-70B   Van Hool Alizée   1987

2758	MPZ705	**2760**	MPY555	**2762**	MPT905	**2768**	NSY855	**2770**	NST825
2759	MPN885	**2761**	MPH775	**2767**	NTF645	**2769**	NTD625		

2771	NTJ675	Volvo B10M-60	Van Hool Alizée			1987			
2772	NST755	Volvo B10M-60	Van Hool Alizée			1987			
2773	NSP725	Volvo B10M-60	Van Hool Alizée			1987			

2774-2779

Volvo B10M-58B   Van Hool Alizée   1988

2774	NZD708	2776	NZG738	2777	NZE958	2778	NYL628	2779	NZB548
2775	NYM878								

2781	NSX775	Volvo B10M-65	Van Hool Alizée			1987			

2782-2787

Volvo B10M-70B   Van Hool Alizée   1987

2782	NSS505	2784	NTH595	2785	NTD865	2786	NTE945	2787	NST995
2783	NTH975								

2788-2820

Volvo B10M-65*   Säffle   1987   *2797-820 are B10M-70B

2788	DAO603	2796	DBR693	2802	CCN201	2708	DMO362	2714	EJP272
2789	CJK703	2797	CDY251	2803	CFK421	2709	DJR122	2715	GSG523
2790	CSA553	2798	CCH191	2804	CGE381	2710	DDP092	2717	GER553
2792	CSK913	2799	CPL231	2805	DDB142	2711	DPP212	2718	GCW783
2793	DBS773	2800	CBJ201	2806	DDY122	2712	DHA422	2719	GAJ753
2794	CPL813	2801	CNF181	2807	DJJ232	2713	DZR292	2720	FTF663
2795	CZH793								

2821-2839

Volvo B10M-65   Alpus 260SR   1987-88

2821	DKC938	2832	NDX665	2834	NDY745	2836	NEM655	2838	NEM965
2822	BMC644	2833	NDF875	2835	NDS565	2837	NEL955	2839	NEH935

2840-2873

Volvo B10M-70   Säffle   1987-88

2840	NCF525	2846	CAX174	2853	NDE895	2861	NDL915	2869	NDW755
2841	NBS555	2847	BZF354	2854	NBZ985	2862	NDM545	2870	NDX835
2842	NCJ555	2849	NCC805	2855	NDY775	2865	NDZ615	2871	NEP545
2843	NBR855	2850	NBZ505	2856	NDK765	2866	NDJ765	2872	NER795
2844	ASY444	2851	NCA955	2859	NDO565	2867	NDO705	2873	NED785
2845	ASO234	2852	NDZ855	2860	NDG815	2868	NDY915		

2875-2884

Scania CK112   Scania   1988

2875	NCN566	2877	NYM676	2879	NYZ746	2881	NZA886	2883	NLR757
2876	NCY926	2878	NYF626	2880	NZB896	2882	NYL666	2884	NMF737

2885	NKJ827	Scania CN112	Scania			1988			
2886	NKP947	Scania CN112	Scania			1988			

2887-2891

Volvo B10M-70B   Säffle   1988

2887	NMK737	2888	NML817	2889	NMS567	2890	NMN767	2891	NMW897

2892	FFB549	Volvo B10M-70B	Säffle			1985			

2895-2900

Volvo B10M-65   Säffle   1988

2895	NHG528	2897	NHN648	2898	NHW538	2899	NHS688	2900	NHW848
2896	NHP668								

2901	NLO969	Scania K112T	Kutter 10			1988			
2902	LGR980	Volvo B10M-60	Van Hool Alizée			1983			
2903	NTM735	Volvo B10M-60	Van Hool Alizée			1987			
2906	NYX645	Scania K112T	Van Hool Alizée			1988			
2907	NXC081	Volvo B10M-60	Van Hool Alizée			1988			

2908-2923

Volvo B10M-55L   Säffle   1988

2908	NAP243	2912	NBA113	2915	NXB192	2918	NXD112	2921	NNL242
2909	NBE393	2913	NAW283	2916	NXD282	2919	NXP112	2922	NOA152
2910	NAX053	2914	NBD073	2917	NXM322	2920	NXL482	2923	NNM252
2911	NAU283								

2924-2933 Volvo B10M-70B — Säffle — 1988

2924	NXM492	2926	NXC272	2928	NOW292	2930	FJF585	2932	NOF935
2925	NXH152	2927	NXL242	2929	FSU885	2931	FMR665	2933	NOX895

2934-2952 Volvo B10M-70 — Säffle — 1988

2934	NAO303	2938	NAY203	2942	BLE835	2946	NAX293	2950	JLC934
2935	NAR493	2939	NAR323	2943	BGT935	2947	NBB123	2951	JGM614
2936	NBJ263	2940	NBF303	2944	BWW595	2948	NBD213	2952	JCN954
2937	NAS403	2941	BFB535	2945	BWH595	2949	JUF544		

2953-2959 Volvo B10M-65 — Säffle — .1988

2953	DUX545	2955	NRZ615	2957	NRS595	2958	NNW985	2959	NKZ695
2954	FTX555	2956	NNT975						

2960	JBZ096	Volvo B10M-60	Säffle	1988
2961	FDO596	Volvo B10M-50	Säffle	1988

2962-2977 Volvo B10M-65 — Alpus 260SR — 1988

2962	NMN163	2965	NMD323	2972	ABT605	2974	AYH705	2976	ART695
2963	NMC483	2971	AUM575	2973	ARS825	2975	ART525	2977	AWS815
2964	NMH363								

2978-2994 Scania CK113 — Scania — 1989

2978	GAW545	2982	GFX815	2986	BMP996	2989	BEB988	2992	COU808
2979	GGE915	2983	MAR890	2987	CAX716	2990	BGM778	2993	NGT875
2980	GDB595	2984	MCN811	2988	BCX848	2991	BBS918	2994	NFW505
2981	GEF675	2985	BCY548						

2995	BYU112	Volvo B10M-65	Wiima		1986
2996	MEY322	Volvo B10M-60	Wiima Finlandia		1986
2997	NDU182	Scania K112T	Kutter 10		1988
3000	OPM053	Volvo B10M-70B	Van Hool Alizée		1989
3001	MCZ859	Volvo B10M-58B	Van Hool Alizée		1989
3002	LTU899	Volvo B10M-70B	Van Hool Alizée		1989
3003	JKC909	Volvo B10M-60	Van Hool Alizée		1989
3004	JDE999	Volvo B10M-60	Van Hool Alizée		1989
3005	KJH559	Volvo B10M-60	Van Hool Alizée		1989
3006	MWU589	Volvo B9M-46	Säffle		1987
3007	HRX032	Renault Master	Renault	M	1990
3013	EEP513	Volvo B10M-60	Säffle		1983
3016	HCD843	Volvo B10R-59	Säffle		1987
3017	NOD717	Renault Master T35D	Renault	M	1987
3018	AAM826	Auwaerter Neoplan N213	Auwaerter Jetliner		1988

3019-3036 Volvo B10M-65 — Säffle — 1989

3019	OSG361	3023	OSE031	3027	OSC251	3031	OPH123	3034	OPD253
3020	OSF041	3024	OSD191	3028	ORY251	3032	OPC243	3035	OAH332
3021	OSN001	3025	OSJ141	3029	OSA091	3033	OPA153	3036	OAJ102
3022	OSO251	3026	OSK071	3030	ORO351					

3037-3042 Volvo B10M-55L — Säffle — 1989

3037	OAG174	3039	OAK264	3040	OAN434	3041	OZX254	3042	OZW484
3038	OAF164								

3043	OEL243	Volvo B10M-65	Säffle	1989
3044	OED043	Volvo B10M-65	Säffle	1989
3045	ODX333	Volvo B10M-65	Säffle	1989

3046-3051 Volvo B10M-65 — Alpus 260SR — 1989

3046	OHE074	3048	OHD374	3049	OGN384	3050	OHA414	3051	OHE214
3047	OGZ374								

3052	OAA362	Volvo B10M-70	Säffle	DP	1989
3053	OAL112	Volvo B10M-70	Säffle	DP	1989

3054-3059 — Volvo B10M-70B — Van Hool Alizée — 1989

3054	OPA053	3056	OPB063	3057	OPF313	3058	OPS483	3059	OPM433
3055	OPD393								

3060	OWG181	Volvo B10M-60	Van Hool Alizée	1989
3061	OWD391	Volvo B10M-60	Van Hool Alizée	1989
3062	OPO453	Volvo B10M-60	Van Hool Alizée	1989

3063-3079 — Scania CN113 — Scania — 1990

3063	OHW766	3067	OKL628	3071	OKF688	3074	OLA918	3077	OLD638
3064	OHN636	3068	OKH918	3072	OKH608	3075	OLC798	3078	OLA608
3065	OHL546	3069	OKF518	3073	OLC628	3076	OLB548	3079	EDE231
3066	OKN718	3070	OKG908					

3082	OCH595	Volvo B10M-70B	Van Hool Alizée	1989
3083	ODM105	Volvo B10M-60	Van Hool Alizée	1989

3084-3096 — Volvo B10M-70B — Säffle — 1990

3084	OBO185	3087	OYZ745	3090	OYH575	3093	OYX895	3095	OYP535
3085	OBP195	3088	OYJ585	3091	OYL735	3094	OYJ655	3096	OYM675
3086	OBX145	3089	OYL595	3092	OYR855			

3101	HDC391	Volvo B10M-70B	Van Hool Alizée		1984
3102	GZJ723	Volvo B10M-65	Alpus 260SR		1985
3104	AUX778	Volvo B10M-70B	Van Hool Alizée		1985
3106	MPF020	Volvo B10M-70B	Van Hool Alizée		1985
3107	NJX607	Scania CN112	Scania		1988
3108	NKF897	Scania CN112	Scania		1988
3109	NJX777	Scania CN112	Scania		1988
3110	OEJ422	Renault Master T30	Renault	M	1989
3112	GNT759	Volvo B10M-65	Kutter		1984
3113	LDL707	Volvo B9M-60	Kutter		1983
3115	MLG698	Volvo B10M-58	Berkhof		1987
3117	MTC565	Volvo B10M-60	Van Hool Alizée		1987
3118	OUR299	Ford Transit VE6	Ford	M	1989
3119	OHB895	Volvo B10M-70B	Säffle		1990
3120	OGN995	Volvo B10M-70B	Säffle		1990
3121	OOP129	Volvo B10M-60	Lahti 450 Eagle		1988
3122	OSL331	Scania K113T	Lahti 450 Eagle		1989
3123	OOU184	Hino RB145SA	Hino		1989
3124	OOB545	Hino RB145SA	Hino		1989
3125	OWF749	Hino RB145SA	Hino		1989
3126	OAM658	Renault Master T35B	Renault	M	1990
3127	PAF264	Ontario II	Ontario		1990
3128	PAF334	Ontario II	Ontario		1990
3129	PAF337	Ontario II	Ontario		1990
3130	OWD659	Hino RB145	Hino		1990
3131	OUW929	Hino RB145	Hino		1990

3132-3142 — Volvo B10M-55L — Säffle — 1990

3132	AKL170	3135	AER424	3137	AMG180	3139	ANL320	3141	ALF030
3133	AMK340	3136	ALX200	3138	AJS080	3140	AMX100	3142	ANL250
3134	AGC064							

3143	AKF370	Volvo B10M-70	Säffle	1990
3144	AGL220	Volvo B10M-70	Säffle	1990
3145	AET320	Volvo B10M-70	Säffle	1990
3146	AJN350	Volvo B10M-65	Säffle	1990
3147	BAU402	Volvo B10M-50	Säffle	1990
3148	BCG122	Volvo B10M-50	Säffle	1990
3149	AOE100	Volvo B10M-60	Säffle	1990
3150	ASJ142	Volvo B10R-59	Säffle	1990

3151-3159 — Volvo B10M-65 — Säffle — 1990

3151	ASC252	3153	ASW062	3155	BBA192	3157	AYU262	3159	AKD350
3152	AYA122	3154	AZG392	3156	BBZ022	3158	ANH230	

The Swebus operation extends beyond Sweden with some operations in Norway and Denmark. Full details are now yet available, but here we see a Danish registered DAB. Some Copenhagen city services have been won on tender and we hope to include the vehicle used on these services in the 1998 edition. *Malcolm Tranter*

3160-3164 — Volvo B10M-70B — Säffle — 1990

3160	AYU332	3161	BDT402	3162	AYN132	3163	BBB412	3164	BCS282

3165	AAT224	Volvo B10M-60	Säffle	1990
3166	ABA234	Volvo B10M-60	Säffle	1990

3167	HYB302	Volvo B10M-65	Ajokki Express	1990
3169	HZL422	Volvo B10M-65	Ajokki Express	1990
3170	HUR242	Volvo B10M-65	Ajokki Express	1990
3171	HZM122	Volvo B10M-60	Van Hool Alizée	1990
3172	HUZ132	Volvo B10M-60	Van Hool Alizée	1990

3173-3183 — Volvo B10M-70B — Van Hool Alizée — 1990

3173	MHP112	3176	LUJ082	3178	MJZ392	3180	DGM313	3182	DGM173
3174	MGW492	3177	NDW092	3179	MAY492	3181	DDG363	3183	LLS232
3175	MGJ402								

3184	MSU515	Volvo B10M-50B	Van Hool Astral	1987
3185	MHP352	Volvo B10M-70B	Ajokki Express	1990
3186	MJF412	Volvo B10M-70B	Ajokki Express	1990
3187	LZC012	Volvo B10M-70B	Ajokki Express	1990
3188	DFG163	Volvo B10M-70B	Ajokki Express	1990
3190	ACM995	Scania K113T	Van Hool Astral	1991
3191	OAG053	Volvo B10M-60	Lahti Eagle 451	1989

3192-3197 — Volvo B10M-70B — Säffle — 1990

3192	JFD213	3194	JDR423	3195	JHE193	3196	KPY165	3197	KLN105
3193	JKH483								

3198	AAU474	Volvo B10M-65	Säffle		1990
3199	ABB314	Volvo B10M-65	Säffle		1990
3200	DDP403	Volvo B10M-65	Van Hool Astral		1990
3202	FLJ455	Scania K113T	Ajokki Express		1990
3203	DDJ453	Volvo B10M-65	Van Hool Astral		1990
3204	DEO145	Scania CK113	Scania		1990
3205	DGS355	Scania CK113	Scania		1990
3206	DKW225	Scania CK113	Scania		1991
3207	DLM395	Scania CK113	Scania		1991
3209	GOJ385	Scania K113T	Ajokki Regal		1990
3210	GPE485	Scania K113T	Ajokki Regal		1990
3211	OMO381	Scania K113	Ajokki Victor		1989
3218	OHD880	Hino RB145	Hino		1990
3219	HGW163	Renault Trafic	Renault	M	1990
3220	OMS140	Ford Transit VE6	Ford	M	1991
3221	DRW240	Ford Transit VE6	Ford	M	1991
3224	OWH529	Hino RB145	Hino		1990
3225	AFG036	Renault Master T35	Floby	M	1990
3226	AHG138	Renault Master T35	Floby	M	1990
3227	ACA045	Renault Master T35	Floby	M	1991
3228	HRU001	Renault Master T35	Boggi	M	1991
3229	HNU301	Renault Master T35	Boggi	M	1991
3230	HPF011	Renault Master T35	Boggi	M	1991
3231	HPW411	Renault Master T35	Boggi	M	1991
3232	OSU173	Renault Master T35	Boggi	M	1991
3233	ORK423	Renault Master T35	Boggi	M	1991
3234	HNU492	Renault Master T35	Boggi	M	1990
3235	HSA192	Renault Master T35	Boggi	M	1990
3236	CFX128	Volvo B10M-55L	Säffle		1991
3237	CFZ388	Volvo B10M-55L	Säffle		1991
3238	BBU200	Volvo B10M-55L	Säffle		1991
3239	ATB350	Volvo B10M-65	Säffle		1991
3240	ARL390	Volvo B10M-65	Säffle		1991
3241	ARS040	Volvo B10M-65	Säffle		1991
3242	ASL050	Volvo B10M-65	Säffle		1991
3243	EBH351	Volvo B10M-70	Säffle		1991
3244	EDW391	Volvo B10M-70	Säffle		1991
3245	CPJ098	Volvo B10M-70B	Ajokki Express		1991
3246	CGF238	Volvo B10M-70B	Säffle		1991
3247	CRM468	Volvo B10M-70B	Ajokki Express		1991
3248	BBC250	Volvo B10M-65	Säffle		1991

3249-3253   Volvo B10M-70B   Säffle   1991

3249	CKY058	3250	AUN320	3251	APW090	3252	CLH178	3253	CGX408

3254	ABF120	Volvo B10M-70B	Ajokki Express		1991
3255	ABG370	Volvo B10M-70B	Ajokki Express		1991
3256	KAT461	Scania K113T	Ajokki Victor		1991
3257	JUW311	Scania K113T	Ajokki Victor		1991
3258	ABC260	Volvo B10M-70B	Ajokki Express		1991
3259	AAS390	Volvo B10M-70B	Ajokki Express		1991
3260	ELX150	Scania K113T	Ajokki Express		1991
3261	JYX031	Scania K113T	Ajokki Express		1991
3262	EAG061	Volvo B10M-70	Säffle		1991
3263	EAM171	Volvo B10M-70	Säffle		1991

3264-3269   Volvo B10M-55L   Säffle   1991

3264	CMD278	3266	CJC008	3267	CKZ208	3268	CJZ088	3269	CHO108
3265	CKT268								

3270-3277   Volvo B10M-70B   Säffle   1991

3270	AWN090	3272	CLE148	3274	CHS448	3276	ATG300	3277	ASX350
3271	ASE310	3273	CJZ468	3275	CJW438				

3278	CGK198	Volvo B10M-55L	Säffle		1991	
3279	BCZ060	Volvo B10R-59	Säffle		1991	
3280	AXT490	Volvo B10R-59	Säffle		1991	
3281	BAF210	Volvo B10R-59	Säffle		1991	
3282	JJF332	Hino RB145	Foreland		1991	
3283	CEN258	Hino RB145	Foreland		1991	

3284-3292   Volvo B10M-65   Säffle   1991

3284	BAS450	3286	AYR060	3288	AZA160	3290	ASS010	3292	ATN280
3285	AYL320	3287	AYZ400	3289	BBJ140	3291	ARZ090		

3293	ARE340	Volvo B10R-70	Säffle		1991
3294	AWB160	Volvo B10R-70	Säffle		1991
3295	FXR361	Volvo B10M-70B	Ajokki Express		1991
3297	OTN065	Renault Master T35	Floby	M	1989
3298	OLA284	Mercedes-Benz 709D	Mercedes-Benz	B	1990
3299	MPO332	Volvo B10M-60	Van Hool Alizée		1991
3300	MWE482	Volvo B10M-60	Van Hool Alizée		1991
3301	NCU252	Volvo B10M-50B	Van Hool Astral		1991
3302	MPO192	Volvo B10M-50B	Van Hool Astral		1991

3303-3310   Volvo B10M-70B   Van Hool Alizée   1991

3303	MRK292	3305	MXC292	3306	MPB492	3309	NBR182	3310	MZC302
3304	MOJ252								

3311-3316   Scania K113T   Ajokki Victor   1991

3311	EGG070	3313	JZY251	3314	JJP051	3315	JNS441	3316	JKB491
3312	EHG420								

3317	PAR989	Volvo B10M-60	Van Hool Alizée		1989

3318-3325   Scania K113T   Van Hool Alizée   1991

3318	COZ396	3320	CYS006	3322	CRZ196	3324	CSU446	3325	CTU106
3319	CMC136	3321	CSM096	3323	CTB146				

3326	OAL073	Mercedes-Benz 410D	Mercedes-Benz	B	1989
3328	CBD078	Renault Master T35	Floby	M	1991
3329	GGD875	Volvo B10M-65	Säffle 2000		1992
3330	DYU099	Mercedes-Benz 614D	Backaryd	B	1991
3331	GFG293	Mercedes-Benz 0303/15RHS	Mercedes-Benz		1991
3332	FPH093	Mercedes-Benz 0303/15RHS	Mercedes-Benz		1991
3333	LPH098	Mercedes-Benz 0303/15RHS	Mercedes-Benz		1991
3334	HRS755	Volvo B10R-55L	Säffle		1992
3335	OJA820	Hino RB145	Hino		1990
3336	EHP913	Volvo B9M-46	Wiima		1991
3337	ETW723	Volvo B10M-70B	Ajokki Regal		1992
3338	ETC773	Volvo B10M-70B	Ajokki Regal		1992
3339	ETY743	Volvo B10M-70B	Ajokki Regal		1992
3340	ETJ733	Volvo B10M-70B	Ajokki Regal		1992
3341	GCG515	Volvo B10M-65	Wiima		1992
3342	GHG705	Volvo B10M-70	Säffle		1992
3343	GHS625	Volvo B10M-70	Säffle		1992
3344	GFX785	Volvo B10M-70	Säffle		1992
3345	GGG595	Volvo B10M-70	Säffle		1992
3346	JNZ766	Volvo B10M-50B	Van Hool Astral		1992

3347-3355   Volvo B10M-70B   Van Hool Alizée   1992

3347	JNZ766	3349	JND866	3351	JOW706	3354	JMT516	3355	JNJ676
3348	JMJ916	3350	JOD696	3352	JRN926				

3356	OOZ697	Scania K113T	Van Hool Alizée		1992
3357	ONW697	Scania K113T	Van Hool Alizée		1992
3358	KEY198	Volvo B10M-70B	Säffle		1991
3359	PEE260	Volvo B10M-70B	Ajokki Victor		1992

Swebus 3407, MZG401, is one of the standard product Van Hool A508 minibuses shown here for the Lugna Line operation. *Malcolm Tranter*

3360	PEH430	Volvo B10M-65	Säffle 2000		1992		
3361	PEA460	Volvo B10M-65	Säffle 2000		1992		
3362	OKT599	Volvo B12-61B	Ajokki Regal		1992		
3363	HCH809	Volvo B10M-55L	Säffle 2000		1992		
3364-3368		Volvo B10M-70B	Van Hool Alizée		1992		
3364	PRU963	**3365**	PRN763	**3366**	PRK593	**3367**	PRK973	**3368**	PRJ733
3369	PDP040	Volvo B10R-59	Säffle		1992		
3370	HDT869	Volvo B10M-65	Säffle 2000		1992		
3371	HDF549	Volvo B10M-65	Säffle 2000		1992		
3372	HCM529	Volvo B10M-70B	Säffle 2000		1992		
3373	PDZ320	Volvo B10M-70B	Ajokki Regal		1992		
3374	PHX380	Volvo B10M-55L	Säffle 2000		1992		
3375	EYB001	Hino RB145	Hino		1991		
3376	PRR933	Volvo B10M-70B	Van Hool Alizée		1992		
3377	PRJ803	Volvo B10M-70B	Van Hool Alizée		1992		
3378	PRC843	Volvo B10M-70B	Van Hool Alizée		1992		
3379	PRF563	Volvo B10M-70B	Van Hool Alizée		1992		
3380	PEJ370	Volvo B10R-59	Säffle		1992		
3381	PDZ010	Volvo B10R-59	Säffle		1992		
3382	PEC480	Volvo B10R-59	Säffle		1992		
3383	PRK803	Volvo B12-61R	Van Hool Alizée		1992		
3384	HDL589	Volvo B10M-70	Säffle 2000		1992		
3385	PRS943	Volvo B10M-50B	Van Hool Astral 460		1992		
3386	HBB879	Volvo B10M-70	Säffle 2000		1992		
3387	HBL619	Volvo B10M-70	Säffle 2000		1992		
3388	HDD839	Volvo B10M-70	Säffle 2000		1992		
3389	HED669	Volvo B10M-55L	Säffle 2000		1992		
3390	HCO549	Volvo B10M-55L	Säffle 2000		1992		
3391	HCK819	Volvo B10M-55L	Säffle 2000		1992		

3392	PEJ200	Volvo B10M-70	Säffle 2000		1992
3393	PEF340	Volvo B10M-70	Säffle 2000		1992
3394	PEL070	Volvo B10M-70	Säffle 2000		1992
3395	PEK130	Volvo B10M-70	Säffle 2000		1992
3396	PDR120	Volvo B10M-70B	Säffle 2000		1992
3397	PDP350	Volvo B10M-70B	Säffle 2000		1992
3398	HDZ979	Volvo B10M-70	Säffle 2000		1992
3399	HCZ839	Volvo B10M-70	Säffle 2000		1992
3400	HCP939	Volvo B10M-70	Säffle 2000		1992
3401	PZT662	Van Hool A508	Van Hool	B	1992
3402	PZZ912	Van Hool A508	Van Hool	B	1992
3403	PYZ632	Van Hool A508	Van Hool	B	1992
3404	PZE882	Van Hool A508	Van Hool	B	1992
3405	PRN833	Volvo B10M-50B	Van Hool Astral 410		1992
3406	PMJ831	Scania K113T	Ajokki Express		1992
3407	MZG401	Van Hool A508	Van Hool	B	1992
3408	HEF829	Volvo B10M-70	Säffle 2000		1992
3409	HCZ909	Volvo B10M-70	Säffle 2000		1992
3410	PFW569	Mercedes-Benz 0404	Mercedes-Benz	F	1992
3411	PGW562	Mercedes-Benz 0404	Mercedes-Benz	F	1992
3412	PEJ130	Volvo B10M-70B	Ajokki Victor		1992
3413	PRX593	Volvo B10M-50B	Van Hool Astral 460		1992
3414	PJL740	Volvo B10M-70	Säffle 2000		1992
3415	PKW603	Renault Master T35	Renault	M	1991
3416	PTC942	Van Hool A508	Van Hool	B	1992
3418	PST842	Van Hool A508	Van Hool	B	1992

3419-3424

Volvo B10M-65 — Säffle 2000 — 1993

3419	PDO979	3421	PDO669	3422	PFD549	3423	PEU689	3424	PFE629
3420	PDO809								

3425	PXB699	Volvo B10M-65	Carrus Fifty		1993
3426	PXL509	Volvo B10M-65	Carrus Fifty		1993
3427	PFA759	Volvo B10M-65	Säffle 2000		1993
3429	PEN629	Volvo B10M-55L	Säffle 2000		1993
3430	PER969	Volvo B10M-65	Säffle 2000		1993
3431	PFB839	Volvo B10M-65	Säffle 2000		1993
3432	PEM619	Volvo B10M-65	Säffle 2000		1993
3433	PEP649	Volvo B10M-65	Säffle 2000		1993

3434-3441

Volvo B10M-70 — Säffle 2000 — 1993

3434	PEU999	3436	PFA519	3438	PFA689	3440	PFA999	3441	PFC609
3435	PEY849	3437	PFE559	3439	PFD619				

3442	PEO949	Volvo B10M-55L	Säffle 2000		1993
3443	PEW759	Volvo B10M-55L	Säffle 2000		1993

3444-3448

Volvo B10M-70 — Säffle 2000 — 1993

3444	PEN559	3445	PEZ619	3446	PEY919	3447	PEW829	3448	PER899

3449	PZP969	Volvo B10M-65	Carrus Fifty		1993

3450-3454

Volvo B10M-70B — Carrus Fifty — 1993

3450	PXK809	3451	PZY929	3452	PXS509	3453	PZY789	3454	PZS749

3455	PSU968	Scania CN113CLL	Scania MAX CI		1993
3456	PSR938	Scania CN113CLL	Scania MAX CI		1993
3457	PSP618	Scania CN113CLL	Scania MAX CI		1993
3458	PKS222	Van Hool A508	Van Hool	B	1993
3459	PKY402	Van Hool A508	Van Hool	B	1993
3460	PPT635	Volvo B12-61B	Carrus Superstar		1993
3461	PKR620	Auwaerter Neoplan N116/3	Auwaerter Cityliner		1993
3462	PBF567	DAB 11-0860S	DAB		1993
3463	PBF568	DAB 11-0860S	DAB		1993
3464	PYD263	Auwaerter Neoplan N318	Auwaerter Transliner		1993

3465-3470

Volvo B10M-65NG — Säffle 2000 — 1994

3465	PJZ397	3467	PHY487	3468	PHZ187	3469	PHY247	3470	PJU437
3466	PJC487								

No.	Reg	Chassis	Body	Year
3471	PTO004	Volvo B10M-70	Carrus Fifty	1994
3472	PJX102	Scania CN113	Scania	1993
3473	DEM684	Scania B86S-47	Delta Mini	1981
3474	NNX707	MAN 9.170	Helmark	1987
3476	FTE149	Volvo B6F	Van Hool Alizée	1982
3477	CXC102	Volvo B10M-60	Van Hool Alizée	1984
3478	FGZ685	Volvo B10M-60	Berkhof	1984
3479	MWC271	Volvo B10M-60	Berkhof	1986
3480	NFF815	Scania F12CLKA	Wiima	1988
3481	NCX080	Scania K112TL	Ajokki Royal	1988
3483	PUW086	Auwaerter Neoplan N128/4	Auwaerter Megaliner	1994
3484	PUM326	Auwaerter Neoplan N128/4	Auwaerter Megaliner	1994
3485	PUX166	Auwaerter Neoplan N128/4	Auwaerter Megaliner	1994
3486	PZK555	Volvo B10B-60	Säffle	1993
3487	PRC223	Volvo B10M-65	Säffle	1993
3488	PMH140	Auwaerter Neoplan N8008	Auwaerter Metroliner	1993
3489	PNA450	Auwaerter Neoplan N8008	Auwaerter Metroliner	1993
3490	PMP340	Auwaerter Neoplan N8008	Auwaerter Metroliner	1993
3491	PMW210	Auwaerter Neoplan N8008	Auwaerter Metroliner	1993
3492	PWH085	Volvo B10BLE-59	Säffle	1993
3493	PEC903	Volvo B10M-70B	Van Hool Alizée	1993
3494	PSG473	Auwaerter Neoplan N116/3	Auwaerter Cityliner	1994
3495	HAA985	Scania K113TLB	Ajokki Victor	1992
3496	CGY211	Volvo B10M-70B	Carrus Regal	1994
3497	OKR403	Volvo B10M-70	Säffle 2000	1994
3498	NUN103	Volvo B10M-70	Säffle 2000	1994
3499	PWG059	Volvo B10M-70B	Carrus Regal	1994
3500	CCT201	Volvo B10M-70B	Carrus Regal	1994

3501-3513

Volvo B10M-65 — Säffle 2000 — 1982-83

3501	OJN323	3504	JPK473	3507	JUA163	3509	JRZ393	3511	ECR024
3502	NWY093	3505	JPW153	3508	JWT103	3510	DUE374	3512	EFS044
3503	OMF143	3506	JTD293						

3514	AKY310	Scania L113CLB	Carrus Fifty	1994
3515	AND430	Scania L113CLB	Carrus Fifty	1994
3516	AKM490	Scania L113CLB	Carrus Fifty	1994

3518-3522

Scania CN113CLL — Scania MAX CI — 1994

3518	EHD444	3519	EKF034	3520	EMO354	3521	EKY454	3522	ELS174

3523	BFD040	Scania L113CLB	Carrus Fifty	1994
3524	BEY100	Scania L113CLB	Carrus Fifty	1994
3525	BAN070	Scania L113CLB	Carrus Fifty	1994
3526	BAK110	Scania L113CLB	Carrus Fifty	1994

3527-3534

Volvo B10M-70B — Säffle — 1994

3527	JRO483	3529	JRL213	3531	DSF341	3533	DML401	3534	DSD011
3528	JWD173	3530	JRU293	3532	DSA461				

3535-3539

Volvo B10M-65 — Säffle — 1994

3535	EED294	3536	EEY254	3537	EFN484	3538	EDB204	3539	EEC424

3540	PHC029	Volvo B10B-70	Carrus K204	1994

3541-3545

Volvo B10M-55L — Säffle — 1994

3541	DWK224	3542	DUL184	3543	DZX304	3544	DUL254	3545	DUS384

3546	CUL404	Volvo B10BLE-59	Säffle 2000	1993
3547	HLX495	Volvo B10BLE-59	Säffle 2000	1994

3548	GPC355	Scania N113CLL	Carrus K204	1994
3549	JCB204	Volvo B12	Säffle 2000	1995
3554	BFE430	Scania K113TLB	Carrus Fifty	1994
3555	BDT410	Scania K113TLB	Carrus Fifty	1994
3556	BCE280	Scania K113TLB	Carrus Fifty	1994
3557	BBD440	Scania K113TLB	Carrus Fifty	1994
3558	BYS321	Scania L113CLB	Carrus Fifty	1994
3559	BAH340	Scania K113TLB	Carrus Regal	1994
3560	CML414	Volvo B10M-70	Säffle 2000	1994
3561	CNZ324	Volvo B10M-70	Säffle 2000	1994
3562	COC484	Volvo B10M-70	Säffle 2000	1994
3563	COP254	Volvo B10M-70	Säffle 2000	1994
3564	EAA044	Volvo B10M-55L	Säffle 2000	1994
3565	DUD294	Volvo B10M-55L	Säffle 2000	1994

3566-3572

Volvo B10M-55L   Säffle   1994

3566	CTJ284	3568	COK064	3570	CPP394	3571	COG114	3572	CSU134
3567	CRL014	3569	CPC454						

3573	CRZ024	Volvo B10M-70	Säffle 2000	1994
3574	CNM324	Volvo B10M-70	Säffle 2000	1994
3575	JOX193	Volvo B10M-55L	Säffle 2000	1994
3576	JMZ003	Volvo B10M-55L	Säffle 2000	1994
3577	JPL003	Volvo B10M-70	Säffle 2000	1994
3578	DXK294	Volvo B10M-70B	Säffle 2000	1994
3579	HPE295	Volvo B10M-70B	Säffle 2000	1995
3580	BCO020	Scania K113TLB	Carrus Fifty	1994
3581	PUM019	Volvo B10M-65	Carrus Fifty	1994
3582	PWB009	Volvo B10M-65	Carrus Fifty	1994
3583	PUN199	Volvo B10M-65	Carrus Fifty	1994
3584	PUD109	Volvo B10M-65	Carrus Fifty	1994
3585	CGN231	Volvo B10M-70B	Carrus Fifty	1994
3586	CRJ131	Volvo B10M-70B	Carrus Fifty	1994
3587	CEC371	Volvo B10M-70B	Carrus Regal	1994
3588	CHS241	Volvo B10M-70B	Carrus Regal	1994
3589	CEX331	Volvo B10M-70B	Carrus Regal	1994
3580	CCR111	Volvo B10M-70B	Carrus Fifty	1994
3591	EGB454	Volvo B10M-70B	Säffle	1994
3592	ELK344	Scania CN113CLB	Scania	1994
3593	AOR100	Scania K113TLB	Carrus Vector	1994

3594-3615

Scania CN113CLL   Scania MAX CI   1994

3594	PTU488	3599	PTR078	3604	PTL490	3608	PST490	3512	PTF070
3595	PUF298	3600	PTL408	3605	PTD120	3609	PTH300	3513	PTD290
3596	PTY198	3601	PSA290	3606	PTK240	3510	PSX340	3514	PTG220
3597	PUE358	3602	PRY210	3607	PTH470	3511	PSZ120	3515	PSU330
3598	PTN288	3603	PTG390						

3616	EFD264	Volvo B10M-70	Säffle	1994
3617	EFF044	Volvo B10M-70	Säffle	1994
3618	EGH034	Volvo B10M-70	Säffle	1994
3619	ECA464	Volvo B10M-70	Säffle	1994
3620	DOO471	Volvo B10M-65	Säffle	1994
3621	DMM341	Volvo B10M-65	Säffle	1994
3622	DPK191	Volvo B10M-65	Säffle	1994
3623	PNL607	DAB 11-0860S	DAB	1994
3624	GEO102	Auwaerter Neoplan N318/3	Auwaerter	1994
3625	GCA142	Auwaerter Neoplan N318/3	Auwaerter	1994
3626	GGH402	Auwaerter Neoplan N318/3	Auwaerter	1994
3627	EGB384	Volvo B10M-70	Säffle	1994
3628	CDK121	Volvo B10M-70	Carrus Regal	1994
3629	PGK488	Volvo B6-45	Säffle 2000	1994
3630	PNH903	DAB 11-0860S	DAB	1994
3631	BGE193	Scania L113CLB	Carrus Fifty	1994
3632	BUP130	Auwaerter Neoplan N316SHD	Auwaerter Transliner	1994
3633	AAJ441	Auwaerter Neoplan N316SHD	Auwaerter Transliner	1994
3634	PUY150	Auwaerter Neoplan N316SHD	Auwaerter Transliner	1994
3635	JYE123	Auwaerter Neoplan N116/3	Auwaerter Cityliner	1994
3636	GDZ112	Auwaerter Neoplan N116/3	Auwaerter Cityliner	1994
3637	LST140	Scania K113TLA	Carrus Star 701	1995

3638-3642

								Scania K113CLA	Carrus Star 602	1995

3638	LLK450	3639	LPN390	3640	LOF050	3641	LLB310	3642	KDA232

3643-3647

Volvo B12-60 — Carrus Star 602 — 1995

3643	HWR018	3644	HUF358	3645	HWA078	3646	HSY358	3647	HWR258

3648-3652

Volvo B10BLE-59 — Säffle 2000 — 1995

3648	BFG080	3649	BBW250	3650	BFU470	3651	BCO410	3652	BDM460

3653-3657

Volvo B10M-70B — Säffle 2000 — 1995

3653	KLJ045	3654	JDA194	3655	KOH115	3656	FDY195	3657	FDR075

3658	JHN018	Scania L113CLB	Carrus Fifty	1995
3659	JHT448	Scania L113CLB	Carrus Fifty	1995
3660	JKD228	Scania L113CLB	Carrus Fifty	1995
3661	KHW495	Volvo B10M-70B	Säffle	1996
3662	KGS405	Volvo B10M-70B	Säffle	1995
3663	KEA105	Volvo B10M-70	Säffle	1996
3664	CPG253	Scania CN113CLL	Scania MAX CI	1995
3665	CNU463	Scania CN113CLL	Scania MAX CI	1995
3666	KHT338	Auwaerter Neoplan N112/3	Auwaerter Skyliner	1995
3667	JTY259	Auwaerter Neoplan N116/3	Auwaerter Cityiner	1995
3668	KHA355	Volvo B10M-70	Säffle	1995
3669	KMD205	Volvo B10M-70	Säffle	1995
3670	KLF255	Volvo B10M-70	Säffle	1995
3671	BFG150	Volvo B10M-70B	Säffle	1995
3672	EBD005	Volvo B10M-65	Säffle	1995
3673	EAN325	Volvo B10M-65	Säffle	1995
3674	DXD205	Volvo B10M-65	Säffle	1995
3675	CZW300	Scania CN113CLL	Scania MAX CI	1995
3676	KLM154	Scania CK113A	Scania	1995
3277	KKC274	Scania CK113A	Scania	1995
3578	JZY150	Volvo B10M-65	Carrus Fifty	1995
3579	JZC250	Volvo B10M-65	Carrus Fifty	1995
3580	BWT385	Scania K113T	Carrus Regal	1995
3581	JYY010	Volvo B10M-65	Carrus Fifty	1995
3582	DKD193	Scania K113	Carrus Vector	1995
3583	DJU463	Scania K113	Carrus Vector	1995
3584	GBH125	Volvo B10M-70B	Carrus Vector	1995
3685	DZP027	Volvo B10M-65	Säffle	1996
3686	ECE487	Volvo B10M-65	Säffle	1996
3687	HWN073	Volvo B10M-60	Carrus Star 602	1995
3688	CLZ372	Volvo B10M-50B	Carrus Star 602	1995
3689	FZL145	Volvo B10M-50B	Carrus Star 602	1996
3690	JWY278	Volvo B10M-70	Säffle	1996
3691	JTY088	Volvo B10M-70	Säffle	1996
3692	LLX062	Volvo B10M-70B	Säffle	1995
3693	JPH203	Auwaerter Neoplan N318SHD/3	Auwaerter Transliner	1995
3694	JRB383	Auwaerter Neoplan N318SHD/3	Auwaerter Transliner	1995
3695	KJF468	Auwaerter Neoplan N116/3	Auwaerter Cityliner	1995

3696-3703

Scania CN113CLL — Scania MAX Ci — 1995

3696	CFW083	3698	CGC003	3700	CLP243	3702	CKE423	3703	CFA323
3697	CKB013	3699	CEM283	3701	CLA213					

3704	OCZ392	Scania DAB	DAB	1995
3705	NSF032	Scania DAB	DAB	1995
3706	OXR002	Scania DAB	DAB	1995
3707	PPW092	Scania DAB	DAB	1995
3708	CPN133	Scania CN113CLL	Scania MAX Ci	1995
3709	JFL051	Auwaerter Neoplan N318SHD/3	Auwaerter Transliner	1995
3710	JEZ231	Auwaerter Neoplan N318SHD/3	Auwaerter Transliner	1995
3711	JCX101	Auwaerter Neoplan N318SHD/3	Auwaerter Transliner	1995
3712	JGG091	Auwaerter Neoplan N318SHD/3	Auwaerter Transliner	1995
3713	FFE255	Volvo B10M-70	Säffle	1995
3714	DWB005	Volvo B10M-70	Säffle	1995

3715-3723 — Volvo B10M-70B — Säffle — 1995

3715	LTP172	3717	LER302	3719	LPP232	3721	LOO182	3723	LRS392
3716	LZG162	3718	LFB342	3720	LUY102	3722	LKE432		

3724	EBA167	Volvo B10MA-55	Säffle	1996
3725	DXD067	Volvo B10MA-55	Säffle	1996
3726	DYB417	Volvo B10MA-55	Säffle	1996
3727	DET206	Volvo B10M-65	Säffle	1996
3728	DFE496	Volvo B10M-65	Säffle	1995
3729	DCZ376	Volvo B10M-65	Säffle	1995
3730	DEL476	Volvo B10M-65	Säffle	1995
3731	CRH222	Volvo B10M-50B	Carrus Regal	1995
3732	GKL061	Volvo B10M-50B	Carrus Regal	1995
3737	CPF003	Scania CN113CLL	Scania MAX Ci	1995
3738	CPE473	Scania CN113CLL	Scania MAX Ci	1995
3739	CRZ193	Scania CN113CLL	Scania MAX Ci	1995
3740	DWW035	Volvo B10MA-70	Säffle	1995
3741	DZW045	Volvo B10MA-70	Säffle	1995
3742	DZF265	Volvo B10MA-70	Säffle	1995
3743	EEP367	Scania L113CLB	Carrus Fifty	1995
3744	LLM300	Scania L113CLB	Carrus Fifty	1995
3745	KZM290	Scania L113CLB	Carrus Fifty	1995
3746	LMR480	Scania L113CLB	Carrus Fifty	1995
3747	FPO275	Volvo B10M-70	Säffle	1995
3748	LUK402	Volvo B10L-60	Säffle	1995
3749	KJU225	Volvo B10L-60	Säffle	1995
3750	KKZ095	Volvo B10L-60	Säffle	1995
3751	JCH024	Volvo B10MA-55	Säffle	1995
3752	JAP114	Volvo B10MA-55	Säffle	1995
3753	HXX404	Volvo B10M-70	Säffle	1995
3754	HWD314	Volvo B10M-70	Säffle	1995

3755-3763 — Auwaerter Neoplan N318K/3 — Auwaerter Transliner — 1995

3755	BCM312	3757	BFA012	3759	BTR013	3761	CBR143	3763	BZC433
3756	BBD062	3758	BXP403	3760	CCO023	3762	CBK183		

3764	ALF253	Volvo B10M-70B	Carrus Regal	1995
3765	AKW063	Volvo B10M-70B	Carrus Regal	1995
3766	DXD065	Volvo B10M-50	Säffle	1995
3767	CTG182	Volvo B10M-70B	Carrus Regal	1995
3768	COC302	Volvo B10M-70B	Carrus Regal	1995

3769-3773 — Volvo B10M-65 — Carrus Fifty — 1995-96

3769	HCU336	3770	HBU126	3771	HCF176	3772	HBH056	3773	HAG386

3774	FFL445	Volvo B10M-70B	Säffle	1995
3775	FFE015	Volvo B10M-70B	Säffle	1995
3776	FCY295	Volvo B10M-70B	Säffle	1995
3777	FFM215	Volvo B10M-70B	Säffle	1995
3778	GBZ398	Volvo B10M-70B	Säffle	1996
3779	GCY118	Volvo B10M-70B	Säffle	1996

3780-3789 — Volvo B10M-65 — Säffle — 1995

3780	DZP175	3782	DXO125	3784	DWH035	3786	DZK125	3788	DWU035
3781	DYN015	3783	EBN465	3785	EAX225	3787	DZH355	3789	DWO115

3790-3795 — Volvo B12-70B — Van Hool Alizée 360NL — 1995

3790	CHP142	3792	EHF393	3793	ELN063	3794	EKR333	3795	ELX273
3791	EDR093								

3796	PTF193	Volvo B10M-60	Vest Ambassador	1995
3797	FZP188	Volvo B10M-70	Säffle	1996
3798	FZT118	Volvo B10M-70	Säffle	1996
3799	GBZ265	Volvo B10M-70	Carrus Fifty	1995
3800	GAG455	Volvo B10M-70	Carrus Fifty	1995
3801	CPS243	Scania CN113CLL	Scania MAX Ci	1995
3802	CNL483	Scania CN113CLL	Scania MAX Ci	1995
3803	CMK023	Scania CN113CLL	Scania MAX Ci	1995

3804	EBL087	Volvo B10M-70B		Säffle			1996	
3805	EAP437	Volvo B10M-70B		Säffle			1996	
3806	DZU137	Volvo B10M-70B		Säffle			1996	
3807	DYU237	Volvo B10M-70B		Säffle			1996	
3808	ECY127	Volvo B10M-50		Säffle			1996	

3809-3818   Volvo B10M-70B   Säffle   1995-96

3809	LZZ032	**3811**	KLL365	**3813**	KLY055	**3815**	KMO055	**3817**	KJW395
3810	KJY485	**3812**	KKD195	**3814**	KMA415	**3816**	KPU225	**3818**	KKD265

3819	PSA076	Volvo B12-61B	Van Hool Altano		1993	
3820	HGZ351	Volvo B12-61B	Van Hool Altano		1995	
3821	HHL481	Volvo B12-61B	Van Hool Altano		1995	
3822	PNR192	Scania DAB	Silkeborg		1995	
3823	PPT392	Scania DAB	Silkeborg		1995	
3824	JOT161	Volvo B10MA-55	Van Hool Alizée	AC F	1995	

3825-3833   Volvo B10M-70B   Säffle   1995-96

3825	LTH282	**3827**	LGN002	**3829**	LGC012	**3831**	LCH462	**3833**	DXL287
3826	LRH002	**3828**	LOC012	**3830**	LFD122	**3832**	LRN422		

3834	GAZ015	Scania L113	Carrus Fifty		1996	
3835	FYO035	Scania L113	Carrus Fifty		1996	
3836	FZP015	Scania L113	Carrus Fifty		1996	
3837	GAB025	Scania L113	Carrus Fifty		1996	
3838	HPT218	Auwaerter Neoplan N112/3	Auwaerter Skyliner		1995	

3839-3844   Scania CN113CLB   Scania   1995

3839	KDM394	**3841**	KFA404	**3842**	KDE264	**3843**	KGC414	**3844**	KCS064
3840	KES314								

3845	KMU024	Scania CN113A	Scania		1995	
3846	KMH164	Scania CN113A	Scania		1995	
3847	COJ063	Scania CN113CLL	Scania MAX Ci		1995	
3848	COW053	Scania CN113CLL	Scania MAX Ci		1995	
3849	KDZ224	Scania CN113	Scania		1995	
3850	KEW024	Scania CN113	Scania		1995	
3851	KHS014	Scania CN113	Scania		1995	

3852-3859   Volvo B10MA-55   Säffle   1995

3852	FKH035	**3854**	FOH185	**3856**	FTA405	**3858**	HGU238	**3859**	HEP258
3853	FNB225	**3855**	FOL405	**3857**	HFC388				

3862	KOF114	Scania CN113CLB	Scania		1995	
3863	KGF424	Scania CN113CLB	Scania		1995	
3864	KHM134	Scania CN113CLB	Scania		1995	

3865-3872   Volvo B10MA-55   Säffle   1996

3865	HHR038	**3867**	HGR208	**3869**	HFC148	**3871**	HGO358	**3872**	HFE098
3866	HFA438	**3868**	HHX078	**3870**	HFF178				

3873-3877   Scania CN113CLB   Scania   1996

3873	JLZ175	**3874**	JMZ145	**3875**	JKC435	**3876**	JKF085	**3877**	JMG345

3878-3884   Volvo B10MA-55   Säffle   1996

3878	EAT227	**3880**	DYH477	**3882**	JYP018	**3883**	BDL429	**3884**	BEL259
3879	DZZ097	**3881**	BBJ169						

3885	GBH055	Volvo B10M-50B	Carrus Regal		1996	
3886	OSW369	Auwaerter Neoplan N8012	Auwaerter Metroliner		1996	
3887	DBH462	Volkswagen Caravelle	Volkswagen		1995	
3888	BED265	Volkswagen Kombi	Volkswagen		1995	
3889	PSC261	Volkswagen Kombi	Volkswagen		1995	
3890	JWT318	Volvo B10L-60	Säffle		1996	
3891	EKL138	Scania N113CLL	Carrus K201L		1996	

As we go to press a picture of Swebus 4164, with Danish MJ95639 index plates. This carries the silver and light blue livery used for rural services in Denmark.

3892-3897

		Volvo B10M-65		Säffle			1996		
3892	BDF693	**3894**	BDG753	**3895**	BDH563	**3896**	BDG933	**3897**	BDH943
3893	BDG713								

3898	ANM721	Volvo B10M-70B	Carrus Regal	1996
3899	ANM811	Volvo B10M-70B	Carrus Regal	1996
3900	FRM070	Volvo B10M-70	Säffle	1996
3901	FSG480	Volvo B10M-70	Säffle	1996

3902-3915

		Volvo B10M-65		Carrus Fifty			1996		
3902	HKE088	**3905**	HJU348	**3908**	ANB901	**3911**	ANL781	**3914**	ANM551
3903	HKO448	**3906**	HMG118	**3909**	ANC761	**3912**	ANL791	**3915**	HMS278
3904	HLU088	**3907**	ANB811	**3910**	ANC951	**3913**	ANL841		

3916	AZA672	Volvo B10B-70	Säffle	1996
3917	HTA230	Volvo B10M-70	Vest Ambassador 340	1996
3918	HUX420	Volvo B10M-70B	Vest Ambassador 340	1996
3919	FPD030	Volvo B10M-70	Säffle	1996
3920	ELY090	Volvo B10M-70	Säffle	1996
3921	FOJ320	Volvo B10M-70	Säffle	1996
3922	AYD603	Scania L113CLB	Carrus Fifty	1996
3923	AYD743	Scania L113CLB	Carrus Fifty	1996
3924	AYD763	Scania L113CLB	Carrus Fifty	1996
3925	AYE733	Scania L113CLB	Carrus Fifty	1996
3926	DYG149	Volvo B10M-72B	Carrus Regal	1996
3927	AXK702	Volvo B10M-72B	Carrus Regal	1996
3928	AYC943	Scania K113TLA	Carrus Regal	1996
3929	BAL873	Volvo B12	Van Hool Alizée 360NL	1996
3936	FOB280	Volvo B10M-70	Säffle	1996
3937	HTC180	Volvo B12	Van Hool Alizée	1996
3938	CGA060	Volvo B12-61	Neoplan N116/3 Cityliner	1996
3939	CGO080	Volvo B12-61	Neoplan N116/3 Cityliner	1996
3940	CFG360	Volvo B12-61	Neoplan N116/3 Cityliner	1996

3941-3964

Scania CN113CLB*   Katrineholm   1995-96 *3951-5/63/4 are CN113ALB

3941	GSF460	**3949**	GOS210	**3953**	GGG080	**3957**	GMZ390	**3961** GOF450
3942	GPK380	**3950**	GPU440	**3954**	GKG310	**3958**	GPE100	**3962** GPG360
3943	GRN210	**3951**	GKE080	**3955**	GMW120	**3959**	GXE440	**3963** AOB532
3948	GSB420	**3952**	GGS140	**3956**	GSF390	**3960**	GWT010	**3964** ANJ622

3980	HUC390	Volvo B10M-62	Van Hool Alizée 360NL	1996
3981	HXX470	Volvo B10M-62	Van Hool Alizée 360NL	1996
3982	HXO410	Volvo B10M-62	Van Hool Alizée 360NL	1996
3983	AUX632	Volvo B10L	Säffle	1996
3984	BDK753	Volvo B10M-65	Säffle	1996
3985	ETY327	Scania L113CLB	Carrus Fifty	1996
3986	ESX347	Scania L113CLB	Carrus Fifty	1996
3987	ESJ107	Scania L113CLB	Carrus Fifty	1996
3988	BDH963	Volvo B10MA-55	Säffle	1996
3991	AUX612	Volvo B10M-70	Säffle	1996
3992	AUX542	Volvo B10M-70	Säffle	1996
3993	AYY962	Volvo B10LA	Säffle	1996
3994	JEH436	Scania L113CLB	Carrus Fifty	1996
3995	JAX086	Scania L113CLB	Carrus Fifty	1996
3996	JCJ336	Scania L113CLB	Carrus Fifty	1996
3997	JDL486	Scania L113CLB	Carrus Fifty	1996
3998	BDJ573	Volvo B10M-50	Säffle	1996
3999	BDJ913	Volvo B10M-70	Säffle	1996
4000	BDJ953	Volvo B10M-70	Säffle	1996
4001	ESA367	Scania L113CLB	Carrus Fifty	1996
4002	EKO478	Scania L113CLB	Carrus Fifty	1996
4003	JET038	Scania L113CLB	DAB 1350L	1996

4016-4021

Volvo B10MA-55   Säffle   1996

4016	AOB952	**4018**	AOC762	**4019**	BDO853	**4020**	BDO843	**4021** BEG923
4017	AOC682							

4032	AYC583	Scania K113TLB	Carrus Regal	1996
4033	AXX522	Volvo B10M-72B	Carrus Regal	1996
4035	AYZ632	Volvo B10LA	Säffle	1996
4036	EAK479	Volvo B10M-72B	Carrus Regal	1996
4039	KPD469	Auwaerter Neoplan N122/3	Auwaerter Skyliner	1996
4041	BHS743	Volvo B10M-72B	Carrus Regal	1996
4042	AYC563	Scania K113TLB	Carrus Regal	1996

4047-4053

Volvo B10M-70   Säffle   1996

4047	EZZ220	**4048**	FBN160	**4049**	FNJ110	**4050**	FSZ040	**4053**

4063	AXJ852	Volvo B10M-70B	Carrus Star 302	1996
4064	JAM478	Scania CN113CLL	Katrineholm	1996
4065	HZJ358	Scania CN113CLL	Katrineholm	1996
4066	AXK682	Scania L113CLB	Carrus Fifty	1996

4067-4071

Volvo B10M-70   Säffle   1996

4067	FOM100	**4068**	FGD060	**4069**	FBX370	**4070**	FFA200	**4071** AJF751

4072-4077

Scania L113CLB   Carrus Fifty   1996

4072	ESH337	**4074**	ETZ027	**4075**	FBE407	**4076**	EYL247	**4077** ETN347
4073	EUE037							

4081	ASY552	Volvo B10MA-70B	Van Hool Alizée	1996
4082	ATG962	Volvo B10MA-70B	Van Hool Alizée	1996
4083	ATH732	Volvo B10MA-70B	Van Hool Alizée	1996
4084	ATH852	Volvo B10MA-70B	Van Hool Alizée	1996
4085	AYF773	Auwaerter Neoplan N128/4	Auwaerter Megaliner	1996
4086	ATG962	Auwaerter Neoplan N128/4	Auwaerter Megaliner	1996
4087	AYH543	Auwaerter Neoplan N128/4	Auwaerter Megaliner	1996
4088	AYH583	Auwaerter Neoplan N128/4	Auwaerter Megaliner	1996
5026	GWD623	Scania K112TL	Delta Star 50	1987
5031	MLE439	Scania K112TL	Van Hool Alizée 260	1986
5263	LTZ662	Scania K112	Van Hool Alizée 210	1984

5265-5273 — Scania CN112 — Scania — 1984-85

5265	CEE163	**5269**	AUJ517	**5271**	BFY737	**5272**	BJO917	**5273**	BMB927
5267	COR413	**5270**	BGF527						

5275	MLH089	Scania K112TL	Van Hool Alizée 260	1986
5276	MLH469	Scania K112TL	Van Hool Alizée 260	1986
5279	MWF053	Scania CN112	Scania	1986
5280	MUZ333	Scania CN112	Scania	1986
5283	AHS460	Scania K112TL	Van Hool Alizée 310	1987
5293	NFO769	Scania K112TL	Van Hool Alizée 360	1988
5295	NPG350	Scania CN112	Scania	1988
5303	OWN344	Scania CN113CLB	Scania	1989
5304	OWX174	Scania CN113CLB	Scania	1989
5305	OBJ945	Volvo B10M-65	Säffle	1989
5306	OBG785	Volvo B10M-65	Säffle	1989
5307	ODY959	Scania K113TLB	Van Hool Alizée 360	1990

5308-5313 — Volvo B10M-60 — Säffle — 1990

5308	OUS810	**5310**	OUF810	**5311**	OUW760	**5312**	OKD549	**5313**	OJR579
5309	OUG680								

5314	DTG092	Scania CN113CLB	Scania	1990
5316	DWX062	Scania CN113CLB	Scania	1990
5317	FHM099	Scania K113TLB	Van Hool Alizée 360	1991
5318	BZY140	Scania CN113CL	Scania	1991
5319	BWS190	Scania CN113CL	Scania	1991
5320	BZL210	Scania CN113CL	Scania	1991
5321	BYL480	Scania CN113CLB	Scania	1991
5322	AJS280	Volvo B10M-55	Säffle	1991
5323	AEL310	Volvo B10M-55	Säffle	1991
5324	CHZ480	Volvo B10M-60	Säffle	1991
5325	CJM140	Volvo B10M-60	Säffle	1991
5328	PEX200	Scania CN113ALB	Scania	1992
5329	PFF310	Scania CN113ALB	Scania	1992
5330	PFB130	Scania CN113ALB	Scania	1992
5331	PYO695	Volvo B10M-55	Säffle	1992
5332	PYW575	Volvo B10M-55	Säffle	1992

5338-5342 — Scania CN113CLL — Scania — 1994

5338	PSY058	**5339**	PTF088	**5340**	PSS018	**5341**	PTO368	**5342**	PTX328

5343	POR478	Volvo B10BLE-59	Carrus K204 City L	1994
5344	GWN223	Volvo B10M-70	Carrus Fifty	1995
5345	GWH113	Volvo B10M-70	Carrus Fifty	1995
5346	AMX035	Volvo B10M-70B	Carrus Fifty	1995
5347	AHP305	Volvo B10M-70	Carrus Fifty	1995
5348	JSD055	Volvo B10M-55	Säffle	1996
5350	JOH465	Volvo B10M-55	Säffle	1996
5351	JSA265	Volvo B10M-55	Säffle	1996
6654	KTH422	Scania BR116	Ajokki 5000	1981
6659	MZW292	Scania K113TLA	Van Hool Astrobel	1990
6660	LXZ432	Scania K113TLA	Van Hool Astrobel	1990
6663	LYY322	Scania K113TLA	Van Hool Astrobel	1990
7629	APZ516	Volvo B58-65	Wiima M301	1978
7658	AOR987	Volvo B58-65	Wiima M301	1980
7659	AHL697	Volvo B58-65	Wiima M301	1980
7667	KUJ499	Vovo B10M-65	Ajokki 5000D	1981
7674	KNB473	Vovo B10M-70B	Wiima M302	1981
7675	KOH193	Vovo B10M-70B	Wiima M302	1981

7676-7685 — Volvo B10M-65 — Wiima M302 — 1981-82

7676	BLO007	**7680**	AYT347	**7681**	HYO407	**7682**	HEP337	**7685**	KOW297
7677	BLK377								

7686	DUX058	Volvo B10M-60	Wiima M302	1982
7687	EGY318	Volvo B10M-60	Wiima M302	1982
7688	EEJ298	Volvo B10M-60	Wiima M302	1982
7689	FPD400	Volvo B10M-65B	Wiima M401	1982
7691	FGP050	Volvo B10M-65	Wiima M401	1982

7694	FOS450	Volvo B10M-65		Wiima M302		1982		
7697	FMK370	Volvo B10M-65B		Wiima M302		1982		
7699	GYF832	Volvo B10M-65B		Wiima M401		1982		

7702-7708   Volvo B10M-65   Wiima M353   1982

7702	FWH822	**7704**	HHO892	**7706**	FYF602	**7707**	GKT652	**7708**	GOA982
7703	FRL782	**7705**	GDC682						

7709	FYS842	Volvo B10M-70B	Wiima M303	1982
7710	GJD642	Volvo B10M-70B	Wiima M303	1982
7711	FWL842	Volvo B10M-65	Wiima M303	1982
7713	MBP642	Volvo B10M-65	Wiima M303	1982
7715	GAN662	Volvo B10M-65	Wiima M303	1982
7716	GER742	Volvo B10M-60	Wiima M401	1982
7717	GGP772	Volvo B10M-60	Wiima M401	1982
7719	LNK034	Volvo B10M-60	Wiima M452	1983
7721	LNE234	Volvo B10M-60	Wiima M452	1983

7722-7729   Volvo B10M-65   Wiima M303   1983

7722	LNA364	**7724**	LMP494	**7725**	LNK274	**7728**	LNL114	**7729**	LNJ414
7723	LNE164								

7731-7736   Volvo B10M-70B   Ajokki 5000E   1983

7731	LNB204	**7733**	LNE474	**7734**	LNM054	**7735**	LNK104	**7736**	LNG014
7732	LNJ274								

7741	DPT587	Volvo B10M-70B	Wiima M452	1985
7742	DKP677	Volvo B10M-70B	Wiima M452	1985
7743	DMR937	Volvo B10M-70B	Wiima M452	1985
7744	DNT978	Volvo B10M-70B	Van Hool Alizée 210	1985
7745	DJE968	Volvo B10M-70B	Van Hool Alizée 210	1985
7746	DLB988	Volvo B10M-65	Van Hool Alizée 310	1985
7747	DGH888	Volvo B10M-65	Van Hool Alizée 310	1985
7748	DSZ828	Volvo B10M-65	Van Hool Alizée 310	1985
7749	DKF578	Volvo B10M-65	Van Hool Alizée 310	1985
7751	LOD430	Volvo B10M-70B	Wiima M303	1985
7752	LJT190	Volvo B10M-70B	Wiima M303	1985
7753	LGW090	Volvo B10M-70B	Wiima M303	1985

7754-7764   Volvo B10M-70B   Wiima M452*   1985   7758/9 are model M303.

7754	DCR951	**7756**	LFD775	**7759**	JSC865	**7761**	KST865	**7763**	JXH665
7755	CYU871	**7758**	LEN855	**7760**	LTG995	**7762**	AUH775	**7764**	KTC965

7765	ABS575	Volvo B10M-65	Wiima M452	1985
7766	ACC755	Volvo B10M-70B	Wiima M500 Finlandia	1986
7767	ACB505	Volvo B10M-70B	Wiima M500 Finlandia	1986

7768-7772   Volvo B10M-56B   Van Hool Alizée 360   1987

7768	MGE966	**7769**	MGC946	**7770**	MGJ836	**7771**	MFZ956	**7772**	MGX836

7773	MHD856	Volvo B10M-70B	Van Hool Alizée 360	1987

7774-7786   Volvo B10M-70B   Wiima M453   1987

7774	MHJ596	**7778**	MHH966	**7781**	MJS606	**7783**	MJL576	**7785**	MJT836
7776	MJA726	**7779**	MHX666	**7782**	MJC746	**7784**	MJE906	**7786**	MJU936
7777	MHS566	**7780**	MJA656						

7787	MXG606	Volvo B10M-70B	Säffle	1987
7788	MWU716	Volvo B10M-70B	Säffle	1987
7789	FLK411	Volvo B10M-60	Wiima M452	1984
7790	NUH738	Volvo B10M-70B	Wiima M453	1988
7791	NUF668	Volvo B10M-70B	Wiima M453	1988
7792	NUK768	Volvo B10M-70B	Wiima M453	1988
7793	GEZ257	Volvo B10M-70B	Wiima M354	1989
7794	FZH217	Volvo B10M-70B	Wiima M354	1989
7795	FYT097	Volvo B10M-70B	Wiima M354	1989
7796	GEG387	Volvo B10M-70B	Wiima M354	1989

7797	GSK047	Volvo B10M-70B	Delta Star 501				1989	
7798	GXF487	Volvo B10M-70B	Delta Star 501				1989	
7800	HCC227	Volvo B10M-70B	Delta Star 501				1989	
7801	HKT197	Volvo B10M-70B	Delta Star 501				1989	
7803	HBW447	Volvo B10M-58B	Delta Star 501				1989	
7804	HTH167	Volvo B10M-58B	Delta Star 501				1989	
7805	OPX351	Volvo B10M-70B	Wiima/Nårk				1989	
7806	NCP116	Volvo B10M-70B	Delta 9000 Superstar				1988	
7889	OHT586	Volvo B10M-59	Säffle				1990	
7810	OHY686	Volvo B10M-59	Säffle				1990	
7811	OSP325	Volvo B10M-70B	Delta Star 501				1989	

7812-7821   Volvo B10M-70B   Van Hool Alizée   1990

7812	OEJ736	7814	OHM836	7816	OHN536	7818	OHP866	7820	OES566
7813	OHY756	7815	OJA736	7817	OHR706	7819	OEF946	7821	OEM686

7822	OHW666	Volvo B10M-65	Van Hool Alizée 310				1990	
7823	OHS886	Volvo B10M-65	Van Hool Alizée 310				1990	
7824	OHM906	Volvo B10M-70B	Wiima M310				1990	
7828	DTS195	Volvo B10M-70B	Säffle				1990	
7829	DPW275	Volvo B10M-70B	Säffle				1990	
7830	DTE325	Volvo B10M-70B	Säffle				1990	

8101-8120   Scania CR112   Scania   1982-83

8101	DKN711	8105	CYL821	8109	GJC537	8113	LHG344	8117	LHU044
8102	CZA801	8106	DLO791	8110	GJY747	8114	LHE014	8118	LHY444
8103	DJW791	8107	DUA786	8111	LHD244	8115	LHN154	8119	LBJ054
8104	CZW871	8108	DPL936	8112	LHE184	8116	LJJ404	8120	LAO164

8191	LAH323	Volvo B10R-59	Ajokki 5000E		1982

8211-8234   Volvo B10M-60   Säffle   1980

8211	KXY513	8214	KXR633	8221	KXT785	8224	KPG555	8231	JPK149
8212	KXU593	8216	KUO555	8222	KPC755	8230	KBM279	8234	KRU099
8213	KXE943								

8401-8406   Mercedes-Benz 0405N   Mercedes-Benz   1991

8401	AMM353	8403	HMM355	8404	EMM356	8405	NMM356	8406	BKH263
8402	FMM354								

Of the Leyland Titan double-deck buses now operating with Western, all have retained their dual-door configuration. Photographed in Kilmarnock is 939, WYV29T.
Tony Wilson

British Vehicle Index

Reg	Operator	Reg	Operator	Reg	Operator	Reg	Operator
13CLT	Western	552OHU	Midland Red	A145MRN	Ribble	A665HNB	Manchester
49CLT	Selkent	5796MX	Western	A156OFR	Ribble	A668HNB	Manchester
83CBD	United Counties	6253VC	Midland Red	A157OFR	Ribble	A669HNB	Manchester
109DRM	Cumberland	6804VC	Cheltenham & G	A158OFR	Ribble	A671HNB	Manchester
126ASV	Bluebird	9258VC	Midland Red	A159OFR	Ribble	A674HNB	Manchester
127ASV	Bluebird	9492SC	Bluebird	A214MCK	Ribble	A675HNB	Manchester
128ASV	Bluebird	9737VC	Midland Red	A227MDD	Red & White	A678HNB	Manchester
145CLT	Bluebird	9984PG	Midland Red	A243YGF	East Midland	A679HNB	Manchester
147YFM	Bluebird	A6GGT	Midland Red	A308RSU	Western	A680HNB	Manchester
230HUE	Midland Red	A7GGT	Midland Red	A314XWG	East Midland	A681KDV	Cambus
283URB	Western	A8GGT	Midland Red	A315XWG	East Midland	A683HNB	Manchester
295UB	Western	A21HNC	Manchester	A316XWG	East Midland	A683KDV	Cambus
331HWD	Midland Red	A22HNC	Manchester	A317XWG	East Midland	A684HNB	Manchester
400DCD	Stagecoach South	A23HNC	Manchester	A318XWG	East Midland	A687HNB	Manchester
401DCD	Stagecoach South	A24HNC	Manchester	A319YWJ	East Midland	A688HNB	Manchester
402DCD	Stagecoach South	A25HNC	Manchester	A320YWJ	East Midland	A690HNB	Manchester
403DCD	Stagecoach South	A26ORJ	Manchester	A321YWJ	East Midland	A693HNB	Manchester
404DCD	Stagecoach South	A27ORJ	Manchester	A322AKU	East Midland	A694HNB	Manchester
405DCD	Stagecoach South	A28ORJ	Manchester	A323AKU	East Midland	A695HNB	Manchester
406DCD	Stagecoach South	A29ORJ	Manchester	A324AKU	East Midland	A696HNB	Manchester
407DCD	Stagecoach South	A30ORJ	Manchester	A325AKU	East Midland	A698HNB	Manchester
408DCD	Stagecoach South	A31ORJ	Manchester	A354BHL	East Midland	A699HNB	Manchester
409DCD	Stagecoach South	A32ORJ	Manchester	A469TUV	Cheltenham & G	A700HNB	Manchester
410DCD	Stagecoach South	A33ORJ	Manchester	A471HNC	Manchester	A702LNC	Manchester
411DCD	Stagecoach South	A39XHE	East Midland	A472HNC	Manchester	A704LNC	Manchester
412DCD	Stagecoach South	A41XHE	East Midland	A473HNC	Manchester	A705LNC	Manchester
413DCD	Stagecoach South	A42XHE	East Midland	A541HAC	Red & White	A706LNC	Manchester
414DCD	Stagecoach South	A43XHE	East Midland	A542HAC	Midland Red	A708LNC	Manchester
415DCD	Stagecoach South	A44FRS	Bluebird	A543HAC	Midland Red	A710LNC	Manchester
416DCD	Stagecoach South	A44XHE	East Midland	A544HAC	Midland Red	A711LNC	Manchester
417DCD	Stagecoach South	A45FRS	Bluebird	A545HAC	Midland Red	A714LNC	Manchester
418DCD	Stagecoach South	A46FRS	Bluebird	A546HAC	Midland Red	A715LNC	Manchester
419DCD	Stagecoach South	A47FRS	Bluebird	A547HAC	Midland Red	A719LNC	Manchester
420DCD	Stagecoach South	A50LHG	Ribble	A548HAC	Red & White	A722LNC	Manchester
420GAC	Midland Red	A65THX	Selkent	A549HAC	Red & White	A725LNC	Manchester
421DCD	Stagecoach South	A66THX	Fife Scottish	A561KWY	Cambus	A726LNC	Manchester
422DCD	Stagecoach South	A67THX	Selkent	A581HDB	Manchester	A728ANH	United Counties
423DCD	Stagecoach South	A71GEE	East Midland	A582HDB	Manchester	A729ANH	United Counties
424DCD	Stagecoach South	A72GEE	East Midland	A583HDB	Manchester	A730LNC	Manchester
439UG	Western	A73GEE	East Midland	A584HDB	Manchester	A734NNA	Manchester
461CLT	East London	A74GEE	East Midland	A585HDB	Manchester	A735NNA	Manchester
467WYA	Cheltenham & G	A75NAC	Midland Red	A603THV	Selkent	A741NNA	Manchester
472YMF	Stagecoach South	A76NAC	Midland Red	A607THV	Fife Scottish	A743NNA	Manchester
485CLT	East London	A76THX	Selkent	A613THV	Selkent	A744NNA	Manchester
490CLT	Bluebird	A77THX	Selkent	A622THV	East London	A745NNA	Manchester
491GAC	Midland Red	A102DAO	Cumberland	A625THV	Selkent	A747NNA	Manchester
495FFJ	Western	A108TRP	United Counties	A626THV	East London	A748NNA	Manchester
498FYB	Midland Red	A110TRP	United Counties	A627THV	Selkent	A749NNA	Manchester
511OHU	Cheltenham & G	A111TRP	United Counties	A628THV	Selkent	A750NNA	Manchester
527CLT	East London	A112TRP	United Counties	A629THV	Selkent	A751NNA	Manchester
630DYE	East London	A113TRP	United Counties	A630THV	Selkent	A752NNA	Manchester
647DYE	United Counties	A114TRP	United Counties	A631THV	Selkent	A754NNA	Manchester
685DYE	United Counties	A116ESA	Bluebird	A632THV	Selkent	A757NNA	Manchester
703DYE	Western	A117ESA	Bluebird	A634THV	Selkent	A759NNA	Manchester
803DYE	Western	A118ESA	Bluebird	A635THV	Selkent	A761NNA	Manchester
837XHW	Transit	A121GSA	Bluebird	A636THV	Selkent	A762NNA	Manchester
866NHT	Bluebird	A122GSA	Bluebird	A645THV	Selkent	A764NNA	Manchester
896HOD	Western	A123GSA	Bluebird	A648THV	Selkent	A823SUL	Stagecoach South
927GTA	Ribble	A124GSA	Bluebird	A650THV	East London	A824SUL	Western
1412NE	Bluebird	A125GSA	Bluebird	A652THV	Selkent	A825FUL	Fife Scottish
3063VC	Midland Red	A126GSA	Bluebird	A657HNB	Manchester	A826SUL	East London
3273AC	Midland Red	A127GSA	Bluebird	A660HNB	Manchester	A827SUL	East London
4012VC	Midland Red	A138MRN	Cumberland	A661HNB	Manchester	A828SUL	Selkent
4585SC	Bluebird	A142MRN	Ribble	A663WSU	Bluebird	A829SUL	Selkent
4828VC	Midland Red	A143MRN	Ribble	A664HNB	Manchester	A830SUL	Selkent

Reg	Operator	Reg	Operator	Reg	Operator	Reg	Operator
A832SUL	East London	A988SYE	Selkent	ANA165Y	Manchester	ASA27T	Western
A833SUL	Western	A996SYE	Selkent	ANA170Y	Manchester	AVK134V	Busways
A834SUL	Selkent	A999SYE	Selkent	ANA173Y	Manchester	AVK135V	Busways
A836SUL	Selkent	AAE644V	Cheltenham & G	ANA179Y	Manchester	AVK136V	Busways
A837SUL	Selkent	AAE648V	Cheltenham & G	ANA180Y	Manchester	AVK138V	Busways
A838SUL	Selkent	AAE649V	Cheltenham & G	ANA190Y	Manchester	AVK139V	Busways
A840SUL	East London	AAE650V	Cheltenham & G	ANA211T	Western	AVK140V	Midland Red
A841SUL	Selkent	AAE651V	Cheltenham & G	ANA231T	Manchester	AVK141V	Busways
A842SUL	Selkent	AAE659V	Cheltenham & G	ANA435Y	Midland Red	AVK143V	Midland Red
A843SUL	Selkent	AAE660V	Cheltenham & G	ANA533Y	Manchester	AVK145V	Midland Red
A845SUL	Selkent	AAE665V	Cheltenham & G	ANA537Y	Manchester	AVK146V	Busways
A846SUL	East London	AAL516A	Red & White	ANA538Y	Manchester	AVK149V	Busways
A847SUL	Selkent	AAL518A	Red & White	ANA543Y	Manchester	AVK150V	Busways
A848SUL	Selkent	AAL538A	Red & White	ANA544Y	Manchester	AVK154V	Busways
A848VML	Midland Red	AAL544A	Red & White	ANA546Y	Manchester	AVK156V	Busways
A849SUL	East London	AAL575A	Red & White	ANA550Y	Manchester	AVK158V	Busways
A850SUL	Selkent	AAP647T	Stagecoach South	ANA552Y	Manchester	AVK159V	Busways
A854SUL	Selkent	AAP660T	Stagecoach South	ANA553Y	Manchester	AVK160V	Busways
A855SUL	Selkent	AAP662T	Stagecoach South	ANA559Y	Manchester	AVK161V	Busways
A856SUL	Selkent	AAP668T	Stagecoach South	ANA564Y	Manchester	AVK163V	Red & White
A857SUL	Selkent	AAP671T	Stagecoach South	ANA568Y	Manchester	AVK166V	Red & White
A858SUL	Selkent	AAX450A	Red & White	ANA569Y	Manchester	AVK167V	Midland Red
A859SUL	Selkent	AAX451A	Red & White	ANA572Y	Manchester	AVK168V	Midland Red
A866SUL	Selkent	AAX465A	Red & White	ANA577Y	Manchester	AVK169V	Midland Red
A867SUL	East London	AAX466A	Red & White	ANA579Y	Manchester	AVK170V	Busways
A868SUL	Selkent	AAX488A	Red & White	ANA582Y	Manchester	AVK171V	Busways
A873SUL	East London	AAX489A	Red & White	ANA585Y	Manchester	AVK172V	Midland Red
A874SUL	Selkent	AAX515A	Red & White	ANA586Y	Manchester	AVK173V	Red & White
A876SUL	Western	AAX516A	Red & White	ANA589Y	Manchester	AVK174V	Midland Red
A877SUL	Selkent	AAX529A	Red & White	ANA592Y	Manchester	AVK179V	Busways
A880SUL	Selkent	AAX589A	Bluebird	ANA593Y	Manchester	AVK180V	Busways
A881SUL	Selkent	AAX600A	Bluebird	ANA596Y	Manchester	AVK181V	Midland Red
A882SUL	Selkent	AAX601A	Bluebird	ANA597Y	Manchester	AVK183V	Busways
A883SUL	Selkent	AAX631A	Bluebird	ANA600Y	Manchester	AYJ89T	Stagecoach South
A885SUL	Selkent	ABA25T	East Midland	ANA601Y	Manchester	AYJ91T	Stagecoach South
A902SYE	East London	ABV669A	Fife Scottish	ANA604Y	Manchester	AYJ92T	Stagecoach South
A905SYE	East London	AET181T	Midland Red	ANA605Y	Manchester	AYJ95T	Stagecoach South
A918SYE	Selkent	AET182T	Stagecoach South	ANA608Y	Manchester	AYJ97T	Stagecoach South
A921SYE	East London	AET185T	Red & White	ANA609Y	Manchester	AYJ100T	Stagecoach South
A922SYE	East London	AET187T	Stagecoach South	ANA612Y	Manchester	AYJ101T	Stagecoach South
A925SYE	Selkent	AFM1W	Ribble	ANA613Y	Manchester	AYJ102T	Stagecoach South
A926SYE	Selkent	AFY191X	Ribble	ANA620Y	Manchester	AYJ103T	Stagecoach South
A935SYE	East London	AHH206T	Ribble	ANA624Y	Manchester	AYJ107T	Stagecoach South
A940XGG	Bluebird	AHH209T	Ribble	ANA625Y	Manchester	AYR322T	East Midland
A941XGG	Bluebird	AIB4053	Midland Red	ANA627Y	Manchester	B21TVU	Manchester
A942XGG	Bluebird	AKG162A	Bluebird	ANA630Y	Manchester	B22TVU	Manchester
A944SYE	East London	AKG232A	Bluebird	ANA631Y	Manchester	B23TVU	Manchester
A945SYE	East London	AKV137V	Cheltenham & G	ANA633Y	Manchester	B24CGA	Western
A949SYE	East London	ALD968B	Bluebird	ANA637Y	Manchester	B24TVU	Manchester
A950SYE	Selkent	ANA1Y	Manchester	ANA639Y	Manchester	B25TVU	Manchester
A951SYE	Selkent	ANA2Y	Manchester	ANA644Y	Manchester	B26TVU	Manchester
A953SYE	East London	ANA3Y	Manchester	ANA646Y	Manchester	B27PAJ	Transit
A960SYE	East London	ANA4Y	Manchester	ANA647Y	Manchester	B27TVU	Manchester
A961SYE	Selkent	ANA6Y	Manchester	ANA651Y	Manchester	B28PAJ	Transit
A965SYE	East London	ANA7Y	Manchester	ANA653Y	Manchester	B28TVU	Manchester
A967YSX	Fife Scottish	ANA8Y	Manchester	ARN888Y	Cumberland	B29PAJ	Transit
A968YSX	Fife Scottish	ANA9Y	Manchester	ARN889Y	Ribble	B29TVU	Manchester
A969YSX	Fife Scottish	ANA10Y	Manchester	ARN890Y	Ribble	B30PAJ	Transit
A970YSX	Fife Scottish	ANA153Y	Manchester	ARN892Y	Cheltenham & G	B30TVU	Manchester
A971SYE	East London	ANA154Y	Manchester	ARP601X	United Counties	B31PAJ	Transit
A971YSX	Fife Scottish	ANA155Y	Manchester	ARP602X	United Counties	B32PAJ	Transit
A972YSX	Fife Scottish	ANA157Y	Manchester	ARP604X	United Counties	B34PJA	Manchester
A973YSX	Fife Scottish	ANA158Y	Manchester	ARP605X	United Counties	B35PJA	Manchester
A974YSX	Fife Scottish	ANA158Y	Manchester	ARP606X	United Counties	B36PJA	Manchester
A975OST	Cumberland	ANA159Y	Manchester	ARP607X	United Counties	B39PJA	Manchester
A976SYE	Selkent	ANA160Y	Manchester	ARP608X	United Counties	B43MAO	Cumberland
A977OST	Cumberland	ANA161Y	Manchester	ARP609X	United Counties	B49DWE	East Midland
A978OST	Ribble	ANA162Y	Manchester	ARP610X	United Counties	B49PJA	Manchester
A978SYE	Selkent	ANA163Y	Manchester	ARP611X	United Counties	B51XFV	Ribble
A979OST	Ribble	ANA164Y	Manchester	ASA23T	Western	B52DWE	East Midland

216

Reg	Operator	Reg	Operator	Reg	Operator	Reg	Operator
B53DWJ	East Midland	B124WUV	Selkent	B891UAS	Ribble	BUH211V	Red & White
B53PJA	Manchester	B125TVU	Manchester	B892UAS	Cumberland	BUH214V	Red & White
B54DWJ	East Midland	B125WUV	Selkent	B893UAS	Cumberland	BUH232V	Red & White
B55PJA	Manchester	B126WNB	Manchester	B894UAS	Ribble	BUH237V	Red & White
B56PJA	Manchester	B132WNB	Manchester	B895UAS	Cumberland	BUH239V	Burnley & Pendle
B57PJA	Manchester	B133WNB	Manchester	B896UAS	Ribble	BUH240V	Burnley & Pendle
B58PJA	Manchester	B135WNB	Manchester	B897UAS	Ribble	BUH241V	Burnley & Pendle
B60PJA	Manchester	B137WNB	Manchester	B898UAS	Ribble	BUT24Y	Transit
B60WKH	Transit	B138WNB	Manchester	B899UAS	Cumberland	BVP771V	Midland Red
B65PJA	Manchester	B139WNB	Manchester	B900WRN	Cumberland	BVP772V	Midland Red
B67PJA	Manchester	B143WNB	Manchester	B901TVR	Manchester	BVP808V	Midland Red
B69PJA	Manchester	B145WNB	Manchester	B902TVR	Manchester	BVP816V	Midland Red
B70PJA	Manchester	B146XNA	Manchester	B903TVR	Manchester	BVP817V	Midland Red
B72PJA	Manchester	B147XNA	Manchester	B904TVR	Manchester	BVP818V	Midland Red
B74PJA	Manchester	B149XNA	Manchester	B905TVR	Manchester	BYJ919Y	Western
B77PJA	Manchester	B150DHL	East Midland	B906TVR	Manchester	C23CHM	Selkent
B79WUV	Selkent	B150XNA	Manchester	B907TVR	Manchester	C28CHM	Selkent
B80PJA	Manchester	B151DHL	East Midland	B908TVR	Manchester	C29CHM	Selkent
B81WUV	Selkent	B151WRN	Cumberland	B909TVR	Manchester	C30CHM	Selkent
B82PJA	Manchester	B152DHL	East Midland	B910ODU	Midland Red	C42CHM	Selkent
B83WUV	Selkent	B152TRN	Ribble	B910TVR	Manchester	C43CHM	Selkent
B84PJA	Manchester	B152WRN	Ribble	B911ODU	Midland Red	C44CHM	Selkent
B84WUV	Selkent	B153DHL	East Midland	B911TVR	Manchester	C45CHM	Selkent
B86SJA	Manchester	B153WRN	Cumberland	B912ODU	Midland Red	C51CHM	Selkent
B87SJA	Manchester	B153XNA	Manchester	B912TVR	Manchester	C53CHM	Selkent
B88SJA	Manchester	B154DHL	East Midland	B913TVR	Manchester	C54CHM	Selkent
B89SJA	Manchester	B154WRN	Cumberland	B914TVR	Manchester	C55CHM	Selkent
B89WUV	Selkent	B154XNA	Manchester	B915TVR	Manchester	C57CHM	Selkent
B91SJA	Manchester	B155DHL	East Midland	B916TVR	Manchester	C61CHM	Selkent
B91WUV	Selkent	B155XNA	Manchester	B917TVR	Manchester	C62CHM	Selkent
B92WUV	Selkent	B158WRN	Ribble	B918TVR	Manchester	C64CHM	Selkent
B93WUV	Selkent	B162WRN	Cumberland	B919TVR	Manchester	C67CHM	Selkent
B94SJA	Manchester	B177FFS	Fife Scottish	B920TVR	Manchester	C68CHM	Selkent
B95SJA	Manchester	B178FFS	Fife Scottish	B960ODU	Midland Red	C69CHM	Selkent
B96WUV	Selkent	B179FFS	Fife Scottish	B961ODU	Midland Red	C70CHM	Selkent
B97WUV	Selkent	B180FFS	Fife Scottish	BAU178T	United Counties	C71CHM	Selkent
B99WUV	Selkent	B181FFS	Fife Scottish	BAU179T	United Counties	C72CHM	Selkent
B100WUV	Selkent	B182FFS	Fife Scottish	BAU180T	Stagecoach South	C73CHM	Selkent
B101WUV	Selkent	B183FFS	Fife Scottish	BCS865T	Western	C74CHM	Selkent
B103HAO	Cumberland	B184FFS	Fife Scottish	BCS869T	Western	C75CHM	Selkent
B103WUV	Selkent	B185FFS	Fife Scottish	BCS870T	Western	C76CHM	Selkent
B105HAO	Cumberland	B186FFS	Fife Scottish	BCS871T	Western	C77CHM	Selkent
B106HAO	Cumberland	B214OAJ	Transit	BCW827V	Stagecoach South	C80CHM	Selkent
B106UAT	Transit	B215OAJ	Transit	BFV221Y	Ribble	C80OCW	Burnley & Pendle
B106WUV	Selkent	B216OAJ	Transit	BFV222Y	Ribble	C81CHM	Selkent
B107UAT	Transit	B217OAJ	Transit	BFW136W	East Midland	C82CHM	Selkent
B108CCS	Fife Scottish	B218OAJ	Transit	BHO441V	East Midland	C83CHM	Selkent
B108UAT	Transit	B291YSL	Fife Scottish	BHY996V	Cheltenham & G	C86CHM	Selkent
B108WUV	Selkent	B348LSO	Bluebird	BHY997V	Cheltenham & G	C87CHM	Selkent
B109UAT	Transit	B349LSO	Bluebird	BHY998V	Cheltenham & G	C92CHM	Selkent
B110SJA	Manchester	B350LSO	Bluebird	BIW4977	Midland Red	C94CHM	Selkent
B110UAT	Transit	B351LSO	Bluebird	BJG671V	Stagecoach South	C97CHM	Selkent
B110WUV	Selkent	B352LSO	Bluebird	BJG672V	Stagecoach South	C98CHM	Selkent
B112WUV	Selkent	B353LSO	Bluebird	BJG673V	Stagecoach South	C100HSJ	Transit
B113WUV	Selkent	B354LSO	Bluebird	BJG674V	Stagecoach South	C101KDS	Western
B114SJA	Manchester	B355LSO	Bluebird	BJG675V	Stagecoach South	C103CHM	Selkent
B114WUV	Selkent	B356LSO	Bluebird	BJV103L	East Midland	C104CHM	Selkent
B115WUV	Selkent	B357LSO	Bluebird	BKE849T	Stagecoach South	C104KDS	Western
B116WUV	Selkent	B358LSO	Bluebird	BKE850T	Stagecoach South	C105CHM	Selkent
B117TVU	Manchester	B359LSO	Bluebird	BKE859T	Stagecoach South	C105KDS	Western
B117WUV	Selkent	B360LSO	Bluebird	BNC936T	Western	C106CHM	Selkent
B118TVU	Manchester	B625DWF	East Midland	BOU6V	Cheltenham & G	C106KDS	Western
B118WUV	Selkent	B626DWF	East Midland	BPT903S	Red & White	C107CHM	Selkent
B119TVU	Manchester	B627DWF	East Midland	BSJ895T	Western	C108CHM	Selkent
B119WUV	Selkent	B628DWF	East Midland	BSJ896T	Western	C109CHM	Selkent
B121TVU	Manchester	B629DWF	East Midland	BSJ917T	Western	C110CHM	Selkent
B121WUV	Selkent	B630DWF	East Midland	BSJ930T	Western	C111CAT	Transit
B122TVU	Manchester	B631DWF	East Midland	BSJ931T	Western	C111CHM	Selkent
B122WUV	Selkent	B632DWF	East Midland	BSK756	Bluebird	C111JCS	Bluebird
B124TVU	Manchester	B633DWF	East Midland	BTU33W	Transit	C112CAT	Transit

C112CHM	Selkent	C230ENE	Manchester	C633LFT	Busways	C800HCS	Western
C113CAT	Transit	C234ENE	Manchester	C633SFH	Cheltenham & G	C800USG	Fife Scottish
C114CHM	Selkent	C236EVU	Manchester	C634LFT	Busways	C801USG	Fife Scottish
C115CHM	Selkent	C255FRJ	Manchester	C635LFT	Busways	C802USG	Fife Scottish
C116CHM	Selkent	C310ENA	Manchester	C636LFT	Busways	C803USG	Fife Scottish
C117CHM	Selkent	C326HWJ	East Midland	C636SFH	Cheltenham & G	C804USG	Fife Scottish
C118CHM	Selkent	C327HWJ	East Midland	C637LFT	Busways	C805USG	Fife Scottish
C119CHM	Selkent	C328HWJ	East Midland	C637SFH	Cheltenham & G	C806USG	Fife Scottish
C120CHM	Selkent	C329HWJ	East Midland	C638LFT	Busways	C807BYY	Selkent
C120PNV	United Counties	C330HWJ	East Midland	C639LFT	Busways	C807USG	Fife Scottish
C121CHM	Selkent	C331HWJ	East Midland	C639SFH	Cheltenham & G	C809BYY	Selkent
C121PNV	United Counties	C332HWJ	East Midland	C640LFT	Busways	C810BYY	Selkent
C122CAT	Transit	C333HWJ	East Midland	C640SFH	Cheltenham & G	C811BYY	Selkent
C122CHM	Selkent	C334HWJ	East Midland	C641LFT	Busways	C812BYY	Selkent
C122PNV	United Counties	C335HWJ	East Midland	C641SFH	Cheltenham & G	C815BYY	Selkent
C123CAT	Transit	C336HWJ	East Midland	C642LFT	Busways	C818BYY	Selkent
C124CAT	Transit	C336SFL	Cambus	C642SFH	Cheltenham & G	C819BYY	Selkent
C125CAT	Transit	C382SAO	Cumberland	C643LFT	Busways	C901HWF	Bluebird
C128CAT	Transit	C383SAO	Cumberland	C643SFH	Cheltenham & G	C962XVC	Midland Red
C129CAT	Transit	C447NNV	MK Metro	C644LFT	Busways	C963XVC	Midland Red
C131CAT	Transit	C448NNV	MK Metro	C644SFH	Cheltenham & G	C964XVC	Midland Red
C156YBA	Manchester	C461SSO	Bluebird	C645LFT	Busways	CBD902T	United Counties
C158YBA	Manchester	C462SSO	Bluebird	C645SFH	Cheltenham & G	CBD903T	United Counties
C164YBA	Manchester	C463SSO	Bluebird	C646LFT	Busways	CBV2S	Cumberland
C165YBA	Manchester	C466SSO	Bluebird	C647LFT	Busways	CBV6S	Red & White
C166YBA	Manchester	C467SSO	Bluebird	C648LFT	Busways	CBV9S	MK Metro
C167YBA	Manchester	C468SSO	Bluebird	C649LFT	Busways	CBV16S	Midland Red
C169YBA	Manchester	C469SSO	Bluebird	C650LFT	Busways	CBV19S	MK Metro
C170YBA	Manchester	C470SSO	Bluebird	C651LFT	Busways	CBV21S	Ribble
C171ECK	Ribble	C499BFB	Cheltenham & G	C651XDF	Cheltenham & G	CBV776S	Stagecoach South
C172ECK	Ribble	C544RAO	Transit	C652LFT	Busways	CD7045	Stagecoach South
C172YBA	Manchester	C591SHC	Western	C653LFT	Busways	CEO720W	Ribble
C173ECK	Ribble	C594SHC	Western	C654LFT	Busways	CEO721W	Cumberland
C173YBA	Manchester	C601LFT	Busways	C655LFT	Busways	CHH210T	Ribble
C174YBA	Manchester	C602LFT	Busways	C656LFT	Busways	CHH211T	Ribble
C175ECK	Cumberland	C603LFT	Busways	C657LFT	Busways	CHH214T	Ribble
C175YBA	Manchester	C604LFT	Busways	C658LFT	Busways	CJH117V	Stagecoach South
C176ECK	Cumberland	C605LFT	Busways	C659LFT	Busways	CJH119V	Stagecoach South
C176YBA	Manchester	C606LFT	Busways	C659XDF	Cheltenham & G	CJH120V	Stagecoach South
C177ECK	Cumberland	C608LFT	Busways	C660LFT	Busways	CJH142V	Stagecoach South
C178ECK	Ribble	C609LFT	Busways	C661LFT	Busways	CJH145V	Stagecoach South
C178YBA	Manchester	C60CHM	Selkent	C662LFT	Busways	CJJ677W	Stagecoach South
C179ECK	Cumberland	C610LFT	Busways	C663LFT	Busways	CJJ679W	Stagecoach South
C179YBA	Manchester	C611LFT	Busways	C664LFT	Busways	CPO98W	Stagecoach South
C181YBA	Manchester	C612LFT	Busways	C665LFT	Busways	CPO100W	Stagecoach South
C184YBA	Manchester	C613LFT	Busways	C693VAD	Cheltenham & G	CRS60T	Bluebird
C185YBA	Manchester	C614LFT	Busways	C694VAD	Cheltenham & G	CRS61T	Bluebird
C191YBA	Manchester	C615LFT	Busways	C696VAD	Cheltenham & G	CRS62T	Bluebird
C193YBA	Manchester	C616LFT	Busways	C697VAD	Cheltenham & G	CRS63T	Bluebird
C195YBA	Manchester	C617LFT	Busways	C705FKE	Midland Red	CRS68T	Bluebird
C196YBA	Manchester	C617SFH	Cheltenham & G	C714FKE	Midland Red	CRS69T	Bluebird
C197YBA	Manchester	C618LFT	Busways	C738CUC	Cheltenham & G	CRS70T	Bluebird
C198YBA	Manchester	C619LFT	Busways	C752YBA	Manchester	CRS71T	Bluebird
C199YBA	Manchester	C620LFT	Busways	C753YBA	Manchester	CRS73T	Bluebird
C205CBU	Manchester	C621LFT	Busways	C754YBA	Manchester	CRS74T	Bluebird
C207CBU	Manchester	C621SFH	Cheltenham & G	C758YBA	Manchester	CSF158W	Fife Scottish
C208CBU	Manchester	C622LFT	Busways	C769YBA	Manchester	CSF159W	Fife Scottish
C210CBU	Manchester	C623LFT	Busways	C787USG	Fife Scottish	CSF160W	Fife Scottish
C212CBU	Manchester	C624LFT	Busways	C788USG	Fife Scottish	CSF161W	Fife Scottish
C213CBU	Manchester	C625LFT	Busways	C789USG	Fife Scottish	CSF162W	Fife Scottish
C214CBU	Manchester	C626LFT	Busways	C790USG	Fife Scottish	CSF163W	Fife Scottish
C215CBU	Manchester	C626SFH	Cheltenham & G	C791USG	Fife Scottish	CSF164W	Fife Scottish
C216CBU	Manchester	C627LFT	Busways	C792USG	Fife Scottish	CSF165W	Fife Scottish
C219WAJ	Transit	C628LFT	Busways	C793USG	Fife Scottish	CSF166W	Fife Scottish
C220WAJ	Transit	C629LFT	Busways	C794USG	Fife Scottish	CSF167W	Fife Scottish
C221CBU	Manchester	C630LFT	Busways	C795USG	Fife Scottish	CSF168W	Fife Scottish
C221WAJ	Transit	C631LFT	Busways	C796USG	Fife Scottish	CSF169W	Fife Scottish
C222WAJ	Transit	C631SFH	Cheltenham & G	C797USG	Fife Scottish	CSO386Y	Western
C224CBU	Manchester	C632LFT	Busways	C798USG	Fife Scottish	CSO390Y	Western
C226ENE	Manchester	C632SFH	Cheltenham & G	C799USG	Fife Scottish	CSO526Y	Western

Reg	Operator	Reg	Operator	Reg	Operator	Reg	Operator
CSU920	Bluebird	D107NUS	Western	D134VRP	MK Metro	D511RCK	East Midland
CSU921	Bluebird	D107VRP	MK Metro	D135VRP	MK Metro	D512CSF	Fife Scottish
CSU922	Bluebird	D108NUS	Western	D136FYM	Selkent	D516DSX	Fife Scottish
CSU923	Bluebird	D108VRP	MK Metro	D136NUS	Western	D517DSX	Fife Scottish
CSU978	Stagecoach South	D109NDW	Red & White	D136VRP	MK Metro	D518DSX	Fife Scottish
CSU992	Stagecoach South	D109NUS	Western	D137FYM	Selkent	D518RCK	East Midland
CSV219	Midland Red	D109VRP	MK Metro	D137VRP	MK Metro	D519DSX	Fife Scottish
CUB72Y	Western	D110NUS	Western	D138VRP	MK Metro	D519RCK	East Midland
CUB73Y	Western	D110PTT	Devon	D139VRP	MK Metro	D520DSX	Fife Scottish
CUL79V	Stagecoach South	D110VRP	MK Metro	D140VRP	MK Metro	D520RCK	Cumberland
CUL80V	East London	D111NUS	Western	D141FYM	Selkent	D521DSX	Fife Scottish
CUL86V	Selkent	D111PTT	Devon	D141VRP	MK Metro	D522DSX	Fife Scottish
CUL98V	Selkent	D111VRP	MK Metro	D142FYM	Selkent	D522RCK	East Midland
CUL114V	Selkent	D112PTT	Devon	D142VRP	MK Metro	D523DSX	Fife Scottish
CUL120V	Selkent	D112VRP	MK Metro	D143VRP	MK Metro	D523KSE	Bluebird
CUL130V	Selkent	D113NUS	Western	D144FYM	Selkent	D524DSX	Fife Scottish
CUL137V	Selkent	D113PTT	Devon	D144VRP	MK Metro	D525RCK	Cumberland
CUL140V	Selkent	D113VRP	MK Metro	D145FYM	Selkent	D528RCK	Cumberland
CUL142V	Selkent	D114NUS	Western	D145VRP	MK Metro	D529RCK	Cumberland
CUL163V	East London	D114PTT	Devon	D147VRP	MK Metro	D530RCK	Cumberland
CUL168V	Stagecoach South	D114VRP	MK Metro	D155VRP	MK Metro	D531RCK	Cumberland
CUL169V	Stagecoach South	D115NUS	Western	D156VRP	MK Metro	D533RCK	Cumberland
CUL175V	Selkent	D115VRP	MK Metro	D164VRP	MK Metro	D534RCK	Cumberland
CUL179V	Western	D116NUS	Western	D177VRP	MK Metro	D539RCK	East Midland
CUL180V	Stagecoach South	D116PTT	Devon	D181VRP	MK Metro	D547RCK	East Midland
CUL189V	Western	D116VRP	MK Metro	D183VRP	MK Metro	D558RCK	Cumberland
CUL190V	Stagecoach South	D117NUS	Western	D192VRP	MK Metro	D559RCK	Cumberland
CUL193V	Selkent	D117PTT	Devon	D211VEV	Stagecoach South	D560RCK	Cumberland
CUL197V	Western	D117VRP	MK Metro	D230UHC	Western	D561RCK	East Midland
CUL198V	Stagecoach South	D118NUS	Western	D260JVR	Manchester	D581VBV	Cheltenham & G
CUL208V	Western	D118PTT	Devon	D268JVR	Manchester	D601MDB	Manchester
CUL209V	Western	D118VRP	MK Metro	D269JVR	Manchester	D604HTC	Cheltenham & G
CUL214V	Selkent	D119VRP	MK Metro	D272JVR	Manchester	D605HTC	Cheltenham & G
CUL215V	Stagecoach South	D120PTT	Devon	D277FAS	Fife Scottish	D606HTC	Cheltenham & G
CUL222V	Selkent	D120VRP	MK Metro	D277JVR	Manchester	D606MDB	Manchester
CUL223V	Selkent	D121NUS	Western	D278FAS	Fife Scottish	D611MDB	Manchester
CUL224V	Selkent	D121VRP	MK Metro	D279FAS	Fife Scottish	D614ASG	Fife Scottish
CUL225V	Stagecoach South	D122NUS	Western	D322MNC	Bluebird	D615ASG	Fife Scottish
CUV272C	East London	D122VRP	MK Metro	D367JJD	Selkent	D618MDB	Manchester
CUV286C	East London	D123FYM	Selkent	D380XRS	Cumberland	D619MDB	Manchester
CUV300C	East London	D123NUS	Western	D381XRS	Cumberland	D623MDB	Manchester
CUV303C	East London	D123VRP	MK Metro	D383XRS	United Counties	D624MDB	Manchester
CUV311C	East London	D124FYM	Selkent	D384XAO	Cumberland	D627MDB	Manchester
CWR525Y	Ribble	D124NUS	Western	D385XRS	Bluebird	D628MDB	Manchester
CWR526Y	Ribble	D124VRP	MK Metro	D386XRS	Bluebird	D630MDB	Manchester
CWX669T	Ribble	D125FYM	Selkent	D387XRS	Bluebird	D632MDB	Manchester
CYJ492Y	Red & White	D125PTT	Devon	D388XRS	Bluebird	D634MDB	Manchester
CYJ493Y	Red & White	D125VRP	MK Metro	D389XRS	Bluebird	D636MDB	Manchester
D34UAO	East Midland	D126FYM	Selkent	D401TFT	Busways	D636NOD	Devon
D35UAO	Cumberland	D126VRP	MK Metro	D402TFT	Busways	D637NOD	Devon
D36UAO	Cumberland	D127FYM	Selkent	D404TFT	Devon	D638MDB	Manchester
D37UAO	Cumberland	D127VRP	MK Metro	D405TFT	Devon	D639MDB	Manchester
D38UAO	Cumberland	D128FYM	Selkent	D407TFT	Devon	D639NOD	Devon
D39UAO	Cumberland	D128NUS	Western	D408TFT	Devon	D640MDB	Manchester
D41UAO	Western	D128VRP	MK Metro	D409TFT	Devon	D640NOD	Devon
D42UAO	Cumberland	D129FYM	Selkent	D412TFT	Devon	D641MDB	Manchester
D43UAO	Cumberland	D129NUS	Western	D413TFT	Devon	D642NOD	Devon
D44UAO	Cumberland	D129VRP	MK Metro	D414TFT	Devon	D643MDB	Manchester
D45UAO	Cumberland	D130FYM	Selkent	D415TFT	Busways	D644MDB	Manchester
D46UAO	Cumberland	D130NUS	Western	D416TFT	Devon	D645MDB	Manchester
D81UFV	Burnley & Pendle	D130VRP	MK Metro	D417TFT	Devon	D646MDB	Manchester
D82UFV	Burnley & Pendle	D131FYM	Selkent	D418TFT	Devon	D646NOD	Devon
D83UFV	Burnley & Pendle	D131PTT	Devon	D419TFT	Busways	D647MDB	Manchester
D94EKV	Western	D131VRP	MK Metro	D420TFT	Devon	D647NOD	Devon
D101VRP	MK Metro	D132FYM	Selkent	D435RYS	Bluebird	D648MDB	Manchester
D102VRP	MK Metro	D132VRP	MK Metro	D436RYS	Bluebird	D648NOD	Devon
D103WPM	MK Metro	D133FYM	Selkent	D473WPM	Stagecoach South	D649MDB	Manchester
D104VRP	MK Metro	D133VRP	MK Metro	D476PON	East London	D649NOD	Devon
D105VRP	MK Metro	D134FYM	Selkent	D503RCK	East Midland	D650MDB	Manchester
D106VRP	MK Metro	D134PTT	Devon	D504RCK	East Midland	D650NOD	Devon

D651NNE	Manchester	DBV838W	Ribble	E94LHG	Burnley & Pendle	E439AFT	Devon
D652NOD	Devon	DBV839W	Ribble	E94YWB	East Midland	E440AFT	Busways
D653NNE	Manchester	DBV841W	Ribble	E95YWB	East Midland	E441AFT	Devon
D654NNE	Manchester	DDW433V	Red & White	E96YWB	East Midland	E442AFT	Busways
D655NNE	Manchester	DDW434V	Red & White	E97YWB	East Midland	E443AFT	Busways
D655NOD	Devon	DDZ8844	Bluebird	E98YWB	East Midland	E445AFT	Busways
D656NOD	Devon	DGS625	Bluebird	E101JFV	Burnley & Pendle	E446AFT	Devon
D658NNE	Manchester	DHW350W	Cheltenham & G	E102JFV	Burnley & Pendle	E447AFT	Busways
D659NNE	Manchester	DHW352W	Cheltenham & G	E102OUH	Cheltenham & G	E449AFT	Busways
D661NNE	Manchester	DMS20V	Red & White	E113RBO	Red & White	E450AFT	Busways
D666NNE	Manchester	DMS22V	Red & White	E114SDW	Red & White	E451AFT	Busways
D667NNE	Manchester	DNE545Y	Cheltenham & G	E115SDW	Red & White	E452AFT	Busways
D668NNE	Manchester	DSV943	Cumberland	E130ORP	United Counties	E453AFT	Busways
D670NNE	Manchester	DWF22V	East Midland	E131ORP	United Counties	E454AFT	Busways
D671NNE	Manchester	DWF23V	East Midland	E132ORP	United Counties	E455AFT	Busways
D672NNE	Manchester	DWF24V	East Midland	E132SAT	Transit	E456AFT	Busways
D673NNE	Manchester	DWF26V	East Midland	E133ORP	United Counties	E457AFT	Busways
D674NNE	Manchester	DWF188V	Bluebird	E133SAT	Transit	E458AFT	Busways
D675NNE	Manchester	DWF190V	Bluebird	E134ORP	United Counties	E459AFT	Busways
D676NNE	Manchester	DWF191V	Bluebird	E134SAT	Transit	E500LFL	Cambus
D677NNE	Manchester	DWF193V	Bluebird	E135SAT	Transit	E501LFL	Cambus
D678NNE	Manchester	DWF194V	Midland Red	E136SAT	Transit	E502LFL	Cambus
D679NNE	Manchester	DWF195V	Midland Red	E137SAT	Transit	E510PVV	Cumberland
D680NNE	Manchester	DWF198V	Fife Scottish	E138SAT	Transit	E511PVV	Cumberland
D713CSC	Fife Scottish	DWF199V	Fife Scottish	E139SAT	Transit	E512PVV	Cumberland
D744BRS	Bluebird	DWF200V	Fife Scottish	E140SAT	Transit	E635BVK	Busways
D777NDV	Devon	E26GCK	Ribble	E141SAT	Transit	E637BVK	Busways
D778NDV	Devon	E47CHH	Cumberland	E142BKH	Transit	E638YUS	Western
D779NDV	Devon	E47HFE	East Midland	E143BKH	Transit	E643DCK	Western
D780NDV	Devon	E48CHH	Cumberland	E144BKH	Transit	E644KYW	Fife Scottish
D781NDV	Devon	E48HFE	East Midland	E145BKH	Transit	E645KYW	Western
D784NDV	Devon	E49CHH	Cumberland	E146BKH	Transit	E646DCK	Western
D785NDV	Devon	E49HFE	East Midland	E147BKH	Transit	E663JAD	Cheltenham & G
D786NDV	Devon	E50CHH	Cumberland	E148BKH	Transit	E665JAD	Cheltenham & G
D787NDV	Devon	E50HFE	East Midland	E149BKH	Transit	E667JAD	Cheltenham & G
D792NDV	Devon	E51HFE	East Midland	E150BKH	Transit	E676KDG	Cheltenham & G
D794NDV	Devon	E52WAG	Transit	E151BKH	Transit	E705LYU	Stagecoach South
D795NDV	Devon	E56HFE	East Midland	E155CGJ	East London	E709MFV	Transit
D796NDV	Devon	E57HFE	East Midland	E200BDV	Devon	E712LYU	East London
D797NDV	Devon	E58HFE	East Midland	E201EPB	Stagecoach South	E713LYU	Bluebird
D798NDV	Devon	E60WDT	East Midland	E203EPB	Stagecoach South	E714LYU	Bluebird
D799NDV	Devon	E61JFV	Burnley & Pendle	E205BDV	Devon	E721BVO	East Midland
D799USB	Western	E61WDT	East Midland	E209BDV	Devon	E746SKR	Stagecoach South
D860FOT	Ribble	E62JFV	Burnley & Pendle	E210BDV	Devon	E747SKR	Stagecoach South
D918GRU	Western	E63JFV	Burnley & Pendle	E211BDV	Devon	E748SKR	Stagecoach South
DAK201V	Red & White	E64JFV	Burnley & Pendle	E213BDV	Devon	E749SKR	Stagecoach South
DBV24W	Cumberland	E65JFV	Burnley & Pendle	E216BDV	Devon	E750SKR	Stagecoach South
DBV25W	Stagecoach South	E66JFV	Burnley & Pendle	E223BDV	Devon	E751SKR	Stagecoach South
DBV26W	Red & White	E66MVV	MK Metro	E317BRM	Busways	E752SKR	Stagecoach South
DBV29W	Stagecoach South	E67MVV	MK Metro	E364YGB	Bluebird	E753SKR	Stagecoach South
DBV30W	Ribble	E68MVV	MK Metro	E421AFT	Busways	E754UKR	Stagecoach South
DBV32W	Cumberland	E69MVV	MK Metro	E422AFT	Busways	E755UKR	Stagecoach South
DBV38W	Burnley & Pendle	E70MVV	MK Metro	E423AFT	Busways	E800WDV	Devon
DBV39W	Burnley & Pendle	E71MVV	MK Metro	E423AFT	Busways	E801WDV	Devon
DBV40W	Burnley & Pendle	E72MVV	MK Metro	E425AFT	Busways	E802WDV	Devon
DBV41W	Burnley & Pendle	E73MVV	MK Metro	E426AFT	Busways	E806WDV	Devon
DBV42W	Burnley & Pendle	E84HRN	Burnley & Pendle	E427AFT	Busways	E810WDV	Devon
DBV43W	Burnley & Pendle	E85HRN	Burnley & Pendle	E428AFT	Busways	E815WDV	Devon
DBV100W	Cumberland	E86HRN	Burnley & Pendle	E429AFT	Busways	E816WDV	Devon
DBV131Y	Ribble	E87HRN	Burnley & Pendle	E430AFT	Busways	E821WDV	Devon
DBV132Y	Ribble	E88HRN	Burnley & Pendle	E431AFT	Busways	E822WDV	Devon
DBV134Y	Cumberland	E89HRN	Burnley & Pendle	E431AFT	Devon	E823WDV	Devon
DBV137Y	Ribble	E90JHG	Burnley & Pendle	E432AFT	Busways	E824WDV	Devon
DBV199W	Ribble	E90YWB	East Midland	E433AFT	Busways	E825ATT	Devon
DBV829W	Ribble	E91LBV	Burnley & Pendle	E433YHL	Midland Red	E827ATT	Devon
DBV831W	Ribble	E91YWB	East Midland	E434AFT	Busways	E828ATT	Devon
DBV832W	Ribble	E92LHG	Burnley & Pendle	E435AFT	Busways	E830ATT	Devon
DBV833W	Ribble	E92YWB	East Midland	E436AFT	Devon	E842KAS	Bluebird
DBV834W	Cumberland	E93LHG	Burnley & Pendle	E437AFT	Busways	E864RCS	Western
DBV835W	Ribble	E93YWB	East Midland	E438AFT	Devon	E865RCS	Western

E866RCS	Western	EJR118W	Busways	F55EAT	Transit	F157HAT	Transit
E867RCS	Western	EJR119W	Busways	F55RFS	Cheltenham & G	F160FWY	East London
E880DRA	East Midland	EJR122W	Busways	F56RFS	Fife Scottish	F164XCS	Bluebird
E901KYR	Busways	EJR123W	Busways	F57RFS	Cheltenham & G	F165FWY	East London
E905KYR	Busways	EJV31Y	East Midland	F58RFS	Cheltenham & G	F166FWY	East London
E906KYR	Busways	EJV32Y	East Midland	F60RFS	Cheltenham & G	F167SMT	Cambus
E907KYR	Busways	EJV33Y	East Midland	F63RFS	Western	F168SMT	Cambus
E908KYR	Busways	EJV34Y	East Midland	F64RFS	Western	F169FWY	Bluebird
E909KSG	Fife Scottish	EKW614V	East Midland	F65RFS	Western	F170FWY	East London
E909KYR	Busways	EKW615V	East Midland	F71LAL	Midland Red	F171FWY	East London
E910KSG	Fife Scottish	EKW616V	East Midland	F74DCW	Red & White	F171SMT	Cambus
E910KYR	Busways	EKY21V	East Midland	F75TFU	East Midland	F172FWY	East London
E911KYR	Busways	EKY22V	East Midland	F76TFU	East Midland	F173FWY	East London
E912KYR	Busways	EKY23V	East Midland	F77HAU	Bluebird	F174FWY	East London
E914KYR	Busways	EKY24V	East Midland	F77TFU	East Midland	F175FWY	East London
E915KYR	Busways	EKY25V	East Midland	F78TFU	East Midland	F176FWY	East London
E917KYR	Busways	EKY27V	East Midland	F101HVK	Busways	F177FWY	Bluebird
E918KYR	Busways	EKY28V	East Midland	F102HVK	Busways	F178FWY	East London
E919KYR	Busways	EKY29V	East Midland	F103HVK	Busways	F179FWY	East London
E920KYR	Busways	ENJ909V	Stagecoach South	F103XCW	Burnley & Pendle	F180FWY	Bluebird
E921KYR	Busways	ENJ910V	Stagecoach South	F104HVK	Busways	F197ASD	Western
E922KYR	Busways	ENJ911V	Stagecoach South	F104XCW	Burnley & Pendle	F201FHH	Cumberland
E923KYR	Busways	ENJ912V	Stagecoach South	F105HVK	Busways	F202FHH	Cumberland
E924KYR	Busways	ENJ913V	Stagecoach South	F105XCW	Burnley & Pendle	F243OFP	Red & White
E925KYR	Busways	ENJ914V	Stagecoach South	F106HVK	Busways	F251JRM	Transit
E927KYR	Busways	ENJ915V	Stagecoach South	F106XCW	Burnley & Pendle	F252JRM	Transit
E927PBE	East Midland	ENJ916V	Stagecoach South	F107HVK	Busways	F253KAO	Transit
E928PBE	East Midland	ENJ917V	Stagecoach South	F107NRT	United Counties	F277WAF	Bluebird
E929PBE	East Midland	ENJ918V	Stagecoach South	F107XCW	Burnley & Pendle	F282DRJ	Manchester
E930PBE	East Midland	EPW516K	Busways	F108HVK	Busways	F283DRJ	Manchester
E947BHS	Bluebird	ERV115W	Stagecoach South	F108NRT	Transit	F285DRJ	Manchester
EAP973V	Stagecoach South	ERV116W	Stagecoach South	F108XCW	Burnley & Pendle	F286KGK	Fife Scottish
EAP977V	Stagecoach South	ERV117W	Stagecoach South	F109HVK	Busways	F289DRJ	Manchester
EAP978V	Stagecoach South	ERV118W	Stagecoach South	F109XCW	Burnley & Pendle	F291DRJ	Manchester
EAP982V	Stagecoach South	ESU263	Busways	F110HVK	Busways	F294DRJ	Manchester
EAP983V	Bluebird	ESU435	Western	F110NES	United Counties	F295DRJ	Manchester
EAP984V	Stagecoach South	ESU913	Manchester	F110XCW	Burnley & Pendle	F296DRJ	Manchester
EAP985V	Stagecoach South	ESU920	Manchester	F111HVK	Busways	F297DRJ	Manchester
EAP986V	Stagecoach South	EWE202V	Bluebird	F111XCW	Burnley & Pendle	F298DRJ	Manchester
EAP987V	Stagecoach South	EWE203V	East Midland	F112HVK	Busways	F300DRJ	Manchester
EAP988V	Stagecoach South	EWE204V	Fife Scottish	F112XCW	Burnley & Pendle	F301DRJ	Manchester
EAP990V	Stagecoach South	EWE205V	Bluebird	F113HVK	Busways	F301MYJ	Stagecoach South
EAP991V	Stagecoach South	EWE206V	East Midland	F114HVK	Busways	F302MYJ	Stagecoach South
EAP992V	Stagecoach South	EWS740W	Cheltenham & G	F114YVP	Western	F303MYJ	Stagecoach South
EAP996V	Bluebird	EWS743W	Cheltenham & G	F115HVK	Busways	F304DRJ	Manchester
ECS877V	Western	EWS746W	Cheltenham & G	F116HVK	Busways	F304MYJ	Stagecoach South
ECS878V	Western	EWS748W	Cheltenham & G	F117HVK	Busways	F305MYJ	Stagecoach South
ECS879V	Western	EWS751W	Cheltenham & G	F118HVK	Busways	F306MYJ	Stagecoach South
ECS880V	Western	EWY74Y	Western	F118YVP	Western	F307MYJ	Stagecoach South
ECS882V	Western	EWY75Y	Western	F119HVK	Busways	F308MYJ	Stagecoach South
ECU201E	Busways	EWY76Y	Western	F119YVP	Western	F309MYJ	Stagecoach South
EDS50A	Bluebird	EYE229V	Stagecoach South	F120HVK	Busways	F310MYJ	Fife Scottish
EFU935Y	East Midland	EYE230V	Selkent	F121HVK	Busways	F311DET	Cheltenham & G
EHG43S	Ribble	EYE233V	Stagecoach South	F121YVP	Western	F311MYJ	Fife Scottish
EHG44S	Ribble	EYE236V	Western	F122HVK	Busways	F312MYJ	Fife Scottish
EHG45S	Ribble	EYE237V	Stagecoach South	F123HVK	Busways	F334JHS	Western
EHG46S	Ribble	EYE240V	Stagecoach South	F124HVK	Busways	F335JHS	Western
EJR104W	Busways	EYE244V	Stagecoach South	F125HVK	Busways	F359GKN	MK Metro
EJR105W	Busways	EYE246V	Western	F128YVP	Western	F394DHL	Selkent
EJR106W	Midland Red	EYE248V	Western	F135SPX	Cumberland	F404KOD	Devon
EJR107W	Busways	EYE250V	Stagecoach South	F135URP	United Counties	F405KOD	Devon
EJR108W	Busways	F25PSL	Stagecoach South	F136SPX	Cumberland	F406KOD	Devon
EJR109W	Busways	F32CWY	East London	F137SPX	Cumberland	F407KOD	Devon
EJR110W	Busways	F41XCS	Western	F149XCS	Western	F408KOD	Devon
EJR111W	Busways	F50CWY	East London	F152HAT	Transit	F410KOD	Devon
EJR112W	Busways	F51RFS	Western	F153HAT	Transit	F411KOD	Devon
EJR113W	Cheltenham & G	F52RFS	Western	F154HAT	Transit	F412KOD	Devon
EJR114W	Busways	F53EAT	Transit	F155HAT	Transit	F413KOD	Devon
EJR115W	Busways	F53RFS	Western	F156FWY	East London	F424GGB	Bluebird
EJR117W	Busways	F54RFS	Western	F156HAT	Transit	F506NJE	Cambus

F507NJE	Cambus	F705BAT	Transit	F904JRG	Busways	FRP911T	United Counties
F508NJE	Cambus	F706CAG	Transit	F905JRG	Busways	FRP912T	United Counties
F509NJE	Cambus	F714FDV	Devon	F906JRG	Busways	FSL61W	Transit
F510NJE	Cambus	F715FDV	Devon	F907JRG	Busways	FSL62W	Transit
F511NJE	Cambus	F716FDV	Devon	F908JRG	Busways	FSU737	Western
F512NJE	Cambus	F717FDV	Devon	F909JRG	Busways	FSU739	Western
F513NJE	Cambus	F718FDV	Devon	F910JRG	Busways	FUH32V	Burnley & Pendle
F514NJE	Cambus	F719FDV	Devon	F911JRG	Busways	FUH33V	Burnley & Pendle
F515NJE	Cambus	F720FDV	Devon	F912JRG	Busways	FUH34V	Burnley & Pendle
F516NJE	Cambus	F722FDV	Devon	F912YWY	East London	FVR249V	Manchester
F517NJE	Cambus	F723FDV	Devon	F913HTU	Ribble	FVR280V	Manchester
F524WSJ	Western	F726FDV	Devon	F913JRG	Busways	FVR290V	Manchester
F601MSL	Stagecoach South	F728FDV	Devon	F913YWY	East London	FVR291V	Manchester
F601UVN	Transit	F729FDV	Devon	F914HTU	Ribble	FVR294V	Ribble
F602MSL	Stagecoach South	F730FDV	Devon	F914JRG	Busways	FWH461Y	Manchester
F602UVN	Transit	F731FDV	Devon	F915JRG	Busways	FWH462Y	Manchester
F603MSL	Stagecoach South	F732FDV	Devon	F916JRG	Busways	FYX824W	Midland Red
F603UVN	Transit	F733FDV	Devon	F917JRG	Busways	G30PSR	Stagecoach South
F604MSL	Stagecoach South	F735FDV	Devon	F918JRG	Busways	G30TGW	Selkent
F604UVN	Transit	F736FDV	Devon	F919JRG	Busways	G31TGW	Selkent
F605MSL	Stagecoach South	F737FDV	Devon	F920JRG	Busways	G33TGW	Selkent
F605UVN	Transit	F738FDV	Devon	F947NER	Manchester	G34TGW	Selkent
F606MSL	Stagecoach South	F740FDV	Devon	F948NER	Manchester	G35TGW	Selkent
F606UVN	Transit	F741FDV	Devon	F958HTO	Devon	G36TGW	Selkent
F607UVN	Transit	F742FDV	Devon	F995DRN	Burnley & Pendle	G37SSR	Stagecoach South
F608UVN	Transit	F743FDV	Devon	FAO417V	United Counties	G37TGW	Selkent
F609UVN	Transit	F744FDV	Devon	FAO418V	United Counties	G38TGW	Selkent
F609XMS	Devon	F745FDV	Devon	FAO419V	United Counties	G39SSR	Stagecoach South
F610UVN	Transit	F748FDV	Devon	FAO420V	Cumberland	G39TGW	Selkent
F614XMS	Devon	F750FDV	Devon	FAO421V	Cumberland	G40TGW	Selkent
F615XMS	Devon	F754FDV	Devon	FAO422V	Cumberland	G41XBK	Ribble
F616XMS	Devon	F755FDV	Devon	FAO423V	Cumberland	G56SAG	Transit
F617XMS	Devon	F756FDV	Devon	FAO424V	Cumberland	G67PFR	Burnley & Pendle
F619XMS	Devon	F757FDV	Devon	FAO425V	Cumberland	G68PFR	Burnley & Pendle
F620MSL	United Counties	F758FDV	Devon	FAO426V	Cumberland	G71APO	Stagecoach South
F620XMS	Devon	F759FDV	Devon	FAO427V	Cumberland	G72APO	Stagecoach South
F621MSL	United Counties	F760FDV	Devon	FAO428V	Cumberland	G73APO	Stagecoach South
F621XMS	Transit	F761EKM	Stagecoach South	FAO429V	Bluebird	G79VFW	East Midland
F622MSL	United Counties	F762EKM	Stagecoach South	FBR53D	Busways	G80VFW	East Midland
F623MSL	United Counties	F762FDV	Devon	FDV784V	Ribble	G81VFW	East Midland
F624MSL	United Counties	F763EKM	Stagecoach South	FDV799V	Cumberland	G86KUB	Bluebird
F624XMS	Transit	F763FDV	Devon	FDV809V	United Counties	G91KUB	East London
F625MSL	United Counties	F764EKM	Stagecoach South	FDV810V	Bluebird	G93ERP	MK Metro
F625XMS	Transit	F765EKM	Stagecoach South	FDV811V	United Counties	G94ERP	MK Metro
F626MSL	United Counties	F766EKM	Stagecoach South	FDV812V	United Counties	G96ERP	MK Metro
F627MSL	United Counties	F767EKM	Stagecoach South	FDV813V	Ribble	G96MRN	Burnley & Pendle
F628MSL	United Counties	F771EKM	Stagecoach South	FDV816V	Bluebird	G97ERP	MK Metro
F629MSL	United Counties	F771FDV	Devon	FDV817V	Ribble	G97MRN	Burnley & Pendle
F629XMS	Transit	F772EKM	Stagecoach South	FDV818V	Stagecoach South	G98NBD	MK Metro
F630MSL	United Counties	F772FDV	Devon	FDV819V	Bluebird	G98PCK	Burnley & Pendle
F630XMS	Devon	F773EKM	Stagecoach South	FDV829V	Stagecoach South	G99NBD	MK Metro
F631MSL	United Counties	F774EKM	Stagecoach South	FDV830V	Stagecoach South	G99PCK	Burnley & Pendle
F631XMS	Devon	F775EKM	Stagecoach South	FDV831V	Stagecoach South	G100NBD	MK Metro
F632MSL	United Counties	F781KKP	Stagecoach South	FDV832V	United Counties	G101AAD	Cheltenham & G
F633MSL	United Counties	F782KKP	Stagecoach South	FDV833V	Ribble	G102AAD	Cheltenham & G
F634MSP	United Counties	F803FAO	Cumberland	FDV835V	United Counties	G103AAD	Cheltenham & G
F635YRP	United Counties	F804FAO	Cumberland	FDV838V	United Counties	G104AAD	Cheltenham & G
F636YRP	United Counties	F805FAO	Cumberland	FDV839V	Stagecoach South	G105AAD	Cheltenham & G
F637YRP	United Counties	F806FAO	Cumberland	FDV840V	Bluebird	G105KUB	East London
F638YRP	United Counties	F807FAO	Cumberland	FES831W	Ribble	G106KUB	East London
F641XMS	Devon	F808FAO	Cumberland	FFR166S	Burnley & Pendle	G107KUB	East London
F651RBP	Stagecoach South	F809FAO	Cumberland	FFR167S	Burnley & Pendle	G108CEH	Busways
F660PWK	Midland Red	F810FAO	Cumberland	FFR168S	Burnley & Pendle	G113SKX	Busways
F661PWK	Midland Red	F811FAO	Cumberland	FFR172S	Burnley & Pendle	G115OGA	Midland Red
F677PDF	Cheltenham & G	F862FWB	Bluebird	FFR173S	Burnley & Pendle	G119KUB	East London
F695OPA	Stagecoach South	F882CJC	Ribble	FFR174S	Burnley & Pendle	G178PAO	Cumberland
F701BAT	Transit	F883CJC	Ribble	FPR62V	Stagecoach South	G179PAO	Ribble
F702BAT	Transit	F901JRG	Busways	FRP908T	United Counties	G180JHG	Cumberland
F703BAT	Transit	F902JRG	Busways	FRP909T	United Counties	G180PAO	Ribble
F704BAT	Transit	F903JRG	Busways	FRP910T	United Counties	G181JHG	Cumberland

The 1997 Stagecoach Bus Handbook

Reg	Operator	Reg	Operator	Reg	Operator	Reg	Operator	Reg	Operator
G181PAO	Ribble	G285TSL	Bluebird	G641EVV	United Counties	GAJ131V	Transit
G182JHG	Cumberland	G286TSL	Bluebird	G642EVV	United Counties	GAJ132V	Transit
G182PAO	Ribble	G287TSL	Bluebird	G643EVV	United Counties	GAJ133V	Transit
G183JHG	Cumberland	G288TSL	Bluebird	G644EVV	United Counties	GAJ134V	Transit
G183PAO	Ribble	G289TSL	Bluebird	G645EVV	United Counties	GAJ135V	Transit
G184JHG	Cumberland	G290TSL	Bluebird	G646DAG	Stagecoach South	GAJ136V	Transit
G184PAO	Ribble	G291TSL	Bluebird	G646EVV	United Counties	GAZ4381	Cambus
G185JHG	Cumberland	G292TSL	Bluebird	G647EVV	United Counties	GAZ4382	Cambus
G185PAO	Ribble	G293TSL	Cumberland	G648EVV	United Counties	GBU17V	Manchester
G186JHG	Cumberland	G294TSL	Cumberland	G649EVV	United Counties	GBU20V	Manchester
G186PAO	Ribble	G295TSL	Cumberland	G679AAD	Cheltenham & G	GBU22V	Manchester
G187JHG	Ribble	G296TSL	Cumberland	G680AAD	Cheltenham & G	GBU24V	Manchester
G187PAO	Ribble	G297TSL	Cumberland	G681AAD	Cheltenham & G	GBU27V	Manchester
G188JHG	Ribble	G298TSL	Cumberland	G682AAD	Cheltenham & G	GBU28V	Manchester
G188PAO	Ribble	G299TSL	Cumberland	G683AAD	Cheltenham & G	GBU29V	Manchester
G189JHG	Cumberland	G300TSL	Cumberland	G684AAD	Cheltenham & G	GBV101N	Ribble
G189PAO	Ribble	G301WHP	Midland Red	G684KNW	East London	GBV108N	Ribble
G190PAO	Ribble	G302WHP	Midland Red	G701TCD	Stagecoach South	GBV109N	Ribble
G191PAO	Ribble	G303WHP	Midland Red	G702TCD	Stagecoach South	GBV110N	Ribble
G192PAO	Cumberland	G337KKW	Fife Scottish	G703TCD	Stagecoach South	GCK49W	Ribble
G193PAO	Bluebird	G338KKW	Fife Scottish	G704TCD	Stagecoach South	GCS33V	Western
G194PAO	Bluebird	G339KKW	East Midland	G705TCD	Stagecoach South	GCS37V	Western
G195PAO	Bluebird	G340KKW	East Midland	G706TCD	Stagecoach South	GCS38V	Western
G196PAO	Bluebird	G341KKW	East Midland	G707TCD	Stagecoach South	GCS41V	Western
G197PAO	Bluebird	G342KKW	East Midland	G708TCD	Stagecoach South	GCS45V	Western
G198PAO	Bluebird	G343KKW	East Midland	G709TCD	Stagecoach South	GCS47V	Western
G199PAO	Bluebird	G421RYJ	Stagecoach South	G710TCD	Stagecoach South	GCS48V	Western
G200PAO	Bluebird	G461SGB	Western	G767CDU	Ribble	GCS49V	Western
G201PAO	Bluebird	G520LWU	Cambus	G801JRH	Transit	GCS51V	Western
G202PAO	Bluebird	G525LWU	Cambus	G802JRH	Transit	GCS53V	Western
G203PAO	Bluebird	G526LWU	Cambus	G803JRH	Transit	GCS57V	Western
G210SSL	Stagecoach South	G527LWU	Cambus	G804JRH	Transit	GCS58V	Western
G211SSL	Stagecoach South	G528LWU	Midland Red	G805JRH	Transit	GCS60V	Western
G212SSL	Stagecoach South	G529LWU	Midland Red	G806JRH	Transit	GCS61V	Western
G213SSL	Stagecoach South	G530LWU	Midland Red	G807LAG	Transit	GCS62V	Western
G214SSL	Stagecoach South	G531LWU	Midland Red	G807RTS	Stagecoach South	GCS65V	Western
G251TSL	Western	G532LWU	Midland Red	G808LAG	Transit	GCS69V	Western
G252TSL	Western	G533LWU	Cheltenham & G	G808RTS	Stagecoach South	GFN546N	Stagecoach South
G253TSL	Western	G534LWU	Cheltenham & G	G809RTS	Stagecoach South	GFR101W	Ribble
G254TSL	Western	G535LWU	Midland Red	G820KWF	East Midland	GGM80W	Stagecoach South
G255TSL	Western	G546LWU	Cheltenham & G	G821KWF	East Midland	GGM81W	Stagecoach South
G256TSL	Bluebird	G547LWU	Cheltenham & G	G822KWF	East Midland	GGM82W	Stagecoach South
G257TSL	Bluebird	G548LWU	Cheltenham & G	G823KWF	East Midland	GGM86W	Stagecoach South
G258TSL	Bluebird	G565PHH	Cumberland	G824KWF	East Midland	GHB146N	Red & White
G259TSL	Bluebird	G566PHH	Cumberland	G825KWF	East Midland	GHB148N	Red & White
G260TSL	Bluebird	G567PHH	Cumberland	G825VGA	Western	GHV102N	Western
G261TSL	Bluebird	G568PRM	Ribble	G826KWF	East Midland	GHV948N	Western
G262TSL	Bluebird	G569PRM	Ribble	G827KWF	East Midland	GMS285S	Western
G263TSL	Cumberland	G570PRM	Ribble	G864BPD	Stagecoach South	GMS292S	Western
G264TSL	Cumberland	G571PRM	Ribble	G912KWF	Devon	GNF6V	Cheltenham & G
G265TSL	Cumberland	G572PRM	Ribble	G919KWF	Devon	GNF8V	Cheltenham & G
G266TSL	Cumberland	G573PRM	Ribble	G920KWF	Devon	GNF9V	Cheltenham & G
G267TSL	Cumberland	G574FSD	Western	G921TCU	Busways	GNF10V	Cheltenham & G
G268TSL	Cumberland	G574PRM	Ribble	G922TCU	Busways	GNF11V	Cheltenham & G
G269TSL	Cumberland	G575PRM	Ribble	G923TCU	Busways	GOL398N	East Midland
G270TSL	Bluebird	G576PRM	Ribble	G924KWF	Devon	GOL426N	Midland Red
G271TSL	Bluebird	G577PRM	Ribble	G924TCU	Busways	GPJ894N	Stagecoach South
G272TSL	Bluebird	G578PRM	Ribble	G925TCU	Busways	GRM625V	Cumberland
G273TSL	Bluebird	G611CEF	Transit	G926TCU	Busways	GRS343E	Bluebird
G274TSL	Bluebird	G612CEF	Transit	G974ARV	Stagecoach South	GSO1V	Bluebird
G275TSL	Bluebird	G613CEF	Transit	G975ARV	Stagecoach South	GSO2V	United Counties
G276TSL	Bluebird	G614CEF	Transit	G976ARV	Stagecoach South	GSO6V	United Counties
G277TSL	Bluebird	G615CEF	Transit	G977ARV	Stagecoach South	GSO7V	United Counties
G278TSL	Bluebird	G616CEF	Transit	G978ARV	Stagecoach South	GSO8V	East Midland
G279TSL	Bluebird	G617CEF	Transit	GAJ125V	United Counties	GSO77V	Western
G280TSL	Fife Scottish	G618CEF	Transit	GAJ126V	United Counties	GSO82V	Western
G281TSL	Fife Scottish	G619CEF	Transit	GAJ127V	United Counties	GSO83V	Western
G282TSL	Bluebird	G620CEF	Transit	GAJ128V	United Counties	GSO84V	Western
G283TSL	Bluebird	G639EVV	United Counties	GAJ129V	Transit	GSO89V	Bluebird
G284TSL	Bluebird	G640EVV	United Counties	GAJ130V	Transit	GSO90V	Bluebird

GSO91V	Bluebird	H136GVM	Manchester	H429BNL	Busways	H808BKK	Stagecoach South
GSO92V	Bluebird	H137GVM	Manchester	H429EFT	Busways	H809BKK	Stagecoach South
GSO93V	Bluebird	H138GVM	Manchester	H430BNL	Busways	H809WKH	Transit
GSO94V	Bluebird	H139GVM	Manchester	H430EFT	Busways	H810BKK	Stagecoach South
GSO95V	Bluebird	H140GVM	Manchester	H431EFT	Busways	H810WKH	Transit
GSU341	Fife Scottish	H141UUA	Selkent	H432EFT	Busways	H811WKH	Transit
GSU342	Fife Scottish	H142UUA	Selkent	H433EFT	Busways	H812WKH	Transit
GSU343	Fife Scottish	H143UUA	Selkent	H434EFT	Busways	H813WKH	Transit
GSU344	Fife Scottish	H144UUA	East London	H435EFT	Busways	H814WKH	Transit
GSU551	Burnley & Pendle	H145UUA	Selkent	H436EFT	Busways	H815CBP	Stagecoach South
GSU552	Burnley & Pendle	H146UUA	Selkent	H437EFT	Busways	H815WKH	Transit
GSU553	Burnley & Pendle	H147UUA	Selkent	H463GVM	Manchester	H816CBP	Stagecoach South
GSU554	Burnley & Pendle	H148UUA	Selkent	H464GVM	Manchester	H816WKH	Transit
GTX738W	Red & White	H149UUA	Selkent	H465GVM	Manchester	H817CBP	Stagecoach South
GTX743W	Red & White	H150UUA	Selkent	H466GVM	Manchester	H818CBP	Stagecoach South
GTX746W	Midland Red	H151UUA	Selkent	H467GVM	Manchester	H819CBP	Stagecoach South
GTX747W	Red & White	H152UUA	Selkent	H473CEG	Cambus	H882LOX	Fife Scottish
GTX748W	Red & White	H153UUA	Selkent	H474CEG	Cambus	H883LOX	Fife Scottish
GTX750W	Red & White	H154UUA	Selkent	H475CEG	Cambus	H885LOX	Fife Scottish
GTX753W	Red & White	H159EJU	Red & White	H482BEE	East Midland	H889NFS	Devon
GTX754W	Midland Red	H160WWT	Selkent	H483BEE	East Midland	H912XGA	Midland Red
GWE617V	East Midland	H161WWT	Selkent	H484BEE	East Midland	HAH237V	Cheltenham & G
GWE618V	East Midland	H162WWT	Selkent	H485BEE	East Midland	HBD914T	United Counties
GWE619V	East Midland	H163WWT	Selkent	H509AGC	Fife Scottish	HBD915T	United Counties
GXI516	Burnley & Pendle	H165WWT	Selkent	H556TUG	Red & White	HBD916T	United Counties
GXI613	Burnley & Pendle	H166WWT	Selkent	H564WWR	Selkent	HBD917T	United Counties
GYE252W	Western	H167WWT	Selkent	H617ACK	Burnley & Pendle	HBD919T	United Counties
GYE254W	Western	H168WWT	Selkent	H618ACK	Burnley & Pendle	HDS566H	Western
GYE260W	East London	H169WWT	Selkent	H619ACK	Burnley & Pendle	HDV639E	Bluebird
GYE261W	East London	H170WWT	Selkent	H620ACK	Burnley & Pendle	HDZ2601	Transit
GYE262W	East London	H171WWT	Selkent	H621ACK	Burnley & Pendle	HDZ2602	Selkent
GYE263W	East London	H172WWT	Selkent	H622ACK	Burnley & Pendle	HDZ2603	Transit
GYE264W	East London	H173WWT	Selkent	H623ACK	Burnley & Pendle	HDZ2604	Transit
GYE266W	East London	H174WWT	Selkent	H642UWR	Cambus	HDZ2605	Transit
GYE267W	Selkent	H175WWT	Selkent	H643UWR	Cambus	HDZ2606	Transit
GYE268W	East London	H176WWT	Selkent	H649UWR	Cambus	HDZ2607	Transit
GYE272W	East London	H191WFR	Cumberland	H650VVV	United Counties	HDZ2608	Selkent
GYE273W	Western	H192WFR	Cumberland	H651VVV	United Counties	HDZ2609	Transit
GYE281W	Western	H193WFR	Ribble	H652UWR	Cambus	HDZ2610	Transit
GYJ919V	Stagecoach South	H194WFR	Cumberland	H652VVV	United Counties	HDZ2611	Transit
GYJ920V	Stagecoach South	H195WFR	Ribble	H653UWR	Cambus	HDZ2612	Transit
GYJ921V	Stagecoach South	H196WFR	Ribble	H653VVV	United Counties	HDZ2613	Transit
GYJ922V	Stagecoach South	H197WFR	Ribble	H654UWR	East London	HDZ2614	Selkent
H36YCW	Ribble	H257THL	East Midland	H654VVV	United Counties	HDZ2615	Transit
H37YCW	Ribble	H301PAX	Red & White	H655UWR	East London	HDZ2616	Transit
H38YCW	Ribble	H344SWA	East Midland	H657UWR	East London	HDZ8683	Transit
H39YCW	Ribble	H345SWA	East Midland	H667BNL	Busways	HEU122N	Midland Red
H78CFV	Burnley & Pendle	H346SWA	East Midland	H668BNL	Busways	HFG193T	Stagecoach South
H79CFV	Burnley & Pendle	H347SWA	East Midland	H669BNL	Busways	HFG923V	Stagecoach South
H101EKR	Stagecoach South	H348SWA	East Midland	H670BNL	Busways	HFM561D	Bluebird
H103EKR	Stagecoach South	H370PNY	Devon	H671BNL	Busways	HGD213T	Western
H104EKR	Stagecoach South	H401DMJ	Transit	H672BNL	Busways	HGM335E	Bluebird
H112SAO	Cumberland	H401MRW	Midland Red	H673BNL	Busways	HHH370V	Ribble
H113ABV	Burnley & Pendle	H402DEG	East Midland	H674BNL	Busways	HHH372V	Cumberland
H113SAO	Cumberland	H402KPY	Stagecoach South	H675BNL	Busways	HHH373V	Cumberland
H114ABV	Burnley & Pendle	H402MRW	Midland Red	H676BNL	Busways	HIL6075	Cheltenham & G
H114SAO	Cumberland	H403MRW	Midland Red	H679BTP	Stagecoach South	HIL8410	Red & White
H115ABV	Burnley & Pendle	H404MRW	Midland Red	H680BTP	Stagecoach South	HKE690L	Stagecoach South
H115SAO	Cumberland	H405MRW	Midland Red	H721CNC	Manchester	HNE252V	Bluebird
H116SAO	Cumberland	H406MRW	Midland Red	H724CNC	Manchester	HNE253V	Cumberland
H117SAO	Cumberland	H407GAV	Cambus	H726CNC	Manchester	HNE254V	Bluebird
H118SAO	Cumberland	H421BNL	Busways	H727FNC	Manchester	HPK503N	Stagecoach South
H119SAO	Cumberland	H422BNL	Busways	H728FNC	Manchester	HPK505N	Stagecoach South
H126ACU	Busways	H423BNL	Busways	H801BKK	Stagecoach South	HPW522L	Busways
H127ACU	Busways	H424BNL	Busways	H802BKK	Stagecoach South	HPY423V	Transit
H131GVM	Manchester	H425BNL	Busways	H803BKK	Stagecoach South	HSB698Y	Western
H132GVM	Manchester	H426BNL	Busways	H804BKK	Stagecoach South	HSB841Y	Western
H133GVM	Manchester	H427BNL	Busways	H805BKK	Stagecoach South	HSB883Y	Western
H134GVM	Manchester	H428BNL	Busways	H806BKK	Stagecoach South	HSB884Y	Western
H135GVM	Manchester	H428EFT	Busways	H807BKK	Stagecoach South	HSB887Y	Western

Reg	Operator	Reg	Operator	Reg	Operator	Reg	Operator
HSB889Y	Western	J125XHH	Cumberland	J305THP	Midland Red	J511GCD	Stagecoach South
HSK760	Bluebird	J126XHH	Cumberland	J305UKG	Red & White	J512FPS	Bluebird
HSV194	East Midland	J127XHH	Cumberland	J306BRM	Western	J512GCD	Stagecoach South
HSV195	East Midland	J132HMT	East London	J306UKG	Red & White	J513GCD	Stagecoach South
HSV196	East Midland	J133HMT	East London	J307BRM	Western	J514GCD	Stagecoach South
HTG354N	Red & White	J134HMT	East London	J307UKG	Red & White	J515GCD	Stagecoach South
HTY139W	Midland Red	J135HMT	East London	J308BRM	Western	J516GCD	Stagecoach South
HUD475S	Midland Red	J136HMT	East London	J309BRM	Western	J517GCD	Stagecoach South
HUD479S	Midland Red	J137HMT	East London	J310BRM	Western	J518GCD	Stagecoach South
HUD480S	Midland Red	J138HMT	East London	J349XET	East Midland	J519GCD	Stagecoach South
HUF451X	Stagecoach South	J139HMT	East London	J350XET	East Midland	J520GCD	Stagecoach South
HUF579X	Stagecoach South	J140HMT	East London	J351XET	East Midland	J521GCD	Stagecoach South
HUF592X	Stagecoach South	J141HMT	East London	J352XET	East Midland	J522GCD	Stagecoach South
HUF593X	Stagecoach South	J142HMT	East London	J353XET	East Midland	J523GCD	Stagecoach South
HUF603X	Stagecoach South	J143HMT	East London	J371BNW	Busways	J524GCD	Stagecoach South
HUF604X	Stagecoach South	J144HMT	East London	J372BNW	Busways	J525GCD	Stagecoach South
HUF625X	Stagecoach South	J145HMT	East London	J373BNW	Busways	J526GCD	Stagecoach South
HUF626X	Stagecoach South	J176MCW	Burnley & Pendle	J374BNW	Busways	J527GCD	Stagecoach South
HUF639X	Stagecoach South	J177MCW	Burnley & Pendle	J375BNW	Busways	J528GCD	Stagecoach South
HWG207W	Bluebird	J196YSS	Bluebird	J376BNW	Busways	J529GCD	Stagecoach South
HWG208W	Fife Scottish	J197YSS	Bluebird	J377BNW	Busways	J530GCD	Stagecoach South
HWJ620W	East Midland	J198HFR	Ribble	J378BNW	Busways	J531GCD	Stagecoach South
HWJ621W	East Midland	J198YSS	Bluebird	J379BNW	Busways	J532GCD	Stagecoach South
HXI311	Burnley & Pendle	J199HFR	Cumberland	J380BNW	Busways	J533GCD	Stagecoach South
IIL1319	Transit	J199YSS	Bluebird	J401LKO	Stagecoach South	J534GCD	Stagecoach South
IIL1321	Transit	J201HFR	Cumberland	J402LKO	Stagecoach South	J535GCD	Stagecoach South
IIL3503	Stagecoach South	J201JRP	MK Metro	J403LKO	Stagecoach South	J536GCD	Stagecoach South
IIL3504	Fife Scottish	J202HFR	Cumberland	J407PRW	Midland Red	J537GCD	Stagecoach South
IIL3505	Stagecoach South	J202JRP	MK Metro	J408PRW	Midland Red	J538GCD	Stagecoach South
IIL3506	Fife Scottish	J203HFR	Cumberland	J408TEW	Cambus	J539GCD	Stagecoach South
IIL3507	Western	J203JRP	MK Metro	J409PRW	Midland Red	J540GCD	Stagecoach South
J8WSB	Western	J204HFR	Cumberland	J409TEW	Cambus	J541GCD	Stagecoach South
J13WSB	Western	J204JKH	Transit	J410PRW	Midland Red	J542GCD	Stagecoach South
J14WSB	Western	J204JRP	MK Metro	J411PRW	Midland Red	J543GCD	Stagecoach South
J15WSB	Western	J205HFR	Cumberland	J411WSC	Ribble	J544GCD	Stagecoach South
J24MCW	Burnley & Pendle	J205JKH	Transit	J412PRW	Midland Red	J545GCD	Stagecoach South
J25MCW	Burnley & Pendle	J206HFR	Cumberland	J413PRW	Midland Red	J546GCD	Stagecoach South
J91DJV	East Midland	J207HFR	Cumberland	J414PRW	Midland Red	J547GCD	Stagecoach South
J92DJV	East Midland	J208HFR	Cumberland	J415PRW	Midland Red	J548GCD	Stagecoach South
J93DJV	East Midland	J209HFR	Cumberland	J416PRW	Midland Red	J549GCD	Stagecoach South
J94DJV	East Midland	J210HFR	Cumberland	J417PRW	Midland Red	J550GCD	Stagecoach South
J101WSC	Ribble	J213AET	East Midland	J418PRW	Midland Red	J551GCD	Stagecoach South
J102WSC	Ribble	J214AET	East Midland	J430HDS	United Counties	J552GCD	Stagecoach South
J103WSC	Ribble	J215AET	East Midland	J439HDS	United Counties	J553NGS	Transit
J104WSC	Ribble	J216AET	East Midland	J445HDS	United Counties	J620GCR	United Counties
J105WSC	Ribble	J217AET	East Midland	J446HDS	United Counties	J621GCR	United Counties
J106WSC	Ribble	J218AET	East Midland	J450HDS	United Counties	J622GCR	United Counties
J107WSC	Ribble	J219AET	East Midland	J455FSR	Bluebird	J623GCR	Stagecoach South
J108WSC	Ribble	J225JJR	Transit	J456FSR	Bluebird	J624GCR	Stagecoach South
J109WSC	Ribble	J226JJR	Transit	J501FPS	Bluebird	J701KCU	Busways
J110WSC	Ribble	J227JJR	Transit	J501GCD	Stagecoach South	J701YRM	Stagecoach South
J112LKO	Stagecoach South	J228JJR	Transit	J502FPS	Bluebird	J702CWT	Cambus
J112WSC	Ribble	J229JJR	Transit	J502GCD	Stagecoach South	J702KCU	Busways
J113WSC	Ribble	J230JJR	Transit	J503FPS	Bluebird	J702YRM	Stagecoach South
J114WSC	Ribble	J230XKY	East London	J503GCD	Stagecoach South	J703YRM	Stagecoach South
J115WSC	Ribble	J231JJR	Transit	J504FPS	Bluebird	J706CWT	Cambus
J116WSC	Ribble	J231XKY	East London	J504GCD	Stagecoach South	J711CYG	East London
J120AAO	Cumberland	J232JJR	Transit	J505FPS	Bluebird	J712CYG	East London
J120AHH	Cumberland	J233JJR	Transit	J505GCD	Stagecoach South	J714CYG	East London
J120XHH	Bluebird	J263KRN	Ribble	J506FPS	Bluebird	J716CYG	East London
J121AAO	Cumberland	J264KRN	Ribble	J506GCD	Stagecoach South	J717CYG	East London
J121AHH	Cumberland	J301BRM	Western	J507FPS	Bluebird	J718CYG	East London
J121XHH	Bluebird	J302BRM	Western	J507GCD	Stagecoach South	J719CYG	East London
J122AAO	Cumberland	J302TUH	Red & White	J508FPS	Bluebird	J720CYG	East London
J122AHH	Ribble	J303BRM	Western	J508GCD	Stagecoach South	J720GAP	Stagecoach South
J122XHH	Bluebird	J303TUH	Red & White	J509FPS	Bluebird	J721CYG	East London
J123AHH	Ribble	J304BRM	Western	J509GCD	Stagecoach South	J721GAP	Stagecoach South
J123XHH	Cumberland	J304THP	Midland Red	J510FPS	Bluebird	J722CYG	East London
J124AHH	Ribble	J304UKG	Red & White	J510GCD	Stagecoach South	J722GAP	Stagecoach South
J124XHH	Cumberland	J305BRM	Western	J511FPS	Bluebird	J723CYG	East London

Reg	Operator	Reg	Operator	Reg	Operator	Reg	Operator
J724CYG	East London	JDZ2371	Selkent	JWV253W	Stagecoach South	K134DAO	Cumberland
J725CYG	East London	JFR2W	Ribble	JWV255W	Stagecoach South	K134SRH	East London
J726CYG	East London	JFR3W	Ribble	JWV256W	Stagecoach South	K135DAO	Cumberland
J727CYG	East London	JFR4W	Ribble	JWV258W	Stagecoach South	K135SRH	East London
J728CYG	East London	JFR5W	Ribble	JWV266W	Stagecoach South	K150DNV	United Counties
J729CYG	East London	JFR6W	Ribble	JWV267W	Stagecoach South	K151DNV	United Counties
J739CWT	Cambus	JFR7W	Ribble	JWV268W	Stagecoach South	K152DNV	United Counties
J740CWT	Cambus	JFR8W	Ribble	JWV269W	Stagecoach South	K153DNV	United Counties
J741CWT	Cambus	JFR9W	Ribble	JWV274W	Stagecoach South	K154DNV	United Counties
J742CWT	Cambus	JFR10W	Ribble	JWV275W	Stagecoach South	K162FYG	Busways
J743CWT	Cambus	JFR11W	Ribble	JWV976W	Stagecoach South	K163FYG	Busways
J744CWT	Cambus	JFR12W	Ribble	K26WBV	Burnley & Pendle	K164FYG	Busways
J752CWT	United Counties	JFR13W	Ribble	K27WBV	Burnley & Pendle	K165FYG	Busways
J753CWT	United Counties	JFV294N	Ribble	K75XCW	Burnley & Pendle	K166FYG	Busways
J801WFS	Fife Scottish	JFV295N	Ribble	K101JWJ	East Midland	K171CAV	Cambus
J802WFS	Fife Scottish	JHU899X	Cheltenham & G	K101XHG	Bluebird	K172CAV	Cambus
J803WFS	Fife Scottish	JHU912X	Cheltenham & G	K102JWJ	East Midland	K173CAV	Cambus
J804WFS	Fife Scottish	JIL5279	Manchester	K102XHG	Bluebird	K174CAV	Cambus
J805DWW	Cambus	JIL7606	Manchester	K103JWJ	East Midland	K175CAV	Cambus
J805WFS	Fife Scottish	JIL7607	Manchester	K103XHG	Bluebird	K176CAV	Cambus
J806DWW	Cambus	JIL7608	Manchester	K104JWJ	East Midland	K177CAV	Cambus
J806WFS	Fife Scottish	JIL7609	Manchester	K104XHG	Bluebird	K208OHS	Western
J807DWW	Cambus	JIL7610	Manchester	K105JWJ	East Midland	K209OHS	Western
J807WFS	Fife Scottish	JIL8374	Manchester	K105XHG	Bluebird	K211SRH	East London
J808WFS	United Counties	JJD392D	East London	K106JWJ	East Midland	K235NHC	Stagecoach South
J811NKK	Stagecoach South	JJD399D	East London	K106XHG	Bluebird	K236NHC	Stagecoach South
J812NKK	Stagecoach South	JJD402D	East London	K107JWJ	East Midland	K237NHC	Stagecoach South
J813NKK	Stagecoach South	JJD415D	East London	K107XHG	Bluebird	K238NHC	Stagecoach South
J814NKK	Stagecoach South	JJD429D	East London	K108XHG	Bluebird	K239NHC	Stagecoach South
J822HMC	East London	JJD435D	East London	K109SRH	East London	K240NHC	Stagecoach South
J823HMC	East London	JJD437D	East London	K109XHG	Bluebird	K302FYG	East London
J824HMC	East London	JJD444D	East London	K110SRH	East London	K306ARW	Midland Red
J825HMC	East London	JJD445D	East London	K110XHG	Bluebird	K308YKG	Cheltenham & G
J826HMC	East London	JJD450D	East London	K112SRH	East London	K309YKG	Red & White
J827HMC	East London	JJD451D	East London	K112XHG	Ribble	K310YKG	Red & White
J828HMC	East London	JJD456D	East London	K113SRH	East London	K311YKG	Red & White
J829HMC	East London	JJD462D	East London	K113XHG	Cumberland	K312YKG	Red & White
J856NKK	Stagecoach South	JJD470D	East London	K114SRH	East London	K313YKG	Red & White
J901UKV	Transit	JJD481D	East London	K114XHG	Cumberland	K314YKG	Red & White
J909NKP	Stagecoach South	JJD488D	East London	K115SRH	East London	K315YKG	Red & White
J960DWX	Cambus	JJD493D	East London	K115XHG	Ribble	K316YKG	Red & White
J961DWX	Cambus	JJD495D	East London	K116SRH	East London	K317YKG	Red & White
J962DWX	Cambus	JJD496D	East London	K116XHG	Ribble	K318YKG	Red & White
JAH552D	Cambus	JJD497D	East London	K117SRH	East London	K319YKG	Red & White
JAJ137W	Transit	JJD541D	East London	K117XHG	Cumberland	K320YKG	Red & White
JAJ138W	Transit	JJD550D	East London	K118SRH	East London	K321YKG	Red & White
JAJ139W	Transit	JJD565D	East London	K118XHG	Ribble	K322YKG	Red & White
JAJ140W	Transit	JJD581D	East London	K119SRH	East London	K323YKG	Red & White
JAJ141W	Transit	JJD592D	East London	K120SRH	East London	K324YKG	Red & White
JAJ142W	Transit	JJG890P	Stagecoach South	K120XHG	Ribble	K325YKG	Red & White
JAJ143W	Transit	JJG898P	Stagecoach South	K121SRH	East London	K330RCN	Busways
JAJ144W	Transit	JKW286W	Ribble	K121XHG	Cumberland	K331RCN	Busways
JAJ145W	Transit	JMW166P	Busways	K122SRH	East London	K332RCN	Busways
JAJ146W	Transit	JMW167P	Busways	K123SRH	East London	K334RCN	Busways
JAK209W	Bluebird	JMW168P	Busways	K124SRH	East London	K335RCN	Busways
JAK210W	Bluebird	JMW169P	Busways	K125SRH	East London	K336RCN	Busways
JAK211W	East Midland	JMW170P	Busways	K126SRH	East London	K337RCN	Busways
JAK212W	Bluebird	JND260V	Bluebird	K127SRH	East London	K341PJR	Transit
JAO477V	East Midland	JNJ194V	Stagecoach South	K128DAO	Cumberland	K342PJR	Transit
JCK846W	Ribble	JOU160P	Cheltenham & G	K128SRH	East London	K343PJR	Transit
JCK847W	Ribble	JOX502P	Midland Red	K129DAO	Cumberland	K344PJR	Transit
JCK848W	Ribble	JOX503P	Midland Red	K129SRH	East London	K345PJR	Transit
JCK849W	Stagecoach South	JOX504P	Midland Red	K130DAO	Cumberland	K350ANV	United Counties
JDZ2359	Selkent	JPU817	Cumberland	K130SRH	East London	K351ANV	United Counties
JDZ2360	Selkent	JSA101V	Bluebird	K131DAO	Cumberland	K352ANV	United Counties
JDZ2361	Selkent	JSA102V	Bluebird	K131SRH	East London	K353ANV	United Counties
JDZ2362	Selkent	JSA103V	Bluebird	K132DAO	Cumberland	K354ANV	United Counties
JDZ2363	Selkent	JSA104V	Bluebird	K132SRH	East London	K354DWJ	East Midland
JDZ2364	Selkent	JTF971W	Western	K133DAO	Cumberland	K355ANV	United Counties
JDZ2365	Selkent	JWV252W	Stagecoach South	K133SRH	East London	K355DWJ	East Midland

Reg	Operator	Reg	Operator	Reg	Operator	Reg	Operator
K356ANV	United Counties	K567GSA	Bluebird	K629YVN	Transit	K716ASC	Stagecoach South
K356DWJ	East Midland	K567NHC	Stagecoach South	K630HWX	East London	K716DAO	Cumberland
K357ANV	United Counties	K568GSA	Bluebird	K630YVN	Transit	K717ASC	Stagecoach South
K357DWJ	East Midland	K568NHC	Stagecoach South	K631HWX	East London	K717DAO	Cumberland
K358ANV	United Counties	K569GSA	Bluebird	K632HWX	East London	K717PCN	Busways
K358DWJ	East Midland	K569NHC	Stagecoach South	K633HWX	East London	K717UTT	Devon
K359ANV	United Counties	K570GSA	Bluebird	K634HWX	East London	K718ASC	Fife Scottish
K359DWJ	East Midland	K570NHC	Stagecoach South	K635HWX	East London	K718DAO	Cumberland
K360DWJ	East Midland	K571DFS	Transit	K655NHC	Stagecoach South	K718PCN	Busways
K361DWJ	East Midland	K571LTS	Bluebird	K655UNH	United Counties	K719ASC	Fife Scottish
K362DWJ	East Midland	K571NHC	Stagecoach South	K656UNH	United Counties	K719DAO	Cumberland
K363DWJ	East Midland	K572DFS	Transit	K657UNH	United Counties	K719UTT	Devon
K391KUA	Cambus	K572LTS	Bluebird	K658UNH	United Counties	K720ASC	Fife Scottish
K392KUA	Cambus	K572NHC	Stagecoach South	K659UNH	United Counties	K720DAO	Cumberland
K393KUA	Cambus	K573DFS	Transit	K660NHC	Stagecoach South	K720PCN	Busways
K419FAV	MK Metro	K573LTS	Bluebird	K660UNH	United Counties	K720UTT	Devon
K420ARW	Midland Red	K573NHC	Stagecoach South	K661UNH	United Counties	K721ASC	Fife Scottish
K421ARW	Midland Red	K574DFS	Western	K662UNH	United Counties	K721DAO	Cumberland
K422ARW	Midland Red	K574LTS	Bluebird	K663UNH	United Counties	K721PCN	Busways
K423ARW	Midland Red	K574NHC	Stagecoach South	K664UNH	United Counties	K721UTT	Devon
K424ARW	Midland Red	K575DFS	East Midland	K665UNH	United Counties	K722ASC	Fife Scottish
K425ARW	Midland Red	K575LTS	Bluebird	K667UNH	United Counties	K722DAO	Cumberland
K426FAV	MK Metro	K575NHC	Stagecoach South	K668UNH	United Counties	K722PCN	Busways
K428FAV	MK Metro	K576DFS	Transit	K669UNH	United Counties	K722UTT	Devon
K449YCW	Cumberland	K576LTS	Bluebird	K670UNH	United Counties	K723ASC	Fife Scottish
K450YCW	Cumberland	K576NHC	Stagecoach South	K699ERM	Cumberland	K723DAO	Cumberland
K485FFS	Fife Scottish	K577DFS	Transit	K700DAO	Cumberland	K723PNL	Busways
K486FFS	Fife Scottish	K577LTS	Bluebird	K701DAO	Cumberland	K724ASC	Fife Scottish
K487FFS	Fife Scottish	K577NHC	Stagecoach South	K701NDO	East London	K724DAO	Cumberland
K488FFS	Fife Scottish	K578LTS	Bluebird	K702DAO	Cumberland	K724PNL	Busways
K489FFS	Fife Scottish	K578NHC	Stagecoach South	K702NDO	East Midland	K724UTT	Devon
K490FFS	Fife Scottish	K579NHC	Stagecoach South	K702UTT	Devon	K725ASC	Fife Scottish
K491FFS	Fife Scottish	K580NHC	Stagecoach South	K703DAO	Cumberland	K725DAO	Cumberland
K492FFS	Fife Scottish	K584ODY	Stagecoach South	K703NDO	East Midland	K725PNL	Busways
K493FFS	Fife Scottish	K585ODY	Stagecoach South	K703PCN	Busways	K725UTT	Devon
K494FFS	Fife Scottish	K586ODY	Stagecoach South	K704ERM	Cumberland	K726DAO	Cumberland
K508ESS	Bluebird	K587ODY	Stagecoach South	K704NDO	East Midland	K726PNL	Busways
K509ESS	Bluebird	K588ODY	Stagecoach South	K704PCN	Busways	K726UTT	Devon
K510ESS	Bluebird	K601ESH	Fife Scottish	K705DAO	Cumberland	K727DAO	Cumberland
K511ESS	Bluebird	K602ESH	Fife Scottish	K705PCN	Busways	K727PNL	Busways
K515ESS	Bluebird	K603ESH	Fife Scottish	K706DAO	Cumberland	K727UTT	Devon
K518ESS	Bluebird	K604ESH	Fife Scottish	K706PCN	Busways	K728DAO	Cumberland
K521EFL	Midland Red	K605ESH	Fife Scottish	K707DAO	Cumberland	K728PNL	Busways
K522EFL	Midland Red	K610UFR	Ribble	K707PCN	Busways	K729DAO	Cumberland
K523EFL	Midland Red	K611UFR	Ribble	K708DAO	Cumberland	K730DAO	Cumberland
K524EFL	Midland Red	K612UFR	Ribble	K708PCN	Busways	K730UTT	Devon
K525EFL	Midland Red	K613UFR	Ribble	K709ASC	United Counties	K731DAO	Cumberland
K526EFL	Midland Red	K614UFR	Ribble	K709DAO	Cumberland	K731UTT	Devon
K527EFL	Midland Red	K615UFR	Cumberland	K709PCN	Busways	K732DAO	Cumberland
K528EFL	Midland Red	K616UFR	Ribble	K710ASC	United Counties	K732UTT	Devon
K529EFL	Midland Red	K617UFR	Ribble	K710DAO	Cumberland	K733DAO	Cumberland
K530EFL	Midland Red	K618UFR	Ribble	K710PCN	Busways	K734DAO	Cumberland
K553NHC	Stagecoach South	K619UFR	Ribble	K711ASC	United Counties	K735DAO	Cumberland
K554NHC	Stagecoach South	K620UFR	Ribble	K711DAO	Cumberland	K736DAO	Cumberland
K556NHC	Stagecoach South	K620XOD	Devon	K711PCN	Busways	K737DAO	Cumberland
K557NHC	Stagecoach South	K621UFR	Ribble	K711UTT	Devon	K738DAO	Cumberland
K558NHC	Stagecoach South	K622UFR	Cumberland	K712ASC	United Counties	K739DAO	Cumberland
K559NHC	Stagecoach South	K622YVN	Transit	K712DAO	Cumberland	K740DAO	Ribble
K561GSA	Bluebird	K623UFR	Cumberland	K712PCN	Busways	K740DAO	Ribble
K561NHC	Stagecoach South	K623YVN	Transit	K713ASC	United Counties	K741DAO	Cumberland
K562GSA	Bluebird	K624UFR	Ribble	K713DAO	Cumberland	K742DAO	Cumberland
K562NHC	Stagecoach South	K624YVN	Transit	K713PCN	Busways	K743DAO	Cumberland
K563GSA	Bluebird	K625UFR	Cumberland	K713UTT	Devon	K744DAO	Cumberland
K563NHC	Stagecoach South	K625YVN	Transit	K714ASC	Stagecoach South	K745DAO	Cumberland
K564GSA	Bluebird	K626UFR	Cumberland	K714DAO	Cumberland	K746DAO	Cumberland
K564NHC	Stagecoach South	K626YVN	Transit	K714PCN	Busways	K748DAO	Cumberland
K565GSA	Bluebird	K627UFR	Ribble	K714UTT	Devon	K749DAO	Cumberland
K565NHC	Stagecoach South	K627YVN	Transit	K715ASC	Stagecoach South	K750DAO	Cumberland
K566GSA	Bluebird	K628UFR	Ribble	K715DAO	Cumberland	K751DAO	Cumberland
K566NHC	Stagecoach South	K628YVN	Transit	K715PCN	Busways	K752DAO	Cumberland

Reg	Operator	Reg	Operator	Reg	Operator	Reg	Operator
K753DAO	Cumberland	K855ODY	Stagecoach South	K975KUB	Cambus	KYN286X	East London
K754DAO	Cumberland	K856LMK	East London	KAJ214W	Transit	KYN288X	Stagecoach South
K755DAO	Cumberland	K856ODY	Stagecoach South	KAJ215W	Transit	KYN298X	East London
K756DAO	Cumberland	K857LMK	East London	KAJ216W	Transit	KYN305X	Stagecoach South
K757DAO	Cumberland	K857ODY	Stagecoach South	KAJ217W	Transit	KYN306X	East London
K758DAO	Cumberland	K858LMK	East London	KAJ218W	Transit	KYN487X	Stagecoach South
K758FYG	United Counties	K858ODY	Stagecoach South	KAJ219W	Transit	KYV311X	East London
K759DAO	Cumberland	K859LMK	East London	KBB118D	Busways	KYV318X	East London
K759FYG	United Counties	K859ODY	Stagecoach South	KDW342P	Manchester	KYV320X	East London
K760DAO	Cumberland	K860LMK	East London	KGS493Y	Cheltenham & G	KYV326X	East London
K760FYG	United Counties	K860ODY	Stagecoach South	KHG194T	Ribble	KYV331X	East London
K761DAO	Cumberland	K861LMK	East London	KHH375W	Ribble	KYV334X	East London
K761FYG	United Counties	K861ODY	Stagecoach South	KHH376W	Cheltenham & G	KYV340X	East London
K762DAO	Cumberland	K862LMK	East London	KHH377W	Ribble	KYV345X	Stagecoach South
K763DAO	Cumberland	K862ODY	Stagecoach South	KHH378W	Cumberland	KYV348X	Stagecoach South
K764DAO	Cumberland	K863LMK	East London	KHT122P	Midland Red	KYV360X	East London
K765DAO	Cumberland	K863ODY	Stagecoach South	KHT124P	Midland Red	KYV361X	Stagecoach South
K766DAO	Cumberland	K864LMK	East London	KIB8140	Cheltenham & G	KYV366X	East London
K767DAO	Cumberland	K864ODY	Stagecoach South	KKK888V	Stagecoach South	KYV368X	Selkent
K768DAO	Cumberland	K865LMK	East London	KKY220W	Fife Scottish	KYV378X	East London
K769DAO	Cumberland	K865ODY	Stagecoach South	KKY222W	Bluebird	KYV379X	East London
K770DAO	Cumberland	K866LMK	East London	KMA399T	Western	KYV380X	East London
K771DAO	Cumberland	K866ODY	Stagecoach South	KPA366P	Stagecoach South	KYV386X	East London
K772DAO	Cumberland	K867LMK	East London	KPA369P	Stagecoach South	KYV387X	East London
K773DAO	Cumberland	K867ODY	Stagecoach South	KPA374P	Stagecoach South	KYV394X	East London
K774DAO	Cumberland	K868LMK	East London	KPA379P	Stagecoach South	KYV395X	East London
K775DAO	Cumberland	K868ODY	Stagecoach South	KPA387P	Stagecoach South	KYV397X	Stagecoach South
K776DAO	Cumberland	K869LMK	East London	KPA388P	Stagecoach South	KYV406X	East London
K777DAO	Cumberland	K869ODY	Stagecoach South	KPA389P	Stagecoach South	KYV410X	Western
K778DAO	Cumberland	K870LMK	East London	KRM430W	Bluebird	KYV420X	Stagecoach South
K779DAO	Cumberland	K870ODY	Stagecoach South	KRM431W	Cumberland	KYV428X	East London
K780DAO	Cumberland	K871GHH	Cumberland	KRM432W	Cumberland	KYV434X	East London
K781DAO	Cumberland	K871LMK	East London	KRM433W	Cumberland	KYV437X	East London
K783DAO	Cumberland	K871ODY	Stagecoach South	KRM434W	Cumberland	KYV439X	East London
K784DAO	Cumberland	K872GHH	Cumberland	KRM435W	Cumberland	KYV441X	East London
K785DAO	Cumberland	K872ODY	Stagecoach South	KRM436W	Cumberland	KYV442X	Stagecoach South
K786DAO	Cumberland	K873GHH	Cumberland	KRM437W	Cumberland	KYV444X	East London
K787DAO	Cumberland	K873ODY	Stagecoach South	KRN103T	Cumberland	KYV445X	East London
K788DAO	Cumberland	K874GHH	Cumberland	KRN105T	Cumberland	KYV446X	East London
K789DAO	Stagecoach South	K874ODY	Stagecoach South	KRN113T	Cumberland	KYV447X	Selkent
K790DAO	Stagecoach South	K875GHH	Cumberland	KRN119T	Cumberland	KYV448X	East London
K791DAO	Stagecoach South	K875ODY	Stagecoach South	KRS531V	Bluebird	KYV451X	Stagecoach South
K801OMW	Cheltenham & G	K876GHH	Cumberland	KRS532V	Bluebird	KYV453X	East London
K802OMW	Cheltenham & G	K876ODY	Stagecoach South	KRS540V	Western	KYV454X	East London
K803WFJ	Devon	K877GHH	Cumberland	KRS542V	Western	KYV455X	Fife Scottish
K804WFJ	Devon	K877ODY	Stagecoach South	KRU838W	Stagecoach South	KYV456X	East London
K805WFJ	Devon	K878GHH	Cumberland	KRU843W	United Counties	KYV458X	East London
K806WFJ	Devon	K878ODY	Stagecoach South	KRU844W	Stagecoach South	KYV460X	East London
K816WFJ	Devon	K879ODY	Stagecoach South	KRU845W	United Counties	KYV461X	East London
K821TKP	Stagecoach South	K880ODY	Stagecoach South	KRU846W	United Counties	KYV462X	East London
K821WFJ	Devon	K910TKP	Stagecoach South	KRU847W	United Counties	KYV465X	East London
K822TKP	Stagecoach South	K911RGE	Cambus	KRU852W	United Counties	KYV466X	East London
K822WFJ	Devon	K912RGE	Cambus	KSD62W	Western	KYV467X	East London
K823TKP	Stagecoach South	K913VDV	Devon	KSU462	Busways	KYV469X	East London
K823WFJ	Devon	K924VDV	Devon	KSU463	Busways	KYV470X	East London
K824TKP	Stagecoach South	K925VDV	Devon	KSU464	Busways	KYV471X	East London
K824WFJ	Devon	K926VDV	Devon	KVF248V	Red & White	KYV473X	East London
K825TKP	Stagecoach South	K927VDV	Devon	KVF249V	Cheltenham & G	KYV474X	Stagecoach South
K846LMK	East London	K963HUB	Cambus	KWA213W	Bluebird	KYV476X	East London
K847LMK	East London	K964HUB	Cambus	KWA214W	East Midland	KYV480X	East London
K848LMK	East London	K965HUB	Cambus	KWA215W	Bluebird	KYV486X	East London
K849LMK	East London	K966HUB	Cambus	KWA216W	Bluebird	KYV488X	East London
K850LMK	East London	K967HUB	Cambus	KWA217W	Fife Scottish	KYV490X	East London
K851LMK	East London	K968HUB	Cambus	KWA218W	East Midland	KYV492X	East London
K852LMK	East London	K969HUB	Cambus	KWA219W	Bluebird	KYV495X	East London
K853LMK	East London	K970HUB	Cambus	KWA221W	East Midland	KYV496X	East London
K853ODY	Stagecoach South	K971HUB	Cambus	KWA223W	East Midland	KYV497X	East London
K854LMK	East London	K972HUB	Cambus	KWA224W	East Midland	KYV498X	East London
K854ODY	Stagecoach South	K973HUB	Cambus	KYN282X	East London	KYV500X	East London
K855LMK	East London	K974HUB	Cambus	KYN285X	East London	KYV501X	East London

Reg	Fleet	Reg	Fleet	Reg	Fleet	Reg	Fleet
KYV502X	East London	L126DRN	Cumberland	L210YAG	Selkent	L312YDU	Midland Red
KYV503X	East London	L126NAO	Cumberland	L211FDV	Devon	L313YDU	Midland Red
KYV504X	East London	L127DRN	Cumberland	L211YAG	Selkent	L314YDU	Midland Red
KYV505X	East London	L127NAO	Cumberland	L212FDV	Devon	L315JSA	Bluebird
KYV506X	East London	L128DRN	Ribble	L214FDV	Devon	L315YDU	Midland Red
KYV508X	East London	L136VRH	East London	L237CCW	Ribble	L316JSA	Bluebird
KYV511X	Stagecoach South	L137VRH	East London	L238CCW	Transit	L316YDU	Midland Red
KYV512X	East London	L138BFV	Ribble	L239CCW	Ribble	L317YDU	Midland Red
KYV513X	East London	L138VRH	East London	L240CCW	Ribble	L318YDU	Midland Red
KYV514X	East London	L139BFV	Ribble	L241CCK	Ribble	L319YDU	Midland Red
KYV515X	East London	L139VRH	East London	L241SDY	Stagecoach South	L320YDU	Midland Red
KYV517X	East London	L140BFV	Ribble	L242CCK	Transit	L321YDU	Midland Red
KYV521X	East London	L140VRH	East London	L242SDY	Stagecoach South	L322YDU	Midland Red
KYV522X	East London	L141BFV	Ribble	L243CCK	Transit	L323YDU	Midland Red
KYV523X	Stagecoach South	L141VRH	East London	L243SDY	Stagecoach South	L324YDU	Midland Red
KYV525X	East London	L142BFV	Ribble	L244CCK	Transit	L325YDU	Midland Red
KYV526X	East London	L142VRH	East London	L244SDY	Stagecoach South	L326CHB	Red & White
KYV527X	East London	L143BFV	Ribble	L245CCK	Transit	L326YKV	Midland Red
KYV529X	East London	L143VRH	East London	L245SDY	Stagecoach South	L327CHB	Red & White
KYV531X	East London	L144BFV	Ribble	L246CCK	Transit	L327YKV	Midland Red
KYV532X	East London	L144VRH	East London	L246SDY	Stagecoach South	L328CHB	Red & White
KYV533X	East London	L145BFV	Ribble	L247CCK	Transit	L328YKV	Midland Red
KYV535X	East London	L145VRH	East London	L247SDY	Stagecoach South	L329CHB	Red & White
KYV536X	East London	L146BFV	Ribble	L248CCK	Cheltenham & G	L329YKV	Midland Red
KYV537X	East London	L146VRH	East London	L248SDY	Stagecoach South	L330CHB	Cheltenham & G
KYV539X	East London	L148BFV	Ribble	L249CCK	Transit	L330YKV	Midland Red
KYV540X	East London	L149BFV	Ribble	L249SDY	Stagecoach South	L331CHB	Red & White
KYV541X	East London	L150BFV	Ribble	L250CCK	Transit	L334FWO	Red & White
KYV542X	East London	L151BFV	Ribble	L250SDY	Stagecoach South	L335FWO	Red & White
KYV543X	East London	L152BFV	Cumberland	L251CCK	Ribble	L336FWO	Red & White
KYV544X	East London	L153BFV	Ribble	L252CCK	Ribble	L337FWO	Red & White
KYV545X	East London	L154BFV	Cumberland	L253CCK	Ribble	L338FWO	Red & White
KYV546X	East London	L155BFV	Ribble	L254CCK	Transit	L339FWO	Red & White
KYV548X	East London	L155JNH	United Counties	L255CCK	Ribble	L339KCK	East Midland
KYV549X	East London	L156BFV	Ribble	L256CCK	Ribble	L340FWO	Red & White
L26JSA	Bluebird	L156JNH	United Counties	L262VSU	Western	L340KCK	East Midland
L27JSA	Bluebird	L157BFV	Ribble	L267CCK	Fife Scottish	L341FWO	Red & White
L28JSA	Bluebird	L157JNH	United Counties	L268CCK	Fife Scottish	L341KCK	East Midland
L31HHN	Transit	L158BFV	Ribble	L269CCK	Fife Scottish	L342FWO	Red & White
L32HHN	Transit	L158JNH	United Counties	L270LHH	Cumberland	L342KCK	East Midland
L33HHN	Transit	L159CCW	Ribble	L271LHH	Ribble	L343FWO	Red & White
L34HHN	Transit	L159JNH	United Counties	L272LHH	Ribble	L343KCK	East Midland
L35HHN	Transit	L160BFV	Cumberland	L273LHH	Ribble	L344KCK	East Midland
L36HHN	Transit	L160JNH	United Counties	L274LHH	Ribble	L360JBD	United Counties
L37HHN	Transit	L161CCW	Ribble	L275JAO	Cumberland	L361JBD	United Counties
L81YBB	Busways	L161JNH	United Counties	L276JAO	Cumberland	L362JBD	United Counties
L82YBB	Busways	L162JNH	United Counties	L277JAO	Ribble	L363JBD	United Counties
L83YBB	Busways	L178KHG	Burnley & Pendle	L278JAO	Ribble	L364JBD	United Counties
L84YBB	Busways	L179KHG	Burnley & Pendle	L279JAO	Ribble	L365JBD	United Counties
L100JLB	Bluebird	L188SDY	Stagecoach South	L281JAO	Ribble	L366JBD	United Counties
L101GHN	Transit	L193FDV	Devon	L282JAO	Cumberland	L367JBD	United Counties
L101JSA	Bluebird	L194FDV	Devon	L283JAO	Ribble	L368JBD	United Counties
L101SDY	Ribble	L195FDV	Devon	L301JSA	Bluebird	L369JBD	United Counties
L102GHN	Transit	L197FDV	Devon	L301PSC	Fife Scottish	L370JBD	United Counties
L102JSA	Bluebird	L201FDV	Devon	L302JSA	Bluebird	L371JBD	United Counties
L102SDY	Ribble	L201YAG	Selkent	L302PSC	Fife Scottish	L372JBD	United Counties
L103GHN	Transit	L202YAG	Selkent	L303JSA	Bluebird	L373JBD	United Counties
L103SDY	Ribble	L203FDV	Devon	L303PSC	Fife Scottish	L374JBD	United Counties
L104SDY	Ribble	L203YAG	Selkent	L304PSC	Fife Scottish	L375JBD	United Counties
L105SDY	Ribble	L204FDV	Devon	L305PSC	Fife Scottish	L376JBD	United Counties
L106SDY	Ribble	L204YAG	Selkent	L306PSC	Fife Scottish	L377JBD	United Counties
L107SDY	Ribble	L205YAG	Selkent	L307PSC	Fife Scottish	L378JBD	United Counties
L108LHL	East Midland	L206YAG	Selkent	L307SKV	Midland Red	L379JBD	United Counties
L109LHL	East Midland	L207YAG	Selkent	L308PSC	Fife Scottish	L380JBD	United Counties
L119DRN	Ribble	L208FDV	Devon	L308YDU	Midland Red	L381NBD	United Counties
L122DRN	Cumberland	L208PSB	Western	L309PSC	Fife Scottish	L382NBD	United Counties
L123DRN	Cumberland	L208YAG	Selkent	L309YDU	Midland Red	L383NBD	United Counties
L124XHG	Cumberland	L209FDV	Devon	L310PSC	Fife Scottish	L401JBD	United Counties
L125DRN	Ribble	L209YAG	Selkent	L310YDU	Midland Red	L402JBD	United Counties
L125NAO	Cumberland	L210FDV	Devon	L311YDU	Midland Red	L403JBD	United Counties

Reg	Operator	Reg	Operator	Reg	Operator	Reg	Operator
L404JBD	United Counties	L582JSA	Western	L663MSF	Ribble	L737VNL	Busways
L405JBD	United Counties	L583HSG	Fife Scottish	L664MFL	Cambus	L738LWA	East Midland
L406JBD	United Counties	L583JSA	Western	L664MSF	Ribble	L738VNL	Busways
L407JBD	United Counties	L584HSG	Fife Scottish	L665MFL	Cambus	L739LWA	East Midland
L408JBD	United Counties	L584JSA	Western	L665MSF	Ribble	L739VNL	Busways
L409JBD	United Counties	L585HSG	Fife Scottish	L667MFL	Cambus	L740LWA	East Midland
L410JBD	United Counties	L585JSA	Bluebird	L667MSF	Ribble	L740VNL	Busways
L411JBD	United Counties	L586HSG	Fife Scottish	L668MFL	Cambus	L741LWA	East Midland
L412JBD	United Counties	L586JSA	Bluebird	L668MSF	Ribble	L741VNL	Busways
L413JBD	United Counties	L587HSG	Fife Scottish	L669MFL	Cambus	L742LWA	East Midland
L414JBD	United Counties	L587JSA	Bluebird	L669MSF	Ribble	L742VNL	Busways
L415JBD	United Counties	L588HSG	Fife Scottish	L671HNV	United Counties	L743LWA	East Midland
L416JBD	United Counties	L588JSA	Bluebird	L672HNV	United Counties	L743VNL	Busways
L417JBD	United Counties	L589HSG	Fife Scottish	L673HNV	United Counties	L744LWA	East Midland
L418JBD	United Counties	L590HSG	Fife Scottish	L674HNV	United Counties	L744VNL	Busways
L419JBD	United Counties	L601VCD	Stagecoach South	L675HNV	United Counties	L745LWA	East Midland
L420JBD	United Counties	L602VCD	Stagecoach South	L676HNV	United Counties	L745VNL	Busways
L421JBD	United Counties	L603VCD	Stagecoach South	L677HNV	United Counties	L746LWA	East Midland
L422MVV	United Counties	L609TDY	Stagecoach South	L678HNV	United Counties	L746VNL	Busways
L423MVV	Fife Scottish	L616TDY	Stagecoach South	L679HNV	United Counties	L748LWA	East Midland
L423XVV	United Counties	L617TDY	Stagecoach South	L680HNV	United Counties	L748VNL	Busways
L424MVV	Fife Scottish	L618TDY	Stagecoach South	L681HNV	United Counties	L749LWA	East Midland
L424XVV	United Counties	L624TDY	Stagecoach South	L682HNV	United Counties	L749VNL	Busways
L425MVV	Fife Scottish	L625TDY	Stagecoach South	L683HNV	United Counties	L750LWA	East Midland
L425XVV	United Counties	L626TDY	Stagecoach South	L684HNV	United Counties	L750VNL	Busways
L426MVV	Fife Scottish	L627TDY	Stagecoach South	L685CDD	Red & White	L751LHL	East Midland
L426XVV	United Counties	L628TDY	Stagecoach South	L685JBD	United Counties	L751VNL	Busways
L427MVV	Fife Scottish	L629BFV	Ribble	L686CDD	Cheltenham & G	L752VNL	Busways
L427XVV	United Counties	L629TDY	Stagecoach South	L687CDD	Cheltenham & G	L753VNL	Busways
L428MVV	Fife Scottish	L630BFV	Ribble	L688CDD	Cheltenham & G	L754VNL	Busways
L428XVV	United Counties	L630TDY	Stagecoach South	L689CDD	Cheltenham & G	L755VNL	Busways
L435LWA	East Midland	L631BFV	Ribble	L690CDD	Cheltenham & G	L756VNL	Busways
L436LWA	East Midland	L631TDY	Stagecoach South	L691CDD	Cheltenham & G	L757VNL	Busways
L437LWA	East Midland	L632BFV	Ribble	L692CDD	Cheltenham & G	L758VNL	Busways
L438LWA	East Midland	L632TDY	Stagecoach South	L693CDD	Cheltenham & G	L759VNL	Busways
L439LWA	East Midland	L633BFV	Ribble	L694CDD	Cheltenham & G	L760ARG	Busways
L440LWA	East Midland	L633TDY	Stagecoach South	L695CDD	Cheltenham & G	L761ARG	Busways
L441LWA	East Midland	L634BFV	Ribble	L696CDD	Cheltenham & G	L762ARG	Busways
L442LWA	East Midland	L634TDY	Stagecoach South	L701FWO	Red & White	L763ARG	Busways
L443LWA	East Midland	L635BFV	Ribble	L702FWO	Red & White	L764ARG	Busways
L445FFR	Ribble	L635TDY	Stagecoach South	L703FWO	Red & White	L765ARG	Busways
L445LWA	East Midland	L636BFV	Ribble	L704FWO	Red & White	L803XDG	Cheltenham & G
L446FFR	Ribble	L637LDT	East Midland	L705FWO	Red & White	L804XDG	Cheltenham & G
L446LWA	East Midland	L638LDT	East Midland	L705HFU	East Midland	L805XDG	Cheltenham & G
L447FFR	Ribble	L639LDT	East Midland	L706FWO	Red & White	L806XDG	Cheltenham & G
L447LWA	East Midland	L640LDT	East Midland	L706HFU	East Midland	L826BKK	Stagecoach South
L448FFR	Ribble	L641LDT	East Midland	L707FWO	Red & White	L827BKK	Stagecoach South
L448LWA	East Midland	L642LDT	East Midland	L707HFU	East Midland	L828BKK	Stagecoach South
L449LWA	East Midland	L643LDT	East Midland	L708FWO	Red & White	L829BKK	Stagecoach South
L450LWA	East Midland	L651HKS	Fife Scottish	L708HFU	East Midland	L830BKK	Stagecoach South
L451LWA	East Midland	L652HKS	Fife Scottish	L709FWO	Cheltenham & G	L831CDG	Cheltenham & G
L451YAC	Midland Red	L653HKS	Fife Scottish	L709HFU	East Midland	L832CDG	Cheltenham & G
L452LWA	East Midland	L654HKS	Fife Scottish	L710FWO	Cheltenham & G	L833CDG	Cheltenham & G
L452YAC	Midland Red	L655HKS	Fife Scottish	L711FWO	Cheltenham & G	L834CDG	Cheltenham & G
L453LHL	East Midland	L655MFL	Cambus	L712FWO	Cheltenham & G	L835CDG	Cheltenham & G
L453YAC	Midland Red	L656HKS	Fife Scottish	L729VNL	Busways	L836CDG	Cheltenham & G
L454YAC	Midland Red	L656MFL	Cambus	L730VNL	Busways	L837CDG	Cheltenham & G
L455YAC	Midland Red	L657HKS	Fife Scottish	L731LWA	East Midland	L838CDG	Cheltenham & G
L456YAC	Midland Red	L657MFL	Cambus	L731VNL	Busways	L839CDG	Cheltenham & G
L550JFS	Bluebird	L658HKS	Fife Scottish	L732LWA	East Midland	L840CDG	Cheltenham & G
L577NSB	Western	L658MFL	Cambus	L732VNL	Busways	L841CDG	Cheltenham & G
L578HSG	Fife Scottish	L659HKS	Fife Scottish	L733LWA	East Midland	L842CDG	Cheltenham & G
L578NSB	Western	L659MFL	Cambus	L733VNL	Busways	L881SDY	Stagecoach South
L579HSG	Fife Scottish	L660HKS	Ribble	L734LWA	East Midland	L882LFS	Western
L579JSA	Bluebird	L660MFL	Cambus	L734VNL	Busways	L882SDY	Stagecoach South
L580HSG	Fife Scottish	L661MFL	Cambus	L735LWA	East Midland	L883LFS	Western
L580JSA	Bluebird	L661MSF	Ribble	L735VNL	Busways	L883SDY	Stagecoach South
L581HSG	Fife Scottish	L662MFL	Cambus	L736LWA	East Midland	L884SDY	Stagecoach South
L581JSA	Bluebird	L662MSF	Ribble	L736VNL	Busways	L885SDY	Stagecoach South
L582HSG	Fife Scottish	L663MFL	Cambus	L737LWA	East Midland	L886SDY	Stagecoach South

Registration	Operator	Registration	Operator	Registration	Operator	Registration	Operator
L887SDY	Stagecoach South	LFR871X	Ribble	M202LHP	Midland Red	M319DGP	Selkent
L916UGA	Western	LFR873X	Cheltenham & G	M203DRG	Busways	M319RSO	Bluebird
L929CTT	Devon	LFR877X	Ribble	M203LHP	Midland Red	M320DGP	Selkent
L930CTT	Devon	LFV205X	Ribble	M204DRG	Busways	M320RSO	Bluebird
L931CTT	Devon	LFV206X	Ribble	M204LHP	Midland Red	M321RSO	Bluebird
L932CTT	Devon	LHT725P	Midland Red	M205LHP	Midland Red	M331LHP	Midland Red
L933CTT	Devon	LHT726P	Cheltenham & G	M209LHP	Midland Red	M332DRP	United Counties
L934CTT	Devon	LIL3317	Manchester	M210LHP	Midland Red	M332LHP	Midland Red
L935CTT	Devon	LIL4612	Manchester	M223SVN	Transit	M334DRP	United Counties
L936CTT	Devon	LJC800	Cumberland	M224SVN	Transit	M334LHP	Midland Red
L937CTT	Devon	LJY145	Cumberland	M225SVN	Transit	M335DRP	United Counties
L938CTT	Devon	LOD724P	MK Metro	M226SVN	Transit	M335LHP	Midland Red
L939CTT	Devon	LOD725P	MK Metro	M226UTM	Devon	M336DRP	United Counties
L940CTT	Devon	LPF605P	Stagecoach South	M227SVN	Transit	M336LHP	Midland Red
L941CTT	Devon	LSK547	Bluebird	M227UTM	Devon	M337DRP	United Counties
L942CTT	Devon	LSK548	Bluebird	M228UTM	Devon	M337LHP	Midland Red
L943CTT	Devon	LSX16P	Fife Scottish	M229UTM	Devon	M338DRP	United Counties
LAG188V	East Midland	LSX17P	Fife Scottish	M230TBV	Ribble	M338LHP	Midland Red
LAG189V	East Midland	LSX32P	Fife Scottish	M230UTM	Devon	M339DRP	United Counties
LAT505V	Transit	LSX38P	Fife Scottish	M231TBV	Ribble	M339LHP	Midland Red
LAT506V	Transit	LUA273V	Cumberland	M231UTM	Devon	M340DRP	United Counties
LAT512V	Transit	LUA275V	Cumberland	M232TBV	Ribble	M340LHP	Midland Red
LAT514V	Transit	LUL511X	Cheltenham & G	M232UTM	Devon	M341DRP	United Counties
LBD839P	United Counties	LWS33Y	Cheltenham & G	M233TBV	Ribble	M341LHP	Midland Red
LBD920V	United Counties	LWS34Y	Cheltenham & G	M233UTM	Devon	M342DRP	United Counties
LBD921V	United Counties	LWS35Y	Cheltenham & G	M234TBV	Ribble	M342LHP	Midland Red
LBD923V	United Counties	LWS36Y	Cheltenham & G	M234UTM	Devon	M343DRP	United Counties
LBN201P	Busways	LWS37Y	Cheltenham & G	M235TBV	Ribble	M343LHP	Midland Red
LBN202P	Busways	LWS38Y	Cheltenham & G	M235UTM	Devon	M344DRP	United Counties
LCU112	Busways	LWS39Y	Cheltenham & G	M236TBV	Ribble	M344JBO	Red & White
LDS201A	Bluebird	LWS40Y	Cheltenham & G	M236UTM	Devon	M344LHP	Midland Red
LDS210A	Bluebird	LWS41Y	Cheltenham & G	M237UTM	Devon	M345DRP	United Counties
LEO736Y	Fife Scottish	LWU470V	Cambus	M238UTM	Devon	M345JBO	Red & White
LEU261P	United Counties	LWV467V	Devon	M239UTM	Devon	M345LHP	Midland Red
LFF875	East London	LWV468V	Devon	M240UTM	Devon	M346DRP	United Counties
LFJ852W	United Counties	M38PVN	Transit	M241UTM	Devon	M346JBO	Red & White
LFJ853W	United Counties	M39PVN	Transit	M242UTM	Devon	M346KWK	Midland Red
LFJ854W	United Counties	M40PVN	Transit	M243UTM	Devon	M347DRP	United Counties
LFJ855W	United Counties	M41PVN	Transit	M244UTM	Devon	M347JBO	Red & White
LFJ858W	Ribble	M42PVN	Transit	M245UTM	Devon	M348DRP	United Counties
LFJ859W	Ribble	M101CCD	Red & White	M246UTM	Devon	M348JBO	Red & White
LFJ861W	Ribble	M102CCD	Fife Scottish	M247UTM	Devon	M349DRP	United Counties
LFJ862W	United Counties	M103CCD	Fife Scottish	M248UTM	Devon	M349JBO	Red & White
LFJ863W	United Counties	M104CCD	Fife Scottish	M249UTM	Devon	M350JBO	Red & White
LFJ864W	United Counties	M104PVN	Transit	M250UTM	Devon	M351JBO	Red & White
LFJ865W	United Counties	M105CCD	Stagecoach South	M301DGP	Selkent	M352JBO	Red & White
LFJ866W	Ribble	M105PVN	Transit	M302DGP	Selkent	M353JBO	Red & White
LFJ868W	United Counties	M106CCD	Stagecoach South	M303DGP	Selkent	M354JBO	Red & White
LFJ869W	United Counties	M106PVN	Transit	M304DGP	Selkent	M355JBO	Red & White
LFJ870W	Stagecoach South	M107CCD	Red & White	M305DGP	Selkent	M356JBO	Red & White
LFJ874W	Stagecoach South	M107PVN	Transit	M306DGP	Selkent	M357JBO	Red & White
LFJ875W	Stagecoach South	M108CCD	Stagecoach South	M307DGP	Selkent	M358JBO	Red & White
LFJ878W	United Counties	M108PVN	Transit	M308DGP	Selkent	M359JBO	Red & White
LFJ879W	United Counties	M151FGB	Western	M309DGP	Selkent	M360JBO	Red & White
LFJ880W	Stagecoach South	M160CCD	Western	M310DGP	Selkent	M361LAX	Red & White
LFJ881W	Stagecoach South	M161CCD	Western	M311DGP	Selkent	M362LAX	Red & White
LFJ882W	Ribble	M162CCD	Western	M311YSC	Stagecoach South	M363LAX	Red & White
LFJ883W	Ribble	M163CCD	Western	M312DGP	Selkent	M364LAX	Red & White
LFJ884W	Ribble	M164CCD	Western	M312YSC	Stagecoach South	M365LAX	Red & White
LFJ885W	Ribble	M164SCK	Ribble	M313DGP	Selkent	M366LAX	Red & White
LFR857X	Ribble	M165CCD	Western	M313YSC	Stagecoach South	M367LAX	Red & White
LFR858X	Ribble	M165SCK	Ribble	M314DGP	Selkent	M368LAX	Red & White
LFR859X	Ribble	M166CCD	Western	M314PKS	Fife Scottish	M369LAX	Red & White
LFR860X	Cheltenham & G	M191HTT	Devon	M315DGP	Selkent	M370LAX	Red & White
LFR861X	Cheltenham & G	M192HTT	Devon	M315PKS	Fife Scottish	M371LAX	Red & White
LFR862X	United Counties	M193HTT	Devon	M316DGP	Selkent	M401SPY	Transit
LFR864X	United Counties	M194HTT	Devon	M317DGP	Selkent	M402SPY	Transit
LFR866X	Ribble	M201DRG	Busways	M317RSO	Bluebird	M403SPY	Transit
LFR868X	Ribble	M201LHP	Midland Red	M318DGP	Selkent	M404BFG	Stagecoach South
LFR870X	Ribble	M202DRG	Busways	M318RSO	Bluebird	M404OKM	Stagecoach South

Reg	Operator	Reg	Operator	Reg	Operator	Reg	Operator
M404SPY	Transit	M491ASW	Western	M649FYS	Western	M717KRH	Transit
M405BFG	Stagecoach South	M492ASW	Western	M650BCD	Stagecoach South	M718BCS	Western
M405OKM	Stagecoach South	M527RSO	Bluebird	M650FYS	Western	M718KRH	Transit
M405SPY	Transit	M528RSO	Bluebird	M651BCD	Stagecoach South	M719BCS	Western
M406BFG	Stagecoach South	M529RSO	Bluebird	M651FYS	Western	M720BCS	Western
M406OKM	Stagecoach South	M530RSO	Bluebird	M652BCD	Stagecoach South	M721BCS	Western
M406SPY	Transit	M531RSO	Bluebird	M652FYS	Western	M722BCS	Western
M407BFG	Stagecoach South	M532RSO	Bluebird	M653FYS	Western	M723BCS	Western
M407OKM	Stagecoach South	M533RSO	Bluebird	M654FYS	Western	M724BCS	Western
M407SPY	Transit	M534RSO	Bluebird	M655FYS	Western	M725BCS	Western
M408BFG	Stagecoach South	M535RSO	Bluebird	M656FYS	Western	M726BCS	Western
M408OKM	Stagecoach South	M536RSO	Bluebird	M657FYS	Western	M727BCS	Western
M408SPY	Transit	M537RSO	Bluebird	M658FYS	Western	M732BSJ	Western
M409BFG	Stagecoach South	M538RSO	Bluebird	M659FYS	Western	M733BSJ	Western
M409SPY	Transit	M539RSO	Bluebird	M660FYS	Western	M734BSJ	Western
M410BFG	Stagecoach South	M540RSO	Bluebird	M661FYS	Western	M735BSJ	Western
M410SPY	Transit	M541RSO	Bluebird	M662ECD	Stagecoach South	M736BSJ	Western
M411RRN	East Midland	M542RSO	Bluebird	M662FYS	Western	M737BSJ	Western
M412RRN	East Midland	M543RSO	Bluebird	M663ECD	Stagecoach South	M738BSJ	Western
M413RRN	East Midland	M543SPY	Transit	M663FYS	Western	M739BSJ	Western
M414RRN	East Midland	M544RSO	Bluebird	M664ECD	Stagecoach South	M740BSJ	Western
M429BNV	United Counties	M544SPY	Transit	M664FYS	Western	M741BSJ	Western
M430BNV	United Counties	M545SPY	Transit	M665ECD	Stagecoach South	M741PRS	Manchester
M451VCW	Ribble	M546SPY	Transit	M665FYS	Western	M742PRS	Manchester
M452VCW	Ribble	M547SPY	Transit	M667ECD	Stagecoach South	M743PRS	Manchester
M453VCW	Ribble	M548SPY	Transit	M667FYS	Western	M744PRS	Manchester
M454VCW	Ribble	M549SPY	Transit	M668ECD	Stagecoach South	M745PRS	Manchester
M454VHE	Manchester	M550SPY	Transit	M668FYS	Western	M746PRS	Manchester
M455VCW	Cumberland	M551SPY	Transit	M669ECD	Stagecoach South	M748PRS	Manchester
M455VHE	Manchester	M552SPY	Transit	M670ECD	Stagecoach South	M749PRS	Manchester
M456VCW	Cumberland	M589OSO	Bluebird	M670SSX	Fife Scottish	M750LAX	Red & White
M456VHE	Manchester	M590OSO	Bluebird	M671SSX	Fife Scottish	M750PRS	Manchester
M457VCW	Cumberland	M591OSO	Bluebird	M672SSX	Fife Scottish	M751LAX	Red & White
M457VHE	Manchester	M592OSO	Bluebird	M673SSX	Fife Scottish	M752LAX	Red & White
M458VCW	Cumberland	M593OSO	Bluebird	M674SSX	Western	M753LAX	Red & White
M458VHE	Manchester	M594OSO	Bluebird	M675SSX	Western	M754LAX	Red & White
M459VCW	Cumberland	M595OSO	Bluebird	M676SSX	Western	M755LAX	Red & White
M459VHE	Manchester	M596OSO	Bluebird	M677SSX	Western	M756LAX	Red & White
M460VCW	Cumberland	M597OSO	Bluebird	M678SSX	Western	M757LAX	Red & White
M460VHE	Manchester	M598OSO	Bluebird	M679SSX	Western	M758LAX	Red & White
M461VCW	Cumberland	M601VHE	East Midland	M680SSX	Western	M759LAX	Red & White
M461VHE	Manchester	M602VHE	East Midland	M681SSX	Western	M760LAX	Red & White
M462VCW	Cumberland	M603VHE	East Midland	M697EDD	Cheltenham & G	M761LAX	Red & White
M462VHE	Manchester	M604VHE	East Midland	M698EDD	Cheltenham & G	M762LAX	Red & White
M463VCW	Cumberland	M605VHE	East Midland	M699EDD	Cheltenham & G	M763LAX	Red & White
M466ASW	Western	M606VHE	East Midland	M701EDD	Cheltenham & G	M764LAX	Red & White
M467ASW	Western	M607VHE	East Midland	M702EDD	Cheltenham & G	M765RAX	Red & White
M468ASW	Western	M608WET	East Midland	M703EDD	Cheltenham & G	M766DRG	Busways
M469ASW	Western	M609WET	East Midland	M704JDG	Cheltenham & G	M766RAX	Red & White
M470ASW	Western	M615APN	Stagecoach South	M705JDG	Cheltenham & G	M767DRG	Busways
M471ASW	Western	M622HDV	Devon	M706JDG	Cheltenham & G	M767RAX	Red & White
M472ASW	Western	M623HDV	Devon	M707JDG	Cheltenham & G	M768DRG	Busways
M473ASW	Western	M624HDV	Devon	M707KRH	Transit	M768RAX	Red & White
M474ASW	Western	M625HDV	Devon	M708JDG	Cheltenham & G	M769DRG	Busways
M475ASW	Western	M626HDV	Devon	M708KRH	Transit	M769RAX	Red & White
M476ASW	Western	M627HDV	Devon	M709JDG	Cheltenham & G	M770DRG	Busways
M477ASW	Western	M628HDV	Devon	M709KRH	Transit	M770RAX	Red & White
M478ASW	Western	M629HDV	Devon	M710JDG	Cheltenham & G	M770TFS	Fife Scottish
M479ASW	Western	M630HDV	Devon	M710KRH	Transit	M771DRG	Busways
M480ASW	Western	M636BCD	Stagecoach South	M711FMR	Cheltenham & G	M771TFS	Fife Scottish
M481ASW	Western	M636HDV	Devon	M711KRH	Transit	M772BCS	Western
M482ASW	Western	M637BCD	Stagecoach South	M712FMR	Cheltenham & G	M772TFS	Fife Scottish
M483ASW	Western	M637HDV	Devon	M712KRH	Transit	M773BCS	Western
M484ASW	Western	M638BCD	Stagecoach South	M713FMR	Cheltenham & G	M773TFS	Fife Scottish
M485ASW	Western	M638HDV	Devon	M713KRH	Transit	M774TFS	Fife Scottish
M486ASW	Western	M639BCD	Stagecoach South	M714FMR	Cheltenham & G	M775TFS	Fife Scottish
M487ASW	Western	M639HDV	Devon	M714KRH	Transit	M776TFS	Fife Scottish
M488ASW	Western	M640HDV	Devon	M715FMR	Cheltenham & G	M778TFS	Fife Scottish
M489ASW	Western	M641HDV	Devon	M715KRH	Transit	M779TFS	Fife Scottish
M490ASW	Western	M648FYS	Western	M716KRH	Transit	M780TFS	Fife Scottish

Reg	Operator	Reg	Operator	Reg	Operator	Reg	Operator
M782PRS	Ribble	M952DRG	Busways	MRJ409W	Manchester	N150XSA	Bluebird
M783PRS	Ribble	M952TSX	Fife Scottish	MSO10W	Western	N151XSA	Bluebird
M784PRS	Western	M953DRG	Busways	MSO13W	Red & White	N152XSA	Bluebird
M785PRS	Western	M953TSX	Fife Scottish	MSO14W	Red & White	N153XSA	Bluebird
M786PRS	Western	M954DRG	Busways	MSO17W	Ribble	N154XSA	Bluebird
M787PRS	Western	M954TSX	Fife Scottish	MSO18W	Western	N176LCK	Ribble
M788PRS	Western	M955TSX	Fife Scottish	MSU445	Fife Scottish	N177LCK	Ribble
M789PRS	Western	M956TSX	Fife Scottish	MSU465	United Counties	N178LCK	Ribble
M790PRS	Western	M975WWR	Cambus	MSU466	Western	N179LCK	Ribble
M791PRS	Western	M976WWR	Cambus	MSU499	Fife Scottish	N180LCK	Ribble
M792PRS	Western	M977WWR	Cambus	MUA872P	Cheltenham & G	N182CMJ	Midland Red
M793PRS	Western	M978WWR	Cambus	MVK500R	Busways	N183CMJ	Midland Red
M794PRS	Ribble	M979VWY	Cambus	MVK521R	Cheltenham & G	N188GFR	Ribble
M795PRS	Ribble	MAU145P	Midland Red	MVK532R	Busways	N189GFR	Ribble
M796PRS	Ribble	MAU146P	Bluebird	MVK544R	Busways	N190GFR	Ribble
M797PRS	Ribble	MBE613R	East Midland	MVK551R	Busways	N191LPN	Stagecoach South
M798PRS	Ribble	MCL937P	MK Metro	MVK558R	Cheltenham & G	N192LPN	Stagecoach South
M799PRS	Ribble	MDS858V	Ribble	MWG622X	East Midland	N193LPN	Stagecoach South
M808JTY	Busways	MDS859V	Ribble	MWG623X	East Midland	N194LFV	Ribble
M808WWR	Cambus	MDS865V	Western	MWG624X	East Midland	N194LPN	Stagecoach South
M809WWR	Cambus	MDS866V	Ribble	N91RVK	Busways	N195LFV	Ribble
M810WWR	Cambus	MEL559P	MK Metro	N95ALS	Fife Scottish	N195LPN	Stagecoach South
M817KRH	Transit	MFN115R	Stagecoach South	N96ALS	Fife Scottish	N196LFV	Ribble
M818KRH	Transit	MFN946F	Stagecoach South	N97ALS	Fife Scottish	N196LPN	Stagecoach South
M819KRH	Transit	MFV30T	Burnley & Pendle	N116YHH	Cumberland	N197LFV	Ribble
M843EMW	Cheltenham & G	MFV33T	Burnley & Pendle	N117YHH	Cumberland	N197LPN	Stagecoach South
M844EMW	Cheltenham & G	MFV34T	Burnley & Pendle	N118YHH	Cumberland	N198LFV	Ribble
M845EMW	Cheltenham & G	MFV35T	Burnley & Pendle	N119YHH	Cumberland	N198LPN	Stagecoach South
M846HDF	Manchester	MFV36T	Burnley & Pendle	N120YHH	Cumberland	N199LFV	Ribble
M847HDF	Cheltenham & G	MHS4P	Bluebird	N121YHH	Cumberland	N199LPN	Stagecoach South
M847PRS	Manchester	MHS5P	Bluebird	N122YHH	Cumberland	N201LFV	Ribble
M869ASW	Western	MIB7416	Bluebird	N123YHH	Cumberland	N201LPN	Stagecoach South
M870ASW	Western	MNC495W	Manchester	N124YHH	Cumberland	N201LTN	Busways
M871ASW	Western	MNC496W	Manchester	N125YHH	Cumberland	N201UHH	Cumberland
M872ASW	Western	MNC498W	Manchester	N126YRM	Cumberland	N202LFV	Ribble
M889ECD	Stagecoach South	MNC499W	Manchester	N127YRM	Cumberland	N202LPN	Stagecoach South
M890ECD	Stagecoach South	MNC523W	Manchester	N128VAO	Cumberland	N202LTN	Busways
M901DRG	Busways	MNC543W	Manchester	N128YRM	Cumberland	N202UHH	Cumberland
M902DRG	Busways	MNC548W	Manchester	N129VAO	Cumberland	N203LPN	Stagecoach South
M911WJK	Stagecoach South	MNS6Y	Fife Scottish	N129YRM	Cumberland	N203LTN	Busways
M912WJK	Stagecoach South	MNS7Y	Fife Scottish	N130AET	East Midland	N203UHH	Cumberland
M913WJK	Stagecoach South	MNS8Y	Fife Scottish	N130VAO	Cumberland	N204LPN	Stagecoach South
M914WJK	Stagecoach South	MNS9Y	Fife Scottish	N130YRM	Cumberland	N204LTN	Busways
M915WJK	Stagecoach South	MNS10Y	Fife Scottish	N131AET	East Midland	N204UHH	Cumberland
M916WJK	Stagecoach South	MOU739P	Cheltenham & G	N131VAO	Cumberland	N205LTN	Busways
M917WJK	Stagecoach South	MRJ36W	Manchester	N131YRM	Cumberland	N205UHH	Cumberland
M918WJK	Stagecoach South	MRJ37W	Manchester	N132AET	East Midland	N206LTN	Busways
M940JBO	Red & White	MRJ38W	Manchester	N132VAO	Cumberland	N206TDU	Midland Red
M941JBO	Red & White	MRJ40W	Manchester	N132YRM	Cumberland	N206UHH	Cumberland
M942JBO	Red & White	MRJ41W	Manchester	N133AET	East Midland	N207LTN	Busways
M942TSX	East Midland	MRJ42W	Manchester	N133YRM	Cumberland	N207TDU	Midland Red
M943JBO	Red & White	MRJ43W	Manchester	N134AET	East Midland	N207UHH	Cumberland
M943TSX	East Midland	MRJ44W	Manchester	N135AET	East Midland	N208LTN	Busways
M944JBO	Red & White	MRJ45W	Manchester	N136AET	East Midland	N208TDU	Midland Red
M944TSX	Fife Scottish	MRJ46W	Manchester	N136MPN	Stagecoach South	N208UHH	Cumberland
M945JBO	Red & White	MRJ47W	Manchester	N137AET	East Midland	N209LTN	Busways
M945TSX	Fife Scottish	MRJ48W	Manchester	N138AET	East Midland	N209UHH	Cumberland
M946JBO	Red & White	MRJ49W	Manchester	N139AET	East Midland	N210LTN	Busways
M946TSX	Fife Scottish	MRJ51W	Manchester	N140AET	East Midland	N210UHH	Cumberland
M947JBO	Red & White	MRJ52W	Manchester	N141AET	East Midland	N211LTN	Busways
M947TSX	Fife Scottish	MRJ53W	Manchester	N142AET	East Midland	N211TDU	Midland Red
M948JBO	Red & White	MRJ54W	Manchester	N142XSA	Western	N211UHH	Cumberland
M948TSX	Fife Scottish	MRJ66W	Manchester	N143AET	East Midland	N212LTN	Busways
M949JBO	Red & White	MRJ67W	Manchester	N143XSA	Western	N212TDU	Midland Red
M949TSX	Fife Scottish	MRJ71W	Manchester	N144AET	East Midland	N212UHH	Cumberland
M950JBO	Red & White	MRJ270W	East Midland	N144XSA	Western	N213LTN	Busways
M950TSX	Fife Scottish	MRJ275W	Cumberland	N145XSA	Western	N213TDU	Midland Red
M951DRG	Busways	MRJ402W	Manchester	N146XSA	Western	N213UHH	Cumberland
M951JBO	Red & White	MRJ404W	Manchester	N148XSA	Bluebird	N214LTN	Busways
M951TSX	Fife Scottish	MRJ406W	Manchester	N149XSA	Bluebird	N214TDU	Midland Red

Reg	Operator	Reg	Operator	Reg	Operator	Reg	Operator
N214UHH	Cumberland	N325HGK	Selkent	N349MPN	Stagecoach South	N380PNY	Red & White
N215LTN	Busways	N325NPN	Manchester	N350AVV	Midland Red	N381LPN	Stagecoach South
N215TDU	Midland Red	N325VMS	Fife Scottish	N350HGK	Selkent	N381PNY	Red & White
N215UHH	Cumberland	N325XRP	United Counties	N350MPN	Stagecoach South	N382LPN	Stagecoach South
N216LTN	Busways	N326AMC	East London	N350YFL	Cambus	N382PNY	Red & White
N216TDU	Midland Red	N326HGK	Selkent	N351AVV	Midland Red	N383LPN	Stagecoach South
N217LTN	Busways	N326NPN	Manchester	N351HGK	Selkent	N383PNY	Red & White
N247XSA	Western	N326VMS	Fife Scottish	N351MPN	Stagecoach South	N384LPN	Stagecoach South
N301AMC	East London	N326XRP	United Counties	N351YFL	Cambus	N384PNY	Red & White
N301XRP	United Counties	N327AMC	East London	N352AVV	Midland Red	N385LPN	Stagecoach South
N302AMC	East London	N327HGK	Selkent	N352HGK	Selkent	N386LPN	Stagecoach South
N302XRP	United Counties	N327NPN	Manchester	N352MPN	Stagecoach South	N387LPN	Stagecoach South
N303AMC	East London	N327VMS	Fife Scottish	N352YFL	Cambus	N388LPN	Stagecoach South
N303XRP	United Counties	N327XRP	Cumberland	N353AVV	Midland Red	N389LPN	Stagecoach South
N304AMC	East London	N328HGK	Selkent	N353HGK	Selkent	N390LPN	Stagecoach South
N304XRP	United Counties	N328NPN	Manchester	N353MPN	Stagecoach South	N391LPN	Stagecoach South
N305AMC	East London	N328VMS	Fife Scottish	N354AVV	Midland Red	N392LPN	Stagecoach South
N305XRP	United Counties	N328XRP	Cumberland	N354MPN	Stagecoach South	N393LPN	Stagecoach South
N306AMC	East London	N329HGK	Selkent	N355AVV	Midland Red	N394LPN	Stagecoach South
N306XRP	United Counties	N329NPN	Manchester	N355MPN	Stagecoach South	N395LPN	Stagecoach South
N307AMC	East London	N329VMS	Fife Scottish	N356AVV	Midland Red	N396LPN	Stagecoach South
N307XRP	United Counties	N329XRP	Cumberland	N356MPN	Stagecoach South	N397LPN	Stagecoach South
N308AMC	East London	N330HGK	Selkent	N357AVV	Midland Red	N398LPN	Stagecoach South
N308XRP	United Counties	N330NPN	Manchester	N357MPN	Stagecoach South	N399LPN	Stagecoach South
N309AMC	East London	N331HGK	Selkent	N358AVV	Midland Red	N401LDF	Cheltenham & G
N309XRP	United Counties	N331NPN	Manchester	N358MPN	Stagecoach South	N401WVR	Manchester
N310AMC	East London	N332HGK	Selkent	N359AVV	Midland Red	N402LDF	Cheltenham & G
N310XRP	United Counties	N332NPN	Manchester	N359MPN	Stagecoach South	N402WVR	Manchester
N311AMC	East London	N333NPN	Manchester	N360AVV	Midland Red	N403LDF	Cheltenham & G
N311XRP	United Counties	N334HGK	Selkent	N360LPN	Stagecoach South	N403WVR	Manchester
N312AMC	East London	N334NPN	Manchester	N361AVV	Midland Red	N404LDF	Cheltenham & G
N312XRP	United Counties	N335HGK	Selkent	N361LPN	Stagecoach South	N404WVR	Manchester
N313AMC	East London	N335NPN	Manchester	N362AVV	Midland Red	N405LDF	Cheltenham & G
N313XRP	United Counties	N336HGK	Selkent	N362LPN	Stagecoach South	N405WVR	Manchester
N314AMC	East London	N336NPN	Manchester	N363AVV	Midland Red	N406LDF	Cheltenham & G
N314XRP	United Counties	N337HGK	Selkent	N363LPN	Stagecoach South	N406WVR	Manchester
N315AMC	East London	N337NPN	Manchester	N364AVV	Midland Red	N407LDF	Cheltenham & G
N315XRP	United Counties	N338HGK	Selkent	N364LPN	Stagecoach South	N407WVR	Manchester
N316AMC	East London	N338NPN	Manchester	N365AVV	Midland Red	N408LDF	Cheltenham & G
N316VMS	Fife Scottish	N339HGK	Selkent	N365LPN	Stagecoach South	N408WVR	Manchester
N316XRP	United Counties	N339NPN	Manchester	N366AVV	Midland Red	N409LDF	Cheltenham & G
N317AMC	East London	N340HGK	Selkent	N366LPN	Stagecoach South	N409WVR	Manchester
N317VMS	Fife Scottish	N341HGK	Selkent	N367AVV	Midland Red	N410WVR	Manchester
N317XRP	United Counties	N341KKH	Transit	N367LPN	Stagecoach South	N411WVR	Manchester
N318AMC	East London	N341MPN	Stagecoach South	N368AVV	Midland Red	N412WVR	Manchester
N318VMS	Fife Scottish	N342HGK	Selkent	N368LPN	Stagecoach South	N413WVR	Manchester
N318XRP	United Counties	N342KKH	Transit	N369AVV	Midland Red	N414WVR	Manchester
N319AMC	East London	N342MPN	Stagecoach South	N369LPN	Stagecoach South	N415WVR	Manchester
N319VMS	Fife Scottish	N343HGK	Selkent	N370AVV	Midland Red	N416WVR	Manchester
N319XRP	United Counties	N343KKH	Transit	N370LPN	Stagecoach South	N417WVR	Manchester
N320AMC	East London	N343MPN	Stagecoach South	N371AVV	Midland Red	N418WVR	Manchester
N320VMS	Fife Scottish	N344HGK	Selkent	N371LPN	Stagecoach South	N419WVR	Manchester
N320XRP	United Counties	N344KKH	Transit	N372AVV	Midland Red	N420WVR	Manchester
N321AMC	East London	N344MPN	Stagecoach South	N372LPN	Stagecoach South	N421WVR	Manchester
N321HGK	Selkent	N345HGK	Selkent	N372PNY	Red & White	N422WVR	Manchester
N321VMS	Fife Scottish	N345KKH	Transit	N373LPN	Stagecoach South	N423WVR	Manchester
N321XRP	United Counties	N345MPN	Stagecoach South	N373PNY	Red & White	N424WVR	Manchester
N322AMC	East London	N346HGK	Selkent	N374LPN	Stagecoach South	N425WVR	Manchester
N322HGK	Selkent	N346KKH	Transit	N374PNY	Red & White	N426WVR	Manchester
N322VMS	Fife Scottish	N346MPN	Stagecoach South	N375LPN	Stagecoach South	N427WVR	Manchester
N322XRP	United Counties	N347AVV	Midland Red	N375PNY	Red & White	N428WVR	Manchester
N323AMC	East London	N347HGK	Selkent	N376LPN	Stagecoach South	N429WVR	Manchester
N323HGK	Selkent	N347KKH	Transit	N376PNY	Red & White	N430WVR	Manchester
N323VMS	Fife Scottish	N347MPN	Stagecoach South	N377LPN	Stagecoach South	N445XVA	Cambus
N323XRP	United Counties	N348AVV	Midland Red	N377PNY	Red & White	N446XVA	Cambus
N324AMC	East London	N348HGK	Selkent	N378LPN	Stagecoach South	N447XVA	Cambus
N324HGK	Selkent	N348KKH	Transit	N378PNY	Red & White	N448XVA	Cambus
N324VMS	Fife Scottish	N348MPN	Stagecoach South	N379LPN	Stagecoach South	N449XVA	Cambus
N324XRP	United Counties	N349AVV	Midland Red	N379PNY	Red & White	N450XVA	Cambus
N325AMC	East London	N349HGK	Selkent	N380LPN	Stagecoach South	N451PAP	Stagecoach South

Reg	Operator	Reg	Operator	Reg	Operator	Reg	Operator
N451VOD	Ribble	N493RVK	Busways	N619VSS	Cambus	N716LTN	Busways
N451XVA	Cambus	N494RVK	Busways	N620USS	Bluebird	N717KAM	Cheltenham & G
N452PAP	Stagecoach South	N495RVK	Busways	N620VSS	Cambus	N717LTN	Busways
N452VOD	Ribble	N496RVK	Busways	N621VSS	Western	N718LTN	Busways
N452XVA	Cambus	N497RVK	Busways	N622VSS	Western	N718RDD	Cheltenham & G
N453PAP	Stagecoach South	N498RVK	Busways	N623VSS	Western	N719LTN	Busways
N453VOD	Ribble	N499RVK	Busways	N624VSS	Western	N719RDD	Cheltenham & G
N454PAP	Stagecoach South	N501RVK	Busways	N625VSS	Western	N720LTN	Busways
N454VOD	Ribble	N506BJA	Devon	N626VSS	Western	N720RDD	Cheltenham & G
N455PAP	Stagecoach South	N507BJA	Devon	N627VSS	Western	N721LTN	Busways
N455VOD	Ribble	N508BJA	Devon	N628VSS	Western	N721RDD	Cheltenham & G
N456PAP	Stagecoach South	N509BJA	Devon	N629VSS	Western	N722LTN	Busways
N456VOD	Ribble	N510BJA	Devon	N630VSS	Western	N722RDD	Cheltenham & G
N457PAP	Stagecoach South	N511BJA	Devon	N631VSS	Western	N723LTN	Busways
N457VOD	Ribble	N512BJA	Devon	N632VSS	Western	N723RDD	Cheltenham & G
N458PAP	Stagecoach South	N513BJA	Devon	N633VSS	Western	N724LTN	Busways
N458VOD	Ribble	N514BJA	Devon	N634VSS	Western	N724RDD	Cheltenham & G
N459PAP	Stagecoach South	N515BJA	Devon	N635VSS	Western	N725LTN	Busways
N459VOD	Ribble	N516BJA	Devon	N636VSS	Bluebird	N725RDD	Cheltenham & G
N460PAP	Stagecoach South	N517BJA	Devon	N637VSS	Bluebird	N726LTN	Busways
N460VOD	Ribble	N518BJA	Devon	N638VSS	Bluebird	N726RDD	Cheltenham & G
N461PAP	Stagecoach South	N518XER	Cambus	N639VSS	Bluebird	N727LTN	Busways
N461RVK	Busways	N519BJA	Ribble	N640LPN	Stagecoach South	N727RDD	Cheltenham & G
N461VOD	Ribble	N519XER	Cambus	N640VSS	Bluebird	N728LTN	Busways
N462PAP	Stagecoach South	N520BJA	Ribble	N641LPN	Stagecoach South	N728RDD	Cheltenham & G
N462RVK	Busways	N520XER	Cambus	N641VSS	Cambus	N729LTN	Busways
N462VOD	Ribble	N551VDC	Transit	N642LPN	Stagecoach South	N729RDD	Cheltenham & G
N463HRN	Ribble	N552VDC	Transit	N642VSS	Cambus	N730LTN	Busways
N463PAP	Stagecoach South	N553VDC	Transit	N643LPN	Stagecoach South	N730RDD	Cheltenham & G
N463RVK	Busways	N561SJF	Fife Scottish	N643VSS	Cambus	N731LTN	Busways
N463VOD	Ribble	N562SJF	Fife Scottish	N644LPN	Stagecoach South	N731RDD	Cheltenham & G
N464HRN	Ribble	N582XSA	Bluebird	N644VSS	Cambus	N732LTN	Busways
N464PAP	Stagecoach South	N583XSA	Bluebird	N645LPN	Stagecoach South	N732RDD	Cheltenham & G
N464RVK	Busways	N584XSA	Bluebird	N645VSS	Manchester	N733LTN	Busways
N464VOD	Ribble	N601KGF	Selkent	N646VSS	Manchester	N733RDD	Cheltenham & G
N465PAP	Stagecoach South	N601VSS	Western	N647VSS	Manchester	N734LTN	Busways
N465RVK	Busways	N602KGF	Selkent	N648VSS	Manchester	N734RDD	Cheltenham & G
N465VOD	Ribble	N602VSS	Western	N649VSS	Manchester	N735LTN	Busways
N466PAP	Stagecoach South	N603KGF	Selkent	N650VSS	Manchester	N735RDD	Cheltenham & G
N466RVK	Busways	N603VSS	Western	N651VSS	Manchester	N736LTN	Busways
N466VOD	Ribble	N604KGF	Selkent	N652VSS	Manchester	N737LTN	Busways
N467PAP	Stagecoach South	N604VSS	Western	N653VSS	Manchester	N738LTN	Busways
N467RVK	Busways	N605KGF	Selkent	N654VSS	Manchester	N739LTN	Busways
N467VOD	Ribble	N605VSS	Western	N655VSS	Manchester	N740LTN	Busways
N468RVK	Busways	N606KGF	Selkent	N656VSS	Manchester	N752CKU	East Midland
N468VOD	Ribble	N606VSS	Western	N657VSS	Manchester	N753CKU	East Midland
N469RVK	Busways	N607KGF	Selkent	N658VSS	Manchester	N754CKU	East Midland
N470RVK	Busways	N607VSS	Western	N659VSS	Manchester	N755CKU	East Midland
N471RVK	Busways	N608KGF	Selkent	N660VSS	Manchester	N756CKU	East Midland
N472RVK	Busways	N608VSS	Western	N661VSS	Manchester	N757CKU	East Midland
N473RVK	Busways	N609KGF	Selkent	N662VSS	Manchester	N758CKU	East Midland
N474RVK	Busways	N609VSS	Western	N663VSS	Manchester	N759CKU	East Midland
N475RVK	Busways	N610KGF	Selkent	N664VSS	Manchester	N760CKU	East Midland
N476RVK	Busways	N610VSS	Western	N665VSS	Manchester	N761CKU	East Midland
N477RVK	Busways	N611LGC	Selkent	N701LTN	Busways	N762EWG	East Midland
N478RVK	Busways	N611VSS	Western	N702LTN	Busways	N763EWG	East Midland
N479RVK	Busways	N612LGC	Selkent	N703LTN	Busways	N764EWG	East Midland
N480RVK	Busways	N612VSS	Western	N704LTN	Busways	N765EWG	East Midland
N481RVK	Busways	N613LGC	Selkent	N705LTN	Busways	N766EWG	East Midland
N482RVK	Busways	N613VSS	Cambus	N706LTN	Busways	N767EWG	East Midland
N4834VK	Busways	N614LGC	Selkent	N707LTN	Busways	N768EWG	East Midland
N484RVK	Busways	N614VSS	Cambus	N708LTN	Busways	N769EWG	East Midland
N485RVK	Busways	N615VSS	Cambus	N709LTN	Busways	N770EWG	East Midland
N486RVK	Busways	N616USS	Western	N710LTN	Busways	N771EWG	East Midland
N487RVK	Busways	N616VSS	Cambus	N711LTN	Busways	N772EWG	East Midland
N488RVK	Busways	N617USS	Western	N712LTN	Busways	N772RVK	Busways
N489RVK	Busways	N617VSS	Cambus	N713LTN	Busways	N773EWG	East Midland
N490RVK	Busways	N618USS	Bluebird	N714LTN	Busways	N773RVK	Busways
N491RVK	Busways	N618VSS	Cambus	N715LTN	Busways	N774EWG	East Midland
N492RVK	Busways	N619USS	Bluebird	N716KAM	Cheltenham & G	N774RVK	Busways

Reg	Fleet	Reg	Fleet	Reg	Fleet	Reg	Fleet
N775EWG	East Midland	N923NAP	Stagecoach South	NDZ3020	East London	NLS987W	Red & White
N775RVK	Busways	N924NAP	Stagecoach South	NDZ3021	East London	NLS988W	Ribble
N776EWG	East Midland	N925NAP	Stagecoach South	NDZ3022	East London	NLS989W	Western
N776RVK	Busways	N926NAP	Stagecoach South	NDZ3023	East London	NML607E	East London
N777RVK	Busways	N927NAP	Stagecoach South	NDZ3024	East London	NML610E	East London
N778RVK	Busways	N928NAP	Stagecoach South	NDZ3025	East London	NML616E	East London
N779RVK	Busways	N929NAP	Stagecoach South	NDZ3026	East London	NML624E	East London
N789VRM	Cumberland	N930NAP	Stagecoach South	NDZ3133	East London	NML639E	East London
N790VRM	Cumberland	N931NAP	Stagecoach South	NDZ3134	East London	NML641E	East London
N801DNE	Manchester	N932NAP	Stagecoach South	NDZ3135	East London	NML642E	East London
N802DNE	Manchester	N933NAP	Stagecoach South	NDZ3136	East London	NML657E	East London
N803DNE	Manchester	N934NAP	Stagecoach South	NDZ3137	East London	NMY635E	East London
N804DNE	Manchester	N935NAP	Stagecoach South	NDZ3138	East London	NMY640E	East London
N805DNE	Manchester	N936NAP	Stagecoach South	NDZ3139	East London	NMY643E	Bluebird
N806DNE	Manchester	N937NAP	Stagecoach South	NDZ3140	East London	NOE551R	Midland Red
N807DNE	Manchester	N938NAP	Stagecoach South	NDZ3141	East London	NOE552R	Red & White
N808DNE	Manchester	N939NAP	Stagecoach South	NDZ3142	East London	NOE553R	Midland Red
N809DNE	Manchester	N940NAP	Stagecoach South	NDZ3143	East London	NOE554R	Midland Red
N810DNE	Manchester	N941NAP	Stagecoach South	NDZ3144	East London	NOE571R	Midland Red
N811DNE	Manchester	N942NAP	Stagecoach South	NDZ3145	East London	NOE572R	Red & White
N812DNE	Manchester	N943NAP	Stagecoach South	NDZ3146	East London	NOE573R	Red & White
N813DNE	Manchester	N944NAP	Stagecoach South	NDZ3147	East London	NOE576R	Red & White
N814DNE	Manchester	N945NAP	Stagecoach South	NDZ3148	East London	NOE577R	Midland Red
N815DNE	Manchester	N946NAP	Stagecoach South	NDZ3149	East London	NOE578R	Midland Red
N816DNE	Manchester	N947NAP	Stagecoach South	NDZ3150	East London	NOE581R	Midland Red
N817DNE	Manchester	N948NAP	Stagecoach South	NDZ3151	East London	NOE582R	Midland Red
N818DNE	Manchester	N949NAP	Stagecoach South	NDZ3152	East London	NOE586R	Midland Red
N849VHH	Western	N950NAP	Stagecoach South	NDZ3153	East London	NOE587R	Midland Red
N850VHH	Western	N951NAP	Stagecoach South	NDZ3154	East London	NOE589R	Midland Red
N851VHH	Western	N952NAP	Stagecoach South	NDZ3155	East London	NOE590R	Midland Red
N852VHH	Western	N953NAP	Stagecoach South	NDZ3156	East London	NOE595R	Ribble
N853VHH	Western	N954NAP	Stagecoach South	NDZ3157	East London	NOE602R	Midland Red
N854VHH	Western	N955NAP	Stagecoach South	NDZ3158	East London	NOE603R	Midland Red
N855VHH	Western	N956NAP	Stagecoach South	NDZ3159	East London	NOE604R	Midland Red
N856VHH	Western	N957NAP	Stagecoach South	NFB114R	Cheltenham & G	NOE605R	Midland Red
N857VHH	Western	N958NAP	Stagecoach South	NFB603R	Cheltenham & G	NOE606R	Midland Red
N858VHH	Western	N959NAP	Stagecoach South	NFN81R	Stagecoach South	NPA229W	Western
N859VHH	Western	N960NAP	Stagecoach South	NFN88R	Stagecoach South	NPA230W	Midland Red
N860VHH	Western	N961NAP	Stagecoach South	NFR747T	Ribble	NPJ476R	Stagecoach South
N861VHH	Western	N962NAP	Stagecoach South	NFR748T	Ribble	NPJ477R	Stagecoach South
N862VHH	Western	N963NAP	Stagecoach South	NFS170Y	Fife Scottish	NPJ480R	Stagecoach South
N863VHH	Western	N964NAP	Stagecoach South	NFS171Y	Fife Scottish	NPJ482R	Stagecoach South
N864VHH	Western	N965NAP	Stagecoach South	NFS172Y	Fife Scottish	NRP580V	East Midland
N865VHH	Western	N966NAP	Stagecoach South	NFS173Y	Fife Scottish	NSG636A	Bluebird
N866VHH	Western	N967NAP	Stagecoach South	NFS174Y	Fife Scottish	NSP334R	Fife Scottish
N879AVV	Manchester	N968NAP	Stagecoach South	NFS175Y	Fife Scottish	NSP336R	Fife Scottish
N880AVV	Manchester	N969NAP	Stagecoach South	NFS176Y	Fife Scottish	NTC132Y	Cheltenham & G
N881AVV	Manchester	N970NAP	Stagecoach South	NFS177Y	Fife Scottish	NUF276	Bluebird
N882AVV	Manchester	N971NAP	Stagecoach South	NFS178Y	Fife Scottish	NUW550Y	East London
N883AVV	Manchester	N972NAP	Stagecoach South	NFS179Y	Fife Scottish	NUW551Y	East London
N884AVV	Manchester	N973NAP	Stagecoach South	NFX332	Stagecoach South	NUW552Y	East London
N885AVV	Manchester	N974NAP	Stagecoach South	NHH380W	Ribble	NUW553Y	East London
N905NAP	Stagecoach South	N975NAP	Stagecoach South	NHH382W	Cheltenham & G	NUW554Y	East London
N906NAP	Stagecoach South	N976NAP	Stagecoach South	NHL301X	East Midland	NUW555Y	East London
N907NAP	Stagecoach South	N977NAP	Stagecoach South	NHL302X	East Midland	NUW556Y	East London
N908NAP	Stagecoach South	N978NAP	Devon	NHL303X	East Midland	NUW557Y	East London
N909NAP	Stagecoach South	N979NAP	Devon	NHL304X	East Midland	NUW558Y	East London
N910NAP	Stagecoach South	N980NAP	Devon	NHL305X	East Midland	NUW559Y	East London
N911NAP	Stagecoach South	N981NAP	Devon	NHU670R	Cheltenham & G	NUW560Y	East London
N912NAP	Stagecoach South	N982NAP	Devon	NHU671R	Midland Red	NUW562Y	East London
N913NAP	Stagecoach South	NAK28X	Midland Red	NHU672R	Midland Red	NUW563Y	East London
N914NAP	Stagecoach South	NAK29X	Midland Red	NIB4138	Bluebird	NUW564Y	East London
N915NAP	Stagecoach South	NBD102Y	United Counties	NIB5232	Western	NUW565Y	East London
N916NAP	Stagecoach South	NBD103Y	United Counties	NIB5233	Western	NUW566Y	East London
N917NAP	Stagecoach South	NBD104Y	United Counties	NIB5455	Bluebird	NUW568Y	East London
N918NAP	Stagecoach South	NDZ3015	East London	NJA568W	Manchester	NUW569Y	East London
N919NAP	Stagecoach South	NDZ3016	East London	NKY146R	East Midland	NUW571Y	East London
N920NAP	Stagecoach South	NDZ3017	East London	NLP388V	Western	NUW572Y	East London
N921NAP	Stagecoach South	NDZ3018	East London	NLS983W	Western	NUW573Y	East London
N922NAP	Stagecoach South	NDZ3019	East London	NLS985W	Western	NUW574Y	East London

Reg	Operator	Reg	Operator	Reg	Operator	Reg	Operator
NUW575Y	East London	NUW651Y	East London	OHV738Y	East London	OSC55V	Fife Scottish
NUW576Y	East London	NUW652Y	East London	OHV740Y	Selkent	OSC56V	Fife Scottish
NUW577Y	East London	NUW653Y	East London	OHV743Y	East London	OSC57V	Fife Scottish
NUW578Y	East London	NUW654Y	East London	OHV744Y	East London	OSC60V	Fife Scottish
NUW579Y	East London	NUW657Y	East London	OHV748Y	Selkent	OSC61V	Fife Scottish
NUW580Y	East London	NUW658Y	East London	OHV749Y	East London	OSC62V	Fife Scottish
NUW581Y	East London	NUW659Y	East London	OHV751Y	East London	OSC63V	Fife Scottish
NUW582Y	East London	NUW660Y	East London	OHV759Y	East London	OSC64V	Fife Scottish
NUW583Y	East London	NUW662Y	East London	OHV761Y	East London	OSC65V	Fife Scottish
NUW584Y	East London	NUW663Y	East London	OHV762Y	Western	OSC66V	Fife Scottish
NUW585Y	East London	NUW664Y	East London	OHV769Y	East London	OSJ634R	Bluebird
NUW586Y	East London	NUW665Y	East London	OHV770Y	Selkent	OSJ635R	Bluebird
NUW587Y	East London	NUW666Y	East London	OHV771Y	Selkent	OSJ636R	Western
NUW588Y	East London	NUW668Y	East London	OHV772Y	Selkent	OSJ643R	Bluebird
NUW589Y	East London	NUW669Y	East London	OHV780Y	Western	OSJ644R	Bluebird
NUW590Y	East London	NUW670Y	East London	OHV784Y	East London	OSK784	Bluebird
NUW591Y	East London	NUW671Y	East London	OHV785Y	Selkent	OSR193R	Burnley & Pendle
NUW592Y	East London	NUW672Y	East London	OHV789Y	East London	OSR195R	Burnley & Pendle
NUW593Y	East London	NUW673Y	East London	OHV791Y	Selkent	OSR196R	Burnley & Pendle
NUW594Y	Stagecoach South	NUW675Y	East London	OHV797Y	Selkent	OSR197R	Burnley & Pendle
NUW595Y	East London	NWO454R	Red & White	OHV800Y	Western	OSR205R	Burnley & Pendle
NUW596Y	Stagecoach South	NWO457R	Red & White	OHV802Y	East London	OSR206R	Red & White
NUW597Y	East London	NWO461R	Red & White	OHV804Y	Selkent	OSR207R	Red & White
NUW598Y	East London	NWO468R	Red & White	OHV805Y	Selkent	OSR208R	Red & White
NUW600Y	East London	NWS288R	Cheltenham & G	OHV809Y	Western	OSR209R	Red & White
NUW601Y	East London	NWS289R	Cheltenham & G	OHV810Y	Selkent	OUF262W	Stagecoach South
NUW602Y	East London	NXI414	Burnley & Pendle	OHV812Y	Selkent	OVV849R	United Counties
NUW603Y	East London	NXI812	Burnley & Pendle	OHV813Y	Selkent	OVV850R	Fife Scottish
NUW604Y	East London	OBD842P	Midland Red	OHV814Y	Selkent	OVV856R	United Counties
NUW605Y	East London	OCU802R	United Counties	OIJ201	Burnley & Pendle	OWB30X	East Midland
NUW606Y	East London	OCU804R	United Counties	OIW7024	Western	OWB31X	East Midland
NUW608Y	East London	OCU808R	United Counties	OIW7025	Western	OWB32X	East Midland
NUW609Y	East London	OCU815R	Busways	OJL822Y	East Midland	OWB33X	East Midland
NUW610Y	East London	OCU816R	Busways	OJL823Y	East Midland	OWB34X	East Midland
NUW611Y	Stagecoach South	OCU818R	Busways	OJV120S	East Midland	OWC720M	Busways
NUW613Y	East London	OCU819R	Busways	OMS910W	Bluebird	OWC722M	Busways
NUW614Y	East London	OCU820R	Busways	ONH846P	Midland Red	OWC723M	Busways
NUW614Y	Western	OCU821R	Busways	ONH926V	United Counties	P21HMF	East London
NUW615Y	East London	OCU822R	Busways	ORJ72W	Manchester	P23HMF	East London
NUW616Y	Selkent	OCU824R	Busways	ORJ73W	Manchester	P24HMF	East London
NUW617Y	East London	OCU825R	Busways	ORJ74W	Manchester	P25HMF	East London
NUW618Y	Western	OCY910R	Bluebird	ORJ75W	Manchester	P26HMF	East London
NUW619Y	East London	OFV14X	Ribble	ORJ76W	Manchester	P27HMF	East London
NUW621Y	East London	OFV15X	Ribble	ORJ77W	Manchester	P28HMF	East London
NUW622Y	East London	OFV16X	Cumberland	ORJ78W	Manchester	P29HMF	East London
NUW623Y	East London	OFV17X	Cumberland	ORJ79W	Manchester	P31HMF	East London
NUW624Y	East London	OFV18X	Ribble	ORJ80W	Manchester	P92URG	Busways
NUW625Y	East London	OFV19X	Ribble	ORJ81W	Manchester	P101HNH	Midland Red
NUW626Y	East London	OFV20X	Ribble	ORJ91W	Manchester	P102HNH	Midland Red
NUW627Y	East London	OFV21X	Ribble	ORJ92W	Manchester	P103HNH	Midland Red
NUW629Y	East London	OFV22X	Ribble	ORJ93W	Manchester	P104HNH	Midland Red
NUW630Y	East London	OFV23X	Ribble	ORJ94W	Manchester	P105HNH	Midland Red
NUW631Y	East London	OHU801Y	Fife Scottish	ORJ95W	Manchester	P118XCN	Busways
NUW632Y	East London	OHV680Y	Selkent	ORJ98W	Manchester	P119XCN	Busways
NUW633Y	East London	OHV684Y	Western	ORJ100W	Manchester	P120XCN	Busways
NUW634Y	East London	OHV686Y	East London	ORJ362W	Manchester	P121XCN	Busways
NUW636Y	East London	OHV688Y	East London	ORJ368W	Manchester	P122XCN	Busways
NUW637Y	East London	OHV691Y	East London	ORJ377W	Manchester	P123XCN	Busways
NUW639Y	East London	OHV697Y	East London	ORJ381W	Manchester	P124XCN	Busways
NUW640Y	East London	OHV699Y	East London	ORJ393W	Manchester	P125XCN	Busways
NUW641Y	East London	OHV700Y	Western	ORJ395W	Manchester	P126XCN	Busways
NUW642Y	East London	OHV702Y	East London	ORJ396W	Manchester	P127XCN	Busways
NUW643Y	East London	OHV710Y	Western	OSC47V	Fife Scottish	P128XCN	Ribble
NUW644Y	East London	OHV714Y	Western	OSC48V	Fife Scottish	P129XCN	Ribble
NUW645Y	East London	OHV719Y	East London	OSC49V	Fife Scottish	P130XCN	Ribble
NUW646Y	East London	OHV721Y	Selkent	OSC50V	Fife Scottish	P131XCN	Ribble
NUW647Y	East London	OHV724Y	East London	OSC51V	Fife Scottish	P132XCN	Ribble
NUW648Y	East London	OHV728Y	Western	OSC52V	Fife Scottish	P133XCN	Ribble
NUW649Y	East London	OHV729Y	East London	OSC53V	Fife Scottish	P134XCN	Ribble
NUW650Y	East London	OHV731Y	East London	OSC54V	Fife Scottish	P135XCN	Ribble

Registration	Operator	Registration	Operator	Registration	Operator	Registration	Operator
P145KWJ	East Midland	P275VPN	Ribble	P418KWF	East Midland	P555FEF	Transit
P146KWJ	East Midland	P315EFL	Cambus	P419KWF	East Midland	P556EFL	Cambus
P148ASA	Western	P316EFL	Cambus	P420KWF	East Midland	P556FEF	Transit
P148KWJ	East Midland	P317EFL	Cambus	P450KRP	United Counties	P557EFL	Cambus
P149ASA	Western	P318EFL	Cambus	P451KRP	United Counties	P557FEF	Transit
P149KWJ	East Midland	P319EFL	Cambus	P452KRP	United Counties	P558EFL	Cambus
P150ASA	Western	P321JND	Manchester	P455EEF	Transit	P558FEF	Transit
P150KWJ	East Midland	P322JND	Manchester	P456EEF	Transit	P561EFL	Cambus
P151ASA	Western	P323JND	Manchester	P457EEF	Transit	P562EFL	Cambus
P151KWJ	East Midland	P324JND	Manchester	P458EEF	Transit	P563EFL	Cambus
P152ASA	Western	P325JND	Manchester	P459EEF	Transit	P563MSX	Fife Scottish
P152KWJ	East Midland	P326JND	Manchester	P460EEF	Transit	P564EFL	Cambus
P153ASA	Western	P327JND	Manchester	P461EEF	Transit	P564MSX	Fife Scottish
P153KWJ	East Midland	P328JND	Manchester	P491BRS	Bluebird	P565EFL	Cambus
P154ASA	Western	P329JND	Manchester	P492BRS	Bluebird	P565MSX	Fife Scottish
P154KWJ	East Midland	P330JND	Manchester	P493BRS	Bluebird	P566EFL	Cambus
P156ASA	Western	P331JND	Manchester	P494BRS	Bluebird	P566MSX	Fife Scottish
P156KWJ	East Midland	P332JND	Manchester	P495BRS	Bluebird	P567EFL	Cambus
P157ASA	Western	P334JND	Manchester	P496BRS	Bluebird	P567MSX	Fife Scottish
P157KWJ	East Midland	P335JND	Manchester	P497BRS	Bluebird	P568EFL	Cambus
P158ASA	Western	P336JND	Manchester	P498BRS	Bluebird	P568MSX	Fife Scottish
P158KWJ	East Midland	P337JND	Manchester	P499BRS	Bluebird	P569EFL	Cambus
P159ASA	Western	P338JND	Manchester	P526EFL	Cambus	P569MSX	Fife Scottish
P159KAK	East Midland	P339JND	Manchester	P527EFL	Cambus	P570EFL	Cambus
P160ASA	Western	P340JND	Manchester	P527HMP	East London	P571EFL	Cambus
P160KAK	East Midland	P341ASO	Bluebird	P528EFL	Cambus	P572EFL	Cambus
P168KBD	United Counties	P341JND	Manchester	P528HMP	East London	P573EFL	Cambus
P169KBD	United Counties	P342ASO	Bluebird	P529EFL	Cambus	P574EFL	Cambus
P170KBD	United Counties	P342JND	Manchester	P529HMP	East London	P575EFL	Cambus
P171KBD	United Counties	P343ASO	Bluebird	P530EFL	Cambus	P576EFL	Cambus
P172KBD	United Counties	P343JND	Manchester	P530HMP	East London	P577EFL	Cambus
P173KBD	United Counties	P344ASO	Bluebird	P531EFL	Cambus	P578EFL	Cambus
P178DRH	Transit	P344JND	Manchester	P531HMP	East London	P579EFL	Cambus
P179DRH	Transit	P345ASO	Bluebird	P532EFL	Cambus	P601JBU	Manchester
P180DRH	Transit	P345JND	Manchester	P532HMP	East London	P602JBU	Manchester
P181DRH	Transit	P346ASO	Bluebird	P533EFL	Cambus	P603JBU	Manchester
P198OSE	Western	P346JND	Manchester	P533HMP	East London	P604JBU	Manchester
P199OSE	Western	P347ASO	Bluebird	P534EFL	Cambus	P605JBU	Manchester
P217HBD	Midland Red	P347JND	Manchester	P534HMP	East London	P606CMS	Fife Scottish
P218HBD	Midland Red	P348ASO	Bluebird	P535EFL	Cambus	P607CMS	Fife Scottish
P219HBD	Midland Red	P348JND	Manchester	P535HMP	East London	P608CMS	Fife Scottish
P220HBD	Midland Red	P349ASO	Bluebird	P536EFL	Cambus	P609CMS	Fife Scottish
P224VCK	Ribble	P349JND	Manchester	P536HMP	East London	P610CMS	Fife Scottish
P225VCK	Ribble	P349NKH	Transit	P537EFL	Cambus	P611CMS	Fife Scottish
P226VCK	Ribble	P350ASO	Bluebird	P537HMP	East London	P612CMS	Fife Scottish
P227VCK	Ribble	P350JND	Manchester	P538EFL	Cambus	P613CMS	Fife Scottish
P228VCK	Ribble	P350NKH	Transit	P538HMP	East London	P615PGP	Selkent
P229VCK	Ribble	P351ASO	Bluebird	P539EFL	Cambus	P616PGP	Selkent
P230VCK	Ribble	P351JND	Manchester	P539HMP	East London	P617PGP	Selkent
P231VCK	Ribble	P351NKH	Transit	P540EFL	Cambus	P618PGP	Selkent
P232VCK	Ribble	P352ASO	Bluebird	P540HMP	East London	P619PGP	Selkent
P233VCK	Ribble	P352JND	Manchester	P541EFL	Cambus	P620PGP	Selkent
P234VCK	Ribble	P352NKH	Transit	P541EFL	Cambus	P621PGP	Selkent
P235VCK	Ribble	P353JND	Manchester	P541HMP	East London	P622PGP	Selkent
P255ASA	Western	P353NKH	Transit	P542EFL	Cambus	P623PGP	Selkent
P260VPN	Ribble	P354JND	Manchester	P542HMP	East London	P624PGP	Selkent
P261VPN	Ribble	P354NKH	Transit	P543EFL	Cambus	P625NSE	Bluebird
P262VPN	Ribble	P355JND	Manchester	P543HMP	East London	P625PGP	Selkent
P263VPN	Ribble	P356JND	Manchester	P544EFL	Cambus	P626NSE	Bluebird
P264VPN	Stagecoach South	P357JND	Manchester	P545EFL	Cambus	P626PGP	Selkent
P265VPN	Stagecoach South	P364APM	Cambus	P546EFL	Cambus	P627PGP	Selkent
P266VPN	Stagecoach South	P390LPS	Western	P547EFL	Cambus	P628PGP	Selkent
P267VPN	Stagecoach South	P391LPS	Western	P548EFL	Cambus	P629PGP	Selkent
P268VPN	Stagecoach South	P392LPS	Western	P549EFL	Cambus	P630PGP	Selkent
P269VPN	Stagecoach South	P393LPS	Western	P550EFL	Cambus	P631PGP	Selkent
P270VPN	Ribble	P394LPS	Western	P551EFL	Cambus	P632PGP	Selkent
P271VPN	Ribble	P395BRS	Western	P552EFL	Cambus	P633PGP	Selkent
P272VPN	Ribble	P396BRS	Western	P5534FL	Cambus	P634PGP	Selkent
P273VPN	Ribble	P397BRS	Western	P554EFL	Cambus	P636PGP	Selkent
P274VPN	Ribble	P398BRS	Western	P554FEF	Transit	P637PGP	Selkent

Reg	Operator	Reg	Operator	Reg	Operator	Reg	Operator
P638PGP	Selkent	P802GMU	East London	P852GND	Manchester	PRA110R	Bluebird
P639PGP	Selkent	P802XTA	Devon	P852SMR	Cheltenham & G	PRA112R	Bluebird
P640PGP	Selkent	P803GMU	East London	P853GND	Manchester	PRU917R	Fife Scottish
P653FEF	Transit	P803XTA	Devon	P853SMR	Cheltenham & G	PRX189B	Transit
P654FEF	Transit	P804GMU	East London	P854GND	Manchester	PS2743	East Midland
P655FEF	Transit	P804XTA	Devon	P854SMR	Cheltenham & G	PSO178W	Western
P686JBD	United Counties	P805GMU	East London	P855GND	Manchester	PSU443	East Midland
P687JBD	United Counties	P805XTA	Devon	P856GND	Manchester	PSU764	East Midland
P688JBD	United Counties	P806GMU	East London	P857GND	Manchester	PSU775	Ribble
P689JBD	United Counties	P806XTA	Devon	P858GND	Manchester	PSU787	Cumberland
P690JBD	United Counties	P807GMU	East London	P859GND	Manchester	PSU788	Ribble
P691JBD	United Counties	P808GMU	East London	P860GND	Manchester	PSX180Y	Fife Scottish
P692JBD	United Counties	P809GMU	East London	P861GND	Manchester	PSX181Y	Fife Scottish
P701PTA	Devon	P810GMU	East London	P862GND	Manchester	PSX182Y	Fife Scottish
P702PTA	Devon	P811GMU	East London	P863GND	Manchester	PSX183Y	Fife Scottish
P703PTA	Devon	P812GMU	East London	P864GND	Manchester	PSX184Y	Fife Scottish
P704PTA	Devon	P813GMU	East London	P865GND	Manchester	PSX185Y	Fife Scottish
P705PTA	Devon	P814GMU	East London	P866GND	Manchester	PSX186Y	Fife Scottish
P706PTA	Devon	P815GMU	East London	P867GND	Manchester	PSX187Y	Fife Scottish
P707PTA	Devon	P816GMU	East London	P868GND	Manchester	PSX188Y	Fife Scottish
P708PTA	Devon	P817GMU	East London	P901SMR	Cheltenham & G	PSX189Y	Fife Scottish
P709PTA	Devon	P818GMU	East London	P902SMR	Cheltenham & G	PUK621R	Midland Red
P710PTA	Devon	P818GNC	Manchester	P903SMR	Cheltenham & G	PUK622R	Midland Red
P711PTA	Devon	P819GMU	East London	P904SMR	Cheltenham & G	PUK623R	Midland Red
P712PTA	Devon	P819GNC	Manchester	P905SMR	Cheltenham & G	PUK624R	Midland Red
P713PTA	Devon	P820GMU	East London	P906SMR	Cheltenham & G	PUK625R	Midland Red
P714PTA	Devon	P821FVU	Manchester	P907SMR	Cheltenham & G	PUK626R	Midland Red
P716GND	Manchester	P821GMU	East London	P908SMR	Cheltenham & G	PUK627R	Midland Red
P717GND	Manchester	P822FVU	Manchester	P909SMR	Cheltenham & G	PUK628R	Midland Red
P718GND	Manchester	P822GMU	East London	P910SMR	Cheltenham & G	PUK629R	Midland Red
P719GND	Manchester	P823FVU	Manchester	P911SMR	Cheltenham & G	PWY37W	Cambus
P719SKH	Transit	P823GMU	East London	P912SMR	Cheltenham & G	PWY45W	Cambus
P720GND	Manchester	P824FVU	Manchester	P913SMR	Cheltenham & G	PWY45W	Devon
P720SKH	Transit	P824GMU	East London	P914SMR	. Cheltenham & G	PWY47W	Cambus
P721GND	Manchester	P825FVU	Manchester	P973UBV	Ribble	PWY47W	Devon
P721SKH	Transit	P825GMU	East London	P974UBV	Ribble	PWY49W	Cambus
P722GND	Manchester	P826FVU	Manchester	P975UBV	Ribble	PWY50W	Cambus
P722SKH	Transit	P826GMU	East London	P976UBV	Ribble	PYE841Y	East Midland
P723GND	Manchester	P827FVU	Manchester	P978UBV	Ribble	PYE842Y	East Midland
P723SKH	Transit	P828FEF	Transit	P979UBV	Ribble	RAH264W	Cambus
P724GND	Manchester	P828FVU	Manchester	P980UBV	Ribble	RAH265W	Devon
P724SKH	Transit	P829FEF	Transit	PCD73R	Stagecoach South	RAH268W	Devon
P725GND	Manchester	P829FVU	Manchester	PCD79R	Stagecoach South	RAH681F	Busways
P725SKH	Transit	P830FEF	Transit	PCD80R	Stagecoach South	RBD397Y	United Counties
P726GND	Manchester	P830FVU	Manchester	PCK335	Cumberland	RBJ36W	Ribble
P726SKH	Transit	P831FEF	Transit	PEF147X	Transit	RBU180R	East Midland
P727GND	Manchester	P831FVU	Manchester	PEF148X	Transit	RCS382	Western
P728GND	Manchester	P832FEF	Transit	PEF149X	Transit	RCU827S	Busways
P729GND	Manchester	P832FVU	Manchester	PES190Y	Bluebird	RCU828S	Busways
P730GND	Manchester	P833FEF	Transit	PEU511R	Midland Red	RCU832S	Busways
P771TTG	Red & White	P833FVU	Manchester	PEU515R	Cheltenham & G	RCU833S	Busways
P772TTG	Red & White	P834FEF	Transit	PEU516R	Midland Red	RCU834S	Busways
P773TTG	Red & White	P834FVU	Manchester	PEX618W	MK Metro	RCU835S	Busways
P774TTG	Red & White	P835FVU	Manchester	PEX619W	MK Metro	RCU837S	Busways
P780WCN	Busways	P836GND	Manchester	PEX622W	MK Metro	RCU838S	Busways
P781WCN	Busways	P837GND	Manchester	PFN873	Stagecoach South	RDZ6115	East London
P782WCN	Busways	P838GND	Manchester	PHW985S	Red & White	RDZ6116	East London
P783WCN	Busways	P839GND	Manchester	PHW988S	Cheltenham & G	RDZ6117	East London
P784WCN	Busways	P840GND	Manchester	PHW989S	Cheltenham & G	RDZ6118	East London
P785WCN	Busways	P841GND	Manchester	PIB8109	Midland Red	RDZ6119	East London
P786WVK	Busways	P842GND	Manchester	PJI4314	East Midland	RDZ6120	East London
P787WVK	Busways	P843GND	Manchester	PJI4316	East Midland	RDZ6121	East London
P788WVK	Busways	P844GND	Manchester	PJI4983	Western	RDZ6122	East London
P789WVK	Busways	P845GND	Manchester	PJJ16S	Fife Scottish	RDZ6123	East London
P790WVK	Busways	P846GND	Manchester	PJJ344S	Stagecoach South	RDZ6124	East London
P791WVK	Busways	P847GND	Manchester	PJJ345S	Stagecoach South	RDZ6125	East London
P792WVK	Busways	P848GND	Manchester	PJJ346S	Stagecoach South	RDZ6126	East London
P793WVK	Busways	P849GND	Manchester	PKG741R	Red & White	RDZ6127	East London
P801GMU	East London	P850GND	Manchester	PMT199X	Stagecoach South	RDZ6128	East London
P801XTA	Devon	P851GND	Manchester	PRA109R	Bluebird	RDZ6129	East London

RDZ6130	East London	SAG528W	Transit	SMK723F	East London	SUB790W	Cambus
REU310S	Cheltenham & G	SAG529W	Transit	SMK738F	East London	SUB792W	Cambus
REU311S	Cheltenham & G	SAO410R	Bluebird	SMK743F	East London	SUB793W	Cambus
RFS579V	Western	SAO412R	Bluebird	SMK748F	East London	SUB795W	Cambus
RFS582V	Ribble	SCK224X	Ribble	SMK749F	East London	SVK627G	Busways
RFS583V	Western	SCK225X	Ribble	SMK760F	East London	SVV586W	East Midland
RFS584V	Ribble	SCK226X	Ribble	SND82X	Manchester	SVV589W	Midland Red
RGV37W	Ribble	SCN244S	Fife Scottish	SND106X	Manchester	SWC25K	Busways
RGV38W	Ribble	SCN247S	Cheltenham & G	SND107X	Manchester	SWC26K	Busways
RGV39W	Ribble	SCN248S	Busways	SND108X	Manchester	SYC852	Stagecoach South
RGV40W	Ribble	SCN250S	Cheltenham & G	SND109X	Manchester	TAE639S	Midland Red
RHG878X	Ribble	SCN251S	Busways	SND110X	Manchester	TAE641S	Cheltenham & G
RHG878X	Ribble	SCN252S	Midland Red	SND111X	Manchester	TAE642S	Cheltenham & G
RHG880X	Cheltenham & G	SCN253S	Midland Red	SND116X	Manchester	TAE644S	Cheltenham & G
RHG881X	Ribble	SCN254S	Busways	SND117X	Manchester	TBC1X	Busways
RHG884X	Cumberland	SCN255S	Cheltenham & G	SND118X	Manchester	TBC2X	Busways
RHG886X	Ribble	SCN256S	Cheltenham & G	SND119X	Manchester	TCK200X	Ribble
RHL174X	East Midland	SCN257S	Fife Scottish	SND120X	Manchester	TCK212X	Ribble
RIB4309	Bluebird	SCN259S	Busways	SND121X	Manchester	TCK841	Cumberland
RIW3364	Cheltenham & G	SCN264S	Fife Scottish	SND123X	Manchester	TDL567K	Busways
RJA702R	Western	SCN264S	Cheltenham & G	SND124X	Manchester	TEL490R	Stagecoach South
RJA729R	Manchester	SCN265S	Midland Red	SND125X	Manchester	TFN990T	Fife Scottish
RJT146R	Stagecoach South	SCN268S	Busways	SND132X	Manchester	TFU61T	East Midland
RJT153R	Fife Scottish	SCN270S	Busways	SND141X	Manchester	THX401S	East London
RJT155R	Bluebird	SCN276S	Midland Red	SND143X	Manchester	THX402S	East London
RNV413V	Midland Red	SCN277S	Busways	SND144X	Manchester	TJI2488	Manchester
RPR716R	Fife Scottish	SCN281S	Midland Red	SND144X	Manchester	TMS404X	Western
RRM383X	Cumberland	SCN282S	Busways	SND412X	Manchester	TMS405X	Western
RRM384X	Ribble	SCN283S	Busways	SND418X	Manchester	TMS406X	Western
RRM385X	Cheltenham & G	SDA651S	United Counties	SND421X	Manchester	TMS407X	Western
RRM386X	Ribble	SDA715S	United Counties	SND429X	Manchester	TNH870R	United Counties
RRP858R	Ribble	SGS504W	Stagecoach South	SND430X	Manchester	TNH871R	United Counties
RRP862R	United Counties	SHE306Y	East Midland	SND432X	Ribble	TNH872R	United Counties
RRP863R	United Counties	SHE307Y	East Midland	SND440X	Manchester	TNH873R	United Counties
RRS46R	Bluebird	SHE308Y	East Midland	SND450X	Manchester	TOF707S	Midland Red
RRS47R	Bluebird	SHE309Y	East Midland	SND451X	Manchester	TOF708S	Midland Red
RRS48R	Bluebird	SHE310Y	East Midland	SND454X	Manchester	TOF709S	Midland Red
RRS50R	Bluebird	SHE311Y	East Midland	SND455X	Manchester	TOF710S	Midland Red
RRS53R	Bluebird	SHH387X	Ribble	SND465X	Manchester	TPE148S	Stagecoach South
RRS225X	Western	SHH388X	Ribble	SND477X	Manchester	TPE149S	Stagecoach South
RSC190Y	Fife Scottish	SHH389X	Cheltenham & G	SND487X	Manchester	TPE156S	Stagecoach South
RSC191Y	Fife Scottish	SHH390X	Ribble	SND495X	Manchester	TRN476V	Ribble
RSC192Y	Fife Scottish	SHH391X	Ribble	SND496X	Manchester	TRN478V	Ribble
RSC194Y	Fife Scottish	SHH392X	Midland Red	SND501X	Manchester	TRN480V	Ribble
RSG814V	Red & White	SHH393X	Cumberland	SND505X	Manchester	TRN481V	Ribble
RSG815V	Red & White	SHH394X	Ribble	SND506X	Manchester	TRN482V	Cumberland
RSG823V	Red & White	SHN401R	Transit	SND512X	Manchester	TRN806V	Ribble
RSG824V	Red & White	SHN407R	Transit	SND513X	Manchester	TRN810V	Cumberland
RSG825V	Red & White	SIB8243	Stagecoach South	SND514X	Manchester	TRN812V	Ribble
RTH924S	Fife Scottish	SJI2054	Manchester	SND518X	Manchester	TRY118H	Busways
RUF40R	Transit	SJI4558	Manchester	SND519X	Manchester	TSJ31S	Western
RUF41R	Manchester	SJI4559	Manchester	SND521X	Manchester	TSJ32S	Western
RVB973S	Fife Scottish	SJI4560	Manchester	SND526X	Manchester	TSJ33S	Western
RVB974S	Fife Scottish	SKG908S	Red & White	SND527X	Manchester	TSJ67S	Western
RVB978S	Fife Scottish	SKG923S	Red & White	SND530X	Manchester	TSJ70S	Western
RYK815Y*	Selkent	SKL680X	Stagecoach South	SND710X	Cheltenham & G	TSJ71S	Western
RYK816Y	Selkent	SKL681X	Stagecoach South	SNS825W	Cheltenham & G	TSJ76S	Western
RYK818Y	Selkent	SKL682X	Stagecoach South	SNS826W	Western	TSJ78S	Western
RYK819Y	East London	SKL683X	Stagecoach South	SNV930W	United Counties	TSJ79S	Western
RYK820Y	Fife Scottish	SKL684X	Stagecoach South	SNV931W	United Counties	TSJ80S	Western
RYK821Y	Selkent	SKL685X	Stagecoach South	SNV935W	United Counties	TSJ85S	Western
RYK822Y	Selkent	SKY31Y	East Midland	SNV936W	United Counties	TSO12X	Bluebird
SAE752S	Cheltenham & G	SKY32Y	East Midland	SNV937W	United Counties	TSO13X	Bluebird
SAE753S	Midland Red	SMK661F	East London	SSA2X	Bluebird	TSO14X	Bluebird
SAE754S	Cheltenham & G	SMK665F	East London	SSA3X	Bluebird	TSO15X	Bluebird
SAE756S	Cheltenham & G	SMK670F	East London	SSA4X	Bluebird	TSO16X	Bluebird
SAG524W	Transit	SMK671F	East London	SSA5X	Bluebird	TSO17X	Bluebird
SAG525W	Transit	SMK696F	East London	SSA6X	Bluebird	TSO20X	Bluebird
SAG526W	Transit	SMK705F	East London	SSA7X	Bluebird	TSO21X	Bluebird
SAG527W	Transit	SMK709F	East London	STW24W	Cambus	TSO23X	Bluebird

Reg	Operator	Reg	Operator	Reg	Operator	Reg	Operator
TSO24X	Bluebird	UWA159S	East Midland	VLT73	Western	WFS150W	Fife Scottish
TSO29X	Bluebird	UWP105	Western	VLT77	Fife Scottish	WFU466V	East Midland
TSO30X	Bluebird	UWV604S	Devon	VLT104	Western	WFU467V	East Midland
TSO31X	Bluebird	UWV605S	Bluebird	VLT154	Western	WHH415S	Fife Scottish
TSO32X	Bluebird	UWV607S	Western	VLT240	Selkent	WJM825T	Stagecoach South
TSU638	Western	UWV608S	Bluebird	VLT255	United Counties	WJM826T	Stagecoach South
TSU639	United Counties	UWV609S	Bluebird	VLT272	Bluebird	WJM828T	Stagecoach South
TSU640	United Counties	UWV610S	Cumberland	VNB132L	Manchester	WJM829T	Stagecoach South
TSU641	United Counties	UWV611S	Bluebird	VNH157W	Ribble	WJM832T	Stagecoach South
TSU642	United Counties	UWV612S	Cumberland	VOD593S	Cheltenham & G	WLT380	Cumberland
TSV718	Bluebird	UWV613S	Bluebird	VOD596S	Cheltenham & G	WLT415	Western
TSV719	Bluebird	UWV614S	Devon	VOD597S	Cheltenham & G	WLT416	Western
TSV720	Bluebird	UWV617S	Fife Scottish	VOD604S	Stagecoach South	WLT439	Western
TSV721	Bluebird	UWV618S	Cumberland	VOD605S	Stagecoach South	WLT447	Western
TSV722	Bluebird	UWV620S	Cumberland	VPR487S	Fife Scottish	WLT461	Selkent
TSV778	Bluebird	UWV621S	Stagecoach South	VPR491S	Stagecoach South	WLT465	Western
TSV779	Bluebird	UWV622S	Cumberland	VRN827Y	Ribble	WLT491	Selkent
TSV780	Bluebird	UWV622S	Ribble	VRN828Y	Ribble	WLT501	Western
TSV781	Bluebird	UWV623S	Stagecoach South	VRN829Y	Ribble	WLT512	United Counties
TWF201Y	East Midland	UWW3X	Cambus	VRN830Y	Ribble	WLT526	Western
TWF202Y	East Midland	UWW4X	Cambus	VRR447	Cumberland	WLT528	United Counties
TWS906T	Cheltenham & G	UWW7X	Cheltenham & G	VSV564	Stagecoach South	WLT538	Western
TWS909T	Red & White	UWW8X	Cambus	VTV167S	Fife Scottish	WLT546	Western
TWS913T	Cheltenham & G	VAE499T	Cheltenham & G	VTV170S	Midland Red	WLT575	Selkent
TWS914T	Cheltenham & G	VAE501T	Cheltenham & G	VTV171S	Bluebird	WLT613	East London
UCS659	Western	VAE502T	Midland Red	VTV172S	Stagecoach South	WLT682	United Counties
UDT312Y	East Midland	VAE507T	Cheltenham & G	VVV948W	United Counties	WLT697	Western
UDT313Y	East Midland	VAH278X	Cambus	VVV949W	United Counties	WLT706	Cumberland
UF4813	Stagecoach South	VAH279X	Cambus	VVV950W	United Counties	WLT713	Cheltenham & G
UFG48S	Stagecoach South	VAH280X	Cambus	VVV952W	United Counties	WLT720	Western
UFG49S	Transit	VBA161S	Western	VVV953W	United Counties	WLT727	Western
UFG52S	Transit	VBA166S	Red & White	VVV954W	United Counties	WLT774	Western
UFS875R	Fife Scottish	VBA178S	Red & White	VVV961W	United Counties	WLT794	Western
UFS876R	Fife Scottish	VBA188S	Red & White	VVV962W	United Counties	WLT809	Western
UFS877R	Fife Scottish	VBA190S	Red & White	VVV963W	United Counties	WLT824	Cumberland
UFS878R	Fife Scottish	VCS391	Western	VVV965W	United Counties	WLT830	Western
UHG757R	Stagecoach South	VCU301T	Midland Red	VVV966W	United Counties	WLT886	East London
UIB3076	Western	VCU302T	Busways	VVV967W	United Counties	WLT908	United Counties
UIB3541	Western	VCU303T	Busways	VWA34Y	East Midland	WLT978	Western
UIB3542	Western	VCU304T	Midland Red	VWA35Y	East Midland	WPC316X	Ribble
UIB3543	Western	VCU310T	Midland Red	VWA36Y	East Midland	WPR152S	Stagecoach South
ULS660T	Western	VCW196V	Ribble	WAO396Y	Ribble	WSU293	Midland Red
UM7681	Western	VCW197V	Ribble	WAO397Y	Cheltenham & G	WUH167T	Red & White
UMO180N	Stagecoach South	VDV135S	Devon	WAO398Y	Cumberland	WUH168T	Red & White
UNA772S	Western	VEF150Y	Transit	WAO643Y	Bluebird	WVM884S	Western
UNA824S	Western	VEF151Y	Transit	WAO645Y	Cumberland	WVM888S	Western
UNA840S	Western	VEF152Y	Transit	WAS765V	Red & White	WVT618	Stagecoach South
UNA863S	Western	VEF153Y	Transit	WAS767V	Red & White	WWM576W	Ribble
UOT648	Bluebird	VEU231T	Cheltenham & G	WAS771V	Western	WWM920W	Ribble
URF662S	Ribble	VEX289X	Cambus	WAX194S	Red & White	WWM933W	Ribble
URM801Y	Cumberland	VEX291X	Cambus	WBD876S	United Counties	WYJ169S	Stagecoach South
URM802Y	Cumberland	VEX293X	Cambus	WBN474T	Manchester	WYV10T	Selkent
URP939W	United Counties	VEX295X	Cambus	WBN477T	East Midland	WYV11T	East London
URP940W	United Counties	VEX296X	Cambus	WBR248	Busways	WYV12T	East London
URP941W	United Counties	VEX298X	Cambus	WCK213Y	Ribble	WYV13T	East London
URP942W	MK Metro	VEX299X	Cambus	WCK215Y	Ribble	WYV14T	East London
URP943W	Cambus	VEX300X	Cambus	WDA1T	Red & White	WYV15T	East London
URP944W	United Counties	VEX301X	Cambus	WDA2T	Red & White	WYV16T	East London
URP945W	United Counties	VEX303X	Cambus	WDA5T	Red & White	WYV17T	Selkent
USK625	Bluebird	VEX304X	Cambus	WDA994T	Midland Red	WYV18T	East London
USV672	Stagecoach South	VFV7V	Burnley & Pendle	WFM801K	Manchester	WYV19T	Selkent
UTX726S	Red & White	VFX984S	Stagecoach South	WFS135W	Bluebird	WYV20T	Selkent
UVK287T	Busways	VKU73S	East Midland	WFS136W	Western	WYV21T	East London
UVK290T	Busways	VKU77S	East Midland	WFS137W	Bluebird	WYV22T	East London
UVK295T	Busways	VKU79S	East Midland	WFS138W	Western	WYV23T	East London
UVK299T	Busways	VKU80S	Ribble	WFS139W	Fife Scottish	WYV24T	East London
UWA150S	East Midland	VLT14	Selkent	WFS140W	Fife Scottish	WYV25T	East London
UWA154S	East Midland	VLT20	Selkent	WFS141W	Fife Scottish	WYV26T	Selkent
UWA155S	East Midland	VLT37	Western	WFS142W	Western	WYV27T	Western
UWA157S	East Midland	VLT54	Western	WFS147W	Fife Scottish	WYV28T	East London

Reg	Operator	Reg	Operator	Reg	Operator	Reg	Operator
WYV29T	Western	XJJ658V	Stagecoach South	XSJ657T	Western	YFS304W	Western
WYV30T	East London	XJJ659V	Stagecoach South	XSJ658T	Western	YFS308W	Western
WYV30T	East London	XJJ660V	Stagecoach South	XSJ659T	Western	YFS309W	Western
WYV31T	East London	XJJ661V	Stagecoach South	XSJ660T	Western	YFS310W	Western
WYV32T	East London	XJJ662V	Stagecoach South	XSJ661T	Western	YJV806	Cheltenham & G
WYV33T	East London	XJJ663V	Stagecoach South	XSJ662T	Western	YKA8W	Ribble
WYV34T	East London	XJJ664V	Stagecoach South	XSJ665T	Western	YLJ332	East London
WYV35T	East London	XJJ665V	Stagecoach South	XSJ666T	Western	YLJ332	Stagecoach South
WYV36T	East London	XJJ666V	Stagecoach South	XSJ667T	Western	YPD129Y	East Midland
WYV37T	Selkent	XJJ667V	Stagecoach South	XSJ668T	Western	YPD133Y	East Midland
WYV38T	Selkent	XJJ668V	Stagecoach South	XSJ669T	Western	YRN814V	Ribble
WYV39T	East London	XJJ669V	Stagecoach South	XSL596A	Bluebird	YRN815V	Ribble
WYV3T	East London	XJJ670V	Stagecoach South	XSU612	Stagecoach South	YRN816V	Stagecoach South
WYV40T	Selkent	XMS420Y	Fife Scottish	XSU682	Stagecoach South	YRN817V	Ribble
WYV49T	Western	XMS422Y	Western	XSU905	Burnley & Pendle	YRN820V	Ribble
WYV4T	East London	XMS423Y	Western	XSU906	Burnley & Pendle	YRN821V	Stagecoach South
WYV56T	Western	XNV878S	United Counties	XSU907	Burnley & Pendle	YSD350L	Western
WYV5T	Western	XNV879S	United Counties	XSU908	Burnley & Pendle	YSF98S	Western
WYV63T	East London	XNV880S	United Counties	XSU909	Burnley & Pendle	YSF100S	Western
WYV66T	Selkent	XNV885S	United Counties	XSU910	Burnley & Pendle	YSO33Y	Bluebird
WYV6T	East London	XNV886S	United Counties	XVV540S	Red & White	YSO34Y	Bluebird
WYV7T	East London	XNV887S	United Counties	XYK976	Stagecoach South	YSO35Y	Bluebird
WYV8T	East London	XNV888S	United Counties	YAJ154Y	Transit	YSO36Y	Bluebird
WYV9T	Selkent	XNV889S	United Counties	YAJ155Y	Transit	YSO37Y	Bluebird
XAP643S	Fife Scottish	XNV890S	United Counties	YAJ156Y	Transit	YSO38Y	Bluebird
XDU599	Western	XNV891S	United Counties	YAJ157Y	Transit	YSO39Y	Bluebird
XDV602S	Cheltenham & G	XOV753T	Midland Red	YAY21Y	Transit	YSO40Y	Bluebird
XDV606S	Cheltenham & G	XOV754T	Midland Red	YBO16T	Midland Red	YSO41Y	Bluebird
XFF813	East London	XOV755T	Midland Red	YBO18T	Midland Red	YSO42Y	Bluebird
XFF814	East London	XOV756T	Midland Red	YCD73T	Stagecoach South	YSO43Y	Bluebird
XFK305	Burnley & Pendle	XOV760T	Midland Red	YCD74T	Stagecoach South	YSV730	Western
XFU125V	East Midland	XRM772Y	Bluebird	YCD76T	Stagecoach South	YSV735	Western
XFU126V	East Midland	XRN44V	Burnley & Pendle	YCD77T	Stagecoach South	YSX926W	Red & White
XFU129V	East Midland	XRN45V	Burnley & Pendle	YCD82T	Stagecoach South	YSX932W	Red & White
XGR728R	Midland Red	XRN46V	Burnley & Pendle	YDC21Y	Transit	YSX933W	Red & White
XGS736S	East Midland	XRN47V	Burnley & Pendle	YDC23Y	Transit	YSX934W	Red & White
XGS762X	Stagecoach South	XRN48V	Burnley & Pendle	YDC24Y	Transit	YSX935W	Red & White
XIA586	Stagecoach South	XRN49V	Burnley & Pendle	YDC25Y	Transit	YTS820A	Bluebird
XIA857	Stagecoach South	XRN50V	Burnley & Pendle	YDC26Y	Transit	YVN520T	United Counties
XJJ650V	Stagecoach South	XRR175S	Cumberland	YDG616	Cumberland	YVN521T	Transit
XJJ651V	Stagecoach South	XSJ651T	Western	YEL2T	Stagecoach South	YVN522T	United Counties
XJJ652V	Stagecoach South	XSJ653T	Western	YEL4T	Stagecoach South	YVN524T	United Counties
XJJ653V	Stagecoach South	XSJ654T	Western	YEU446V	Midland Red	YWC16L	Busways
XJJ654V	Stagecoach South	XSJ655T	Western	YFB972V	Cheltenham & G	YWC18L	Busways
XJJ655V	Stagecoach South	XSJ656T	Western	YFB973V	Cheltenham & G	YYS174	Western
XJJ657V	Stagecoach South						

ISBN 1 897990 23 4
Published by British Bus Publishing
The Vyne, 16 St Margarets Drive, Wellington,
Telford, Shropshire, TF1 3PH

Printed by Graphics & Print
Unit A13, Stafford Park 15
Telford, Shropshire, TF3 3BB